# AMAZING 500 PUZZLE CHALLENGE

THIS IS A CARLTON BOOK

Design copyright © Carlton Publishing Group 2006
Unless otherwise stated all puzzles © 2006 Puzzler Media Limited, RH1 1EY,
www.puzzler.co.uk

The following puzzles are the copyright of Nikoli (http://www.nikoli.co.jp): 24, 34,
38, 40, 44, 53, 62, 63, 67, 70, 80, 84, 89, 94, 100, 108, 109, 114, 123, 128, 129,
133, 139, 154, 158, 174, 177, 182, 198, 200, 201, 205, 209, 222, 226, 246, 247,
261, 266, 268, 283, 285, 288, 291, 292, 299, 306, 319, 325, 329, 333, 337, 339,
349, 354, 367, 372, 381, 384, 389, 396, 397, 402, 406, 415, 417, 424, 427, 432,
435, 436, 446, 447, 448, 450, 451, 453, 456, 465, 467, 469, 471, 473, 481, 489,
490, 492, 495

The following puzzles are the copyright of Conceptis Puzzles
(http://www.conceptis.tech.com): 6, 15, 23, 37

This edition published in 2006 by Carlton Books Ltd
A Division of the Carlton Publishing Group
20 Mortimer Street
London W1T 3JW

ISBN 13: 978-0-68145-366-1
ISBN 10: 0-68145-366-4

Printed in Dubai

# AMAZING 500 PUZZLE CHALLENGE

**General Editor: Robert Allen**

SEVENOAKS

# INTRODUCTION

With puzzles currently being more popular than ever, this amazing collection of teasing challenges will be a welcome companion to all those who love solving problems. From  logic problems (both the long, classic puzzles and a large number of quick ones that are just the right size for solving over a cup of coffee), picture puzzles and visual reasoning enigmas to number problems, mazes, physical problems, and mathematical crosswords, there really is something to suit everyone's taste and with more than 500 of them you're sure to come across your favourite puzzle at some point. Dots beside the puzzle headings indicate how difficult and time-consuming a puzzle is likely to be – the more dots, the more difficult the puzzle. But don't be put off from trying a difficult puzzle – you may find that those we've rated as being harder are a doddle for you! With that in mind, sit back and enjoy these tempting teasers which will provide you with many hours, weeks and months of fun. Enjoy!

# THE PUZZLES

## 1 HEADS AND TAILS

The diagram shows four coins issued in different reigns by rulers of Monetaria. Can you name the monarch whose head appears on the obverse of each of the coins lettered A to D, describe its reverse design and say in which year it was minted?

1 No female monarch reigned in Monetaria during the 18th century.
2 The coin from the reign of Karl II bears the crossed swords on its reverse.
3 The heraldic dragon appears on coin A, which wasn't issued by William V.
4 The head on the obverse of coin D is that of Josef III.
5 The 1785 coin's reverse shows the value in a wreath of laurel leaves.
6 The coin dated 1865 is somewhere to the right of the one whose reverse design is the shield of Monetaria.

Monarchs: Josef III, Karl II, Maria, William V
Reverse designs: crossed swords, heraldic dragon, shield, wreath of laurels
Dates: 1745, 1785, 1825, 1865

A     B     C     D

Ruler: _____  _____  _____  _____
Reverse: _____  _____  _____  _____
Date: _____  _____  _____  _____

## 2 DOMINO DEAL

A standard set (o–o) to (6–6) is laid out below. Each domino is placed so that the larger number will be on the bottom:
i.e.    3    not    6
        6           3

Those top numbers show the four numbers which form the top half of each domino in that column. The bottom numbers, below the grid, give the four bottom numbers for that column. The seven numbers on the left show the numbers which belong in that row. Can you cross-reference the facts and deduce where each domino has been placed? 3*6 is given as a start.

'TOP' NUMBERS

| | 13 55 | 01 24 | 01 24 | 01 23 | 00 14 | 12 3̶6̶ | 00 26 |
|---|---|---|---|---|---|---|---|
| 0 0 1 2 2 3̶ 5 / 2 2 4 4 5 5̶ 6 | | | | | | 3 / 6 | |
| 0 2 2 2 3 5 6 / 3 4 4 5 6 6 6 | | | | | | | |
| 0 0 0 1 1 3 3 / 0 1 2 3 3 3 5 | | | | | | | |
| A 0 1 1 1 4 4 4 / 1 4 5 5 6 6 | | | | | | | |
| | 55 56 | 23 35 | 14 56 | 04 66 | 24 46 | 13 4̶6̶ | 23 56 |

'BOTTOM' NUMBERS

## 3 PEN PALS

Five school friends went their separate ways to seek their fortunes. They had agreed to write to each other from time to time, but not to be bound by any 'take turns' approach. In their first year after graduation it turned out that:

1 Chris wrote twice as many letters to Gainor as he did to Insley, who wrote twice as many to Al as to Ed.
2 Gainor received twice as many letters from Don as he did from Bob, who wrote four to Insley.
3 Al wrote more to Gainor than he did to Jarrett, who received three letters from Chris.
4 Harkness wrote more to Chris than Chris wrote to Harkness.
5 Don received twice as many letters form Farley as he did from Harkness.
6 No one wrote the same number to any two of the others. Each wrote and received ten letters.

Can you give each writer's surname and say how many letters (at least one) he sent to each of the others?

## 4 SIX SQUARES

The six squares seen highlighted at the top right-hand corner of the grid are repeated in only one other place. Can you see where?

## 5 THE WHEEL THING

Which two of the pictures below form a matching pair?

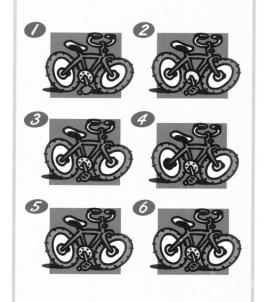

1   2
3   4
5   6

# 6 HANJIE

The numbers alongside each row or column tell you how many blocks of black squares are in a line. For example: 2, 3, 5 tells you that from left to right (or top to bottom) there is a group of two black squares, then at least one white space, then a group of three black squares, then at least one white shape, then a group of five black squares. Each block of black squares on the same line must have at least one white square between it and the next block of black squares.

Sometimes it is possible to tell which squares are going to be black without reference to other lines or columns. In the example below, we can deduce that any block of six black squares must incorporate the two central squares.

6 ▢▢▢▢◼▢▢▢▢

Can you complete this hanjie puzzle, to reveal the hidden pattern or picture?

Column clues (top to bottom, left to right):

| | | | | | | | | 1 | | | | | | | | | | | |
|---|---|---|---|---|---|---|---|---|---|---|---|---|---|---|---|---|---|---|---|
| | | | | | | | | 1 | | | | | | | | | | | |
| | | | | | 2 | | | 1 | | | | | | | | | | | |
| | | 1 | 2 | | 2 | | 1 | 1 | | 1 | | | | | | | | | |
| | 2 | 4 | 2 | 1 | 2 | 1 | 3 | 1 | 1 | | | 2 | 2 | | | 2 | | | |
| | 2 | 2 | 2 | 1 | 2 | 1 | 1 | 5 | 1 | 1 | 2 | 2 | 5 | 6 | 2 | 5 | | | |
| 6 | 2 | 2 | 2 | 1 | 2 | 1 | 5 | 1 | 3 | 9 | 4 | 1 | 5 | 7 | 5 | 2 | 2 | 2 | 2 |
| 1 | 2 | 3 | 11 | 3 | 1 | 2 | 2 | 5 | 8 | 11 | 3 | 6 | 3 | 11 | 8 | 4 | 2 | | |

Row clues:

- 3 1
- 2 3
- 1 1 6
- 2 3 1 1
- 1 2 7
- 1 1 1 5
- 1 1 2 2 4
- 1 2 1 1 4
- 2 3 1 1 1 2
- 2 4 2 3
- 2 11
- 1 3 6
- 1 7
- 1 1 7
- 1 3 4 3
- 1 1 1 2 3
- 1 1 2 3
- 1 1 4 3
- 2 3 1 1 1
- 3 3 3
- 10 3
- 1 6 3
- 1 6
- 1 7
- 2 1 6

(c) Conceptis Puzzles   UK10516

# 7 NUMBER SEARCH

The number 123456 appears just once in this grid, running in either a forward or backward direction, either vertically, horizontally or diagonally. Can you locate it?

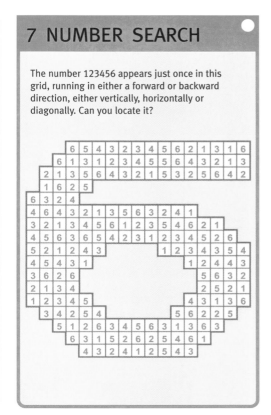

# 8 SMALL HOLDINGS

When Ivan The Not-too-bad-really decided to divide a spare kingdom between four faithful followers, he stipulated that each should hold an identically shaped chunk of territory, the same size as every other. Each, of course, was to have just one castle and one farm. Can you show Ivan's Estate Agent, Manfromm The Prudential, how to achieve his master's wishes?

# 9 LETTER MAZE

The object is to pass through the maze and reach the exit at the top. No diamond may be passed through more than once in any one move nor may you leave a diamond by the gap you came in by. You must not enter diamonds that contain the letters you are told to avoid.

1. Move 4 diamonds. Avoid A, C and F.
2. Move 3 diamonds. Avoid C, E and G.
3. Move 5 diamonds. Avoid A and E.
4. Move 3 diamonds. Avoid C.
5. Move 4 diamonds. Avoid C, D and E.
6. Move 5 diamonds. Avoid B and F.
7. Move 5 diamonds. Avoid C and G.
8. Move 2 diamonds. Avoid B.
9. Move 2 diamonds. Avoid A, C and G.
10. Move 3 diamonds. Avoid A, B and E.

EXIT

```
                     CF
                DG        BE
            AE      CG        DE
         CE      DF      BF      CF
      DG      BE      AF      AE      DF
   AE      BG      CG      BF      CG      AG
BG      DE      AF      CE      BG      DF      CF
   CE      BE      DE      AF      AG      BF
                   START
```

## 10 DROP-OUT

The hippie is trying to choose a waistcoat. In the picture on the right, he's made his choice. Which one did he buy?

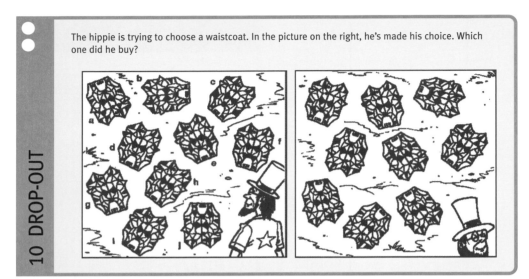

## 11 BIG BREAK

A snooker break is made up by potting red balls (maximum 15) which are each followed by one of six different colours, the point values of the balls are:

RED 1

YELLOW 2

GREEN 3

BROWN 4

BLUE 5

PINK 6

BLACK 7

Snooker player Bob Basher made a break of 70, which ended when he failed to pot a red. In the break he potted the same number of blue and brown and one more pink than yellow, potting all four colours in the break and no other colours.

How was the break compiled?

## 12 SEQUENCE

Which butterfly (a, b, c, d) comes next in this sequence?

a

b

c

d

## 13 DOMINO DEAL

A standard set (o–o) to (6–6) is laid out below. Each domino is placed so that the larger number will be on the bottom:
i.e.   3        not       6
       6                  3
Those top numbers show the four numbers which form the top half of each domino in that column. The bottom numbers, below the grid, give the four bottom numbers for that column. The seven numbers on the left show the numbers which belong in that row. Can you cross-reference the facts and deduce where each domino has been placed? 3*6 is given as a start.

'TOP' NUMBERS

| | 13 | 00 | 01 | 02 | 01 | 01 | 02 |
| | 55 | 13 | 12 | 24 | 23 | 44 | 36 |
| 0 0 1 1 3 4 6 | | | | | | | |
| 1 3 4 4 5 6 6 | | | | | | | |
| 1 2 2 2 3 5 | | | | | 3 | | |
| 2 2 3 5 5 5 6 | | | | | 6 | | |
| 0 0 1 2 2 3 5 | | | | | | | |
| 2 3 4 5 6 6 6 | | | | | | | |
| 0 0 0 1 1 4 4 | | | | | | | |
| 0 1 3 4 4 5 6 | | | | | | | |
| | 44 | 11 | 23 | 36 | 03 | 22 | 34 |
| | 56 | 55 | 56 | 66 | 46 | 45 | 56 |

'BOTTOM' NUMBERS

# 14 SIX SQUARES

The six squares seen highlighted at the top right-hand corner of the grid are repeated in only one other place. Can you see where?

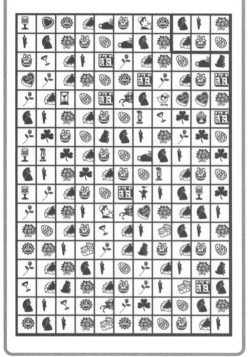

# 16 ABC

Each line, across and down, is to have each of the letters A, B and C, and two empty squares. The letter outside the grid shows the first or second letter in the direction of the arrow. Can you fill in the grid?

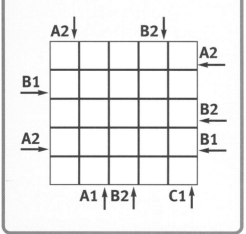

The numbers alongside each row or column tell you how many blocks of black squares are in a line. For example: 2, 3, 5 tells you that from left to right (or top to bottom) there is a group of two black squares, then at least one white space, then a group of three black squares, then at least one white shape, then a group of five black squares. Each block of black squares on the same line must have at least one white square between it and the next block of black squares.

Sometimes it is possible to tell which squares are going to be black without reference to other lines or columns. In the example below, we can deduce that any block of six black squares must incorporate the two central squares.

Can you complete this hanjie puzzle, to reveal the hidden pattern or picture?

## 15 HANJIE

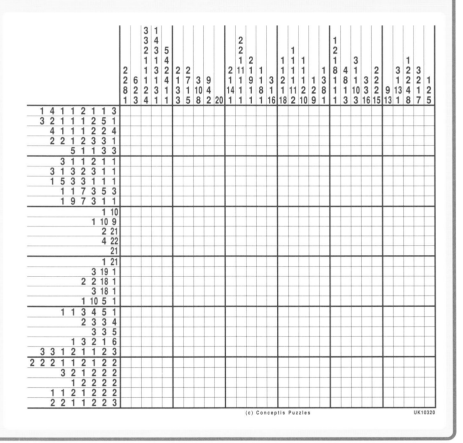

(c) Conceptis Puzzles        UK10320

## 17 COUNTING HOUSE

In Colourland, where the currency rate is 100 cents to the Colourland dollar, the national bank issues coins of a large range of different (and decidedly strange!) denominations, which are distinguishable only by their colour. From the information shown in the four boxes below, can you calculate the individual values of just four of these coins: red, blue, yellow and green?

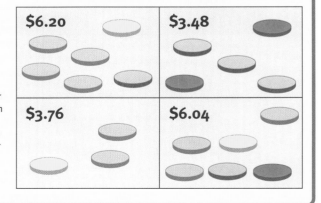

$6.20    $3.48

$3.76    $6.04

At the Little Appenin local fair a plant stall had a display of 25 potted plants. Four customers each bought five plants – taking one from each row and each column. So with just five plants left, each was given a free gift of a plant type she had not already bought. Madge was given the plant next to one of the ferns she purchased. The picture shows one plant bought by each customer. The chart indicates how many of some plants each purchased. At the end of it all, which plant was left on the table and which pots did each buy or was given?

## 18 ODD POT

| | Azalea | Begonia | Cactus | Fern |
|---|---|---|---|---|
| Jackie | | | 3 | |
| Kim | | | | 3 |
| Laura | | 3 | | |
| Madge | | | 2 | 2 |

## 19 BOWLING TEAM

The members of the Basham bowling team make a splendid sight. Can you identify these four colourful characters?
**1** Tom the dustman is not the chap sporting the long beard.
**2** The postman is not Alf who wears a monocle.
**3** George is not the milkman who even bowls in his panama hat.

| ALF | |
|---|---|
| BLACKSMITH | DOCTOR |
| LAWYER | MAIL MAN |
| BEARD | CRAVAT |
| MONOCLE | PANAMA |

| GEORGE | |
|---|---|
| BLACKSMITH | DOCTOR |
| LAWYER | MAIL MAN |
| BEARD | CRAVAT |
| MONOCLE | PANAMA |

| FRED | |
|---|---|
| BLACKSMITH | DOCTOR |
| LAWYER | MAIL MAN |
| BEARD | CRAVAT |
| MONOCLE | PANAMA |

| TOM | |
|---|---|
| BLACKSMITH | DOCTOR |
| LAWYER | MAIL MAN |
| BEARD | CRAVAT |
| MONOCLE | PANAMA |

## 20 NUMBER SEARCH

The number 12478 appears just once in this grid, running in either a forward or backward direction, either vertically, horizontally or diagonally. Can you locate it?

# 21 PAY, STAY AND GO AWAY

Lucy Tayble climbed out of her Rolls Royce and stared at the parking meter. A helpful attendant came up.
'Can I assist you, Ma'am?'
'Certainly not. I was merely wondering how many different ways there were to put in this ridiculous charge of 50 cents.'
'There must be hundreds.'
'No, it's less than that, even though putting in 5 cents then 10 cents is not the same as 10 cents then 5 cents.' The attendant's brain was beginning to spin. 'Isn't it?', he asked. 'Of course not. If one were to drop one's first coin down that drain there, one would rather lose 5 cents than 10 cents, wouldn't one? "I suppose one, err I, would. Did you get the answer?'
'No, you interrupted me. Work it out and tell me when I get back.'
And off Lucy went, knowing that once again she had avoided paying to park and that the attendant would be too busy to notice!
So, how many ways are there to put 50 cents into the machine?

| CHARGES |
| --- |
| 50C PER HOUR |
| ONLY 5C AND |
| 10C COINS |
| ACCEPTED    5C    10C |

## 22 DOMINO DEAL

A standard set (0–0) to (6–6) is laid out below. Each domino is placed so that the larger number will be on the bottom:
i.e.      3         not      6
          6                  3
Those top numbers show the four numbers which form the top half of each domino in that column. The bottom numbers, below the grid, give the four bottom numbers for that column. The seven numbers on the left show the numbers which belong in that row. Can you cross-reference the facts and deduce where each domino has been placed? 3*6 is given as a start.

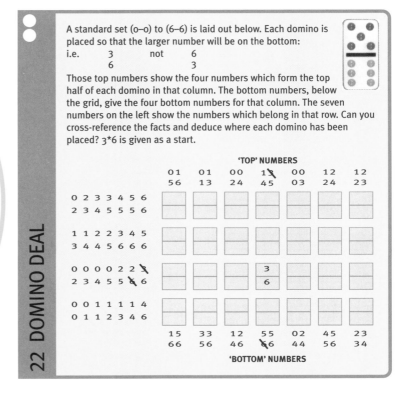

'TOP' NUMBERS

| | 01 | 01 | 00 | 1✗ | 00 | 12 | 12 |
| --- | --- | --- | --- | --- | --- | --- | --- |
| | 56 | 13 | 24 | 45 | 03 | 24 | 23 |
| 0 2 3 3 4 5 6 | | | | | | | |
| 2 3 4 5 5 5 6 | | | | | | | |
| 1 1 2 2 3 4 5 | | | | | | | |
| 3 4 4 5 6 6 6 | | | | | | | |
| 0 0 0 0 2 2 ✗ | | | | | 3 | | |
| 2 3 4 5 5 ✗ 6 | | | | | 6 | | |
| 0 0 1 1 1 1 4 | | | | | | | |
| 0 1 1 2 3 4 6 | | | | | | | |
| | 15 | 33 | 12 | 55 | 02 | 45 | 23 |
| | 66 | 56 | 46 | ✗6 | 44 | 56 | 34 |

'BOTTOM' NUMBERS

## 23 HANJIE

The numbers alongside each row or column tell you how many blocks of black squares are in a line. For example: 2, 3, 5 tells you that from left to right (or top to bottom) there is a group of two black squares, then at least one white space, then a group of three black squares, then at least one white shape, then a group of five black squares. Each block of black squares on the same line must have at least one white square between it and the next block of black squares. Sometimes it is possible to tell which squares are going to be black without reference to other lines or columns. In the example below, we can deduce that any block of six black squares must incorporate the two central squares.

6 ▢▢▢▢■▢▢▢▢

Can you complete this hanjie puzzle, to reveal the hidden pattern or picture?

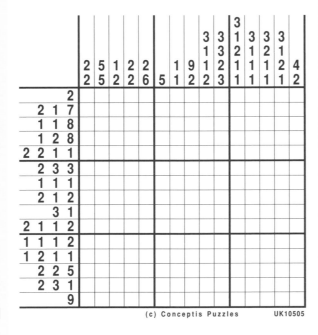

(c) Conceptis Puzzles    UK10505

## 24 CELL STRUCTURE

The object is to create white areas surrounded by black walls, so that:
• Each white area contains only one number
• The number of cells in a white area is equal to the number in it
• The white areas are separated from each other with a black wall
• Cells containing numbers must not be filled in
• The black cells must be linked into a continuous wall
• Black cells cannot form a square of 2x2 or larger

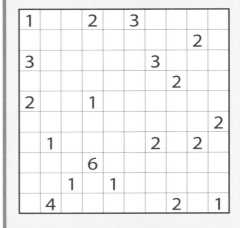

13

## 25 DOMINO DEAL

A standard set (o–o) to (6–6) is laid out below. Each domino is placed so that the larger number will be on the bottom:
i.e.

| 3 | not | 6 |
|---|-----|---|
| 6 |     | 3 |

Those top numbers show the four numbers which form the top half of each domino in that column. The bottom numbers, below the grid, give the four bottom numbers for that column. The seven numbers on the left show the numbers which belong in that row. Can you cross-reference the facts and deduce where each domino has been placed? 3*6 is given as a start.

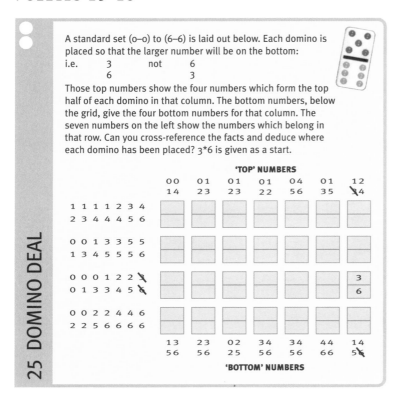

'TOP' NUMBERS

| | 00 14 | 01 23 | 01 23 | 01 22 | 04 56 | 01 35 | 12 ~~3~~4 |
|---|---|---|---|---|---|---|---|
| 1 1 1 1 2 3 4<br>2 3 4 4 4 5 6 | | | | | | | |
| 0 0 1 3 3 5 5<br>1 3 4 5 5 5 6 | | | | | | | |
| 0 0 0 1 2 2 ~~3~~<br>0 1 3 3 4 5 ~~6~~ | | | | | | 3<br>6 | |
| 0 0 2 2 4 4 6<br>2 2 5 6 6 6 6 | | | | | | | |
| | 13 56 | 23 56 | 02 25 | 34 56 | 34 56 | 44 66 | 14 5~~6~~ |

'BOTTOM' NUMBERS

## 27 FRAME UP

Henry is a faithful supporter of Coppleton Basketball Club and he attends matches whenever possible. He has decided that the supporters should have some recognition and he has persuaded Madge, one of the ladies providing refreshments, to take a photo. Henry is in position F and your job is to provide the other names. Left and right are as you look at the photo, and in front and behind are not necessarily directly so unless stated, ie, it is true to say that A is behind K.

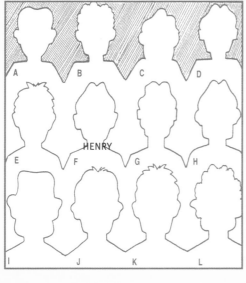

1 Agnes is behind Emily and to the right of Isaac.
2 David is behind Joyce and to the right of Keith.
3 Isaac is behind David and to the right of Lydia.
4 Clive is to the right of Beryl and behind Lydia.
5 Grace is to the left of Isaac and in front of Agnes.
6 Beryl is in front of Felix and to the right of Joyce.
7 Keith is to the right of Henry and behind Agnes.

## 26 COLOUR BLIND

Police Officer Friendly's informer, Slippery Sid, is none too helpful when it comes to pointing out which of various colourful characters keeps their car behind which coloured garage door. The only thing that we do know is that no garage has either a door, car or an owner's name with the same colour in it. From Sid's statement see if you can fill in the form correctly.

LEFT

Owner
Car Make
Car Colour

The red car is two places to the left of the Jaguar and the grey car is one place to the right of Mr Grey's car, which isn't a VW. Mr Green's car, the Lancia and the blue car are in adjoining garages but none has a red door and the green car, the Skoda and Mr Pink's car are also in adjoining garages with the named make being the middle car in each case. There is also an Opel, Mr Blue and Mr White are the other two owners and the other car colour is white.

## 28 NUMBER JIG

Insert the figures into the grid. One has been done for you.

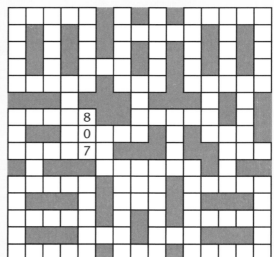

**3 figures**
130
191
219
233
354
419
463
507
588
671
690
~~807~~
876
935

**4 figures**
2190
3253
8491
9725

**5 figures**
12663
13002
19309
20393
26205
29994
31069
31155

32194
33062
40134
48181
50242
50551
52104
53606
60885
62271
65018
77123
83118
89031
90460

91203
92186
93661
93906

**6 figures**
110375
452706
546371
680935
790020

At the Little Appenin local fair a plant stall had a display of 25 potted plants. Four customers each bought five plants – taking one from each row and each column. So with just 5 plants left, each was given a free gift of a plant type they hadn't already bought. One plant bought by each customer is shown. The chart indicates how many of some plants each purchased. The columns are counted from the left as you look. (For non-gardeners the begonia is yellow; the azalea is pink and the other two are, hopefully, obvious.) At the end of it all, which plant was left on the table and which pots did each buy or was given free?

| | Azalea | Begonia | Cactus | Fern |
|---|---|---|---|---|
| Kevin | 2 | | | 2 |
| Len | | 2 | | 2 |
| Mary | 3 | | | |
| Norma | | | 3 | |

## 29 ODD POT

## 30 SQUARE NUMBERS

The numbers 1–25 are entered randomly in a 5 x 5 square so that no two consecutive numbers are adjacent in any direction, or in the same row or column. Column 1 contains four multiples of 5, but not 20, which is in the same row as 5. C3 is one lower than A2 which is four lower than B1 which is one higher than E2 which is one higher than A3 which is a prime number. B4 plus D3 equals D5; E3 plus A5, which are consecutive numbers, equals A4; C2 is an even number. B3, which is one higher than E4, is twice C4; B5 is a multiple of C5, which is not 1. 7 is in the same line diagonally as 8, and 6 is immediately below an even number, whilst 8 is below an odd number. 22 is below and diagonally adjacent to 2 which is in the same row as 14. If the long diagonal from top left to bottom right contains only one odd number, can you complete the grid?

| | 1 | 2 | 3 | 4 | 5 |
|---|---|---|---|---|---|
| A | | | | | |
| B | | | | | |
| C | | | | | |
| D | | | | | |
| E | | | | | |

## 31 LOGI-5

Each line, across and down, is to have each of the letters A, B, C, D and E, appearing once each. Also, every shape – shown by the thick lines – must also have each of the letters in it. Can you fill in the grid?

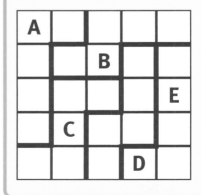

15

## 32 ON THE SCENE

Each of the six objects in the lower boxes can be found in one of the lettered squares in the big picture. Find these squares and transfer the letters to the little boxes below. You should spell out the name of a world – famous university.

## 34 SUDOKU

Place a number from 1 to 9 in each empty cell so that each row, each column and each 3 x 3 block contains all the numbers from 1 to 9.

|   | 2 | 6 |   |   |   |   | 8 | 1 |
|---|---|---|---|---|---|---|---|---|
| 3 |   |   | 7 |   | 8 |   |   | 6 |
| 4 |   |   |   | 5 |   |   |   | 7 |
|   | 5 |   | 1 |   | 7 |   | 9 |   |
|   |   | 3 | 9 |   | 5 | 1 |   |   |
|   | 4 |   | 3 |   | 2 |   | 5 |   |
| 1 |   |   |   | 3 |   |   |   | 2 |
| 5 |   |   | 2 |   | 4 |   |   | 9 |
|   | 3 | 8 |   |   |   | 4 | 6 |   |

## 33 DATE WITH A PLATE

Four couples in Celebration Road have each invited another couple round for a small dinner party. Each party is on a different day. By crossing out the names which do not fit on each invitation and circling those that do, can you name each couple hosting each event and the names of their two guests?

1  Tim is going out the day after Don. Alf is entertaining Dot the day after Joy's dinner party. One hostess is May.
2  Liz's dinner party is on Sunday. Les is going out the day before Jim's dinner party.
3  Fay is not married to Bob who is going out on Friday and neither is the guest of Joy who is not married to Jim.
4  Pam and Tom are married but are not the couple entertaining Kay on Saturday.

| DAY | FROM SHE | & HE | TO SHE | & HE |
|---|---|---|---|---|
|  |  |  |  |  |
|  |  |  |  |  |
|  |  |  |  |  |
|  |  |  |  |  |

## 35 TOFFEE TRAUMA

Guide Greedy Gordon through the maze to collect as many toffees as possible before the end, without going back over his own tracks.

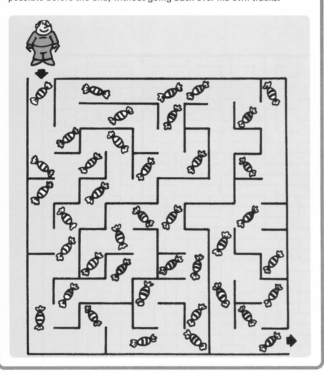

## 36 COLOUR BLIND

Police Officer Friendly's informer, Slippery Sid, is none too helpful when it comes to pointing out which of various colourful characters keeps their car behind which coloured garage door. The only thing that we do know is that no garage has either a door, car or an owner's name with the same colour in it. From Sid's statement see if you can fill in the form correctly.

LEFT
Owner
Car Make
Car Colour

Mr Grey's car is between the red car and the Toyota. The blue car and the Lada are in adjoining garages, neither is Mr Green's car, and none of these is behind the yellow door. The white car is between the Ford and Mr Red's car, and none of these is behind the blue door. Mr White owns the Renault, which is not a red car and is to the left of both Mr Green's car and the black car. There is also a grey car and a Nissan and Mr Black is the other owner.

## 37 HANJIE

The numbers alongside each row or column tell you how many blocks of black squares are in a line. For example: 2, 3, 5 tells you that from left to right (or top to bottom) there is a group of two black squares, then at least one white space, then a group of three black squares, then at least one white shape, then a group of five black squares. Each block of black squares on the same line must have at least one white square between it and the next block of black squares.

Sometimes it is possible to tell which squares are going to be black without reference to other lines or columns. In the example below, we can deduce that any block of six black squares must incorporate the two central squares.

6 ▢▢▢▢■▢▢▢

Can you complete this hanjie puzzle, to reveal the hidden pattern or picture?

| | | | | | | | | | | 2 | 1 | | | 1 | | | | | | | |
|---|---|---|---|---|---|---|---|---|---|---|---|---|---|---|---|---|---|---|---|---|---|
| | | | | 2 | | 2 1 4 | 1 4 1 | 1 1 | | 1 4 | 1 4 | 1 1 | 1 | 1 | | 2 | 1 | 1 | 1 | | |
| | | 1 2 1 | 1 5 1 | 2 1 3 | 5 6 | 2 1 | 1 1 1 | 7 4 | 4 1 1 2 | 1 1 1 | 4 3 2 | 4 3 2 | 1 1 5 | 4 1 | 4 1 | 1 1 | 1 3 | 2 2 | 2 1 | 3 1 | |
| | 3 | | | 2 | | | | | | | | | | | | | | | | | |
| 9 | | | | | | | | | | | | | | | | | | | | | |
| 3 1 | | | | | | | | | | | | | | | | | | | | | |
| 3 1 | | | | | | | | | | | | | | | | | | | | | |
| 15 | | | | | | | | | | | | | | | | | | | | | |
| 2 2 2 2 | | | | | | | | | | | | | | | | | | | | | |
| 2 2 2 2 | | | | | | | | | | | | | | | | | | | | | |
| 4 15 | | | | | | | | | | | | | | | | | | | | | |
| 1 1 1 1 1 | | | | | | | | | | | | | | | | | | | | | |
| 8 3 2 | | | | | | | | | | | | | | | | | | | | | |
| 6 3 2 | | | | | | | | | | | | | | | | | | | | | |
| 4 3 2 | | | | | | | | | | | | | | | | | | | | | |
| 6 5 | | | | | | | | | | | | | | | | | | | | | |
| 2 1 2 2 | | | | | | | | | | | | | | | | | | | | | |
| 2 1 2 2 | | | | | | | | | | | | | | | | | | | | | |
| 1 5 1 | | | | | | | | | | | | | | | | | | | | | |

## 38 MAZE MYSTERY

Travel from the entrance to the exit of the maze, filling the path completely to create a picture.

# 39 DOMINO SEARCH

A set of dominoes has been laid out, using numbers instead of dots for clarity, but the lines which separate the dominoes have been left out. Can you show where each domino in the set has been placed? You may find the check grid useful as each domino is identified by its number pair and the appropriate box can be ticked when the domino has been located. To give you a start 5*2 has been marked in.

| 6 | 1 | 0 | 3 | 4 | 3 | 4 | 1 |
|---|---|---|---|---|---|---|---|
| 1 | 6 | 6 | 3 | 6 | 5 | 2 | 2 |
| 2 | 0 | 3 | 1 | 2 | 3 | 5 | 1 |
| 1 | 3 | 4 | 2 | 6 | 1 | 1 | 0 |
| 5 | 4 | 2 | 6 | 0 | 5 | 2 | 5 |
| 3 | 0 | 4 | 0 | 4 | 6 | 4 | 4 |
| 0 | 3 | 6 | 0 | 2 | 5 | 5 | 5 |

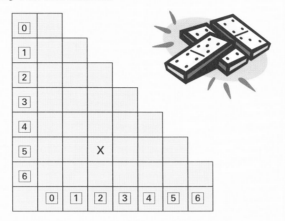

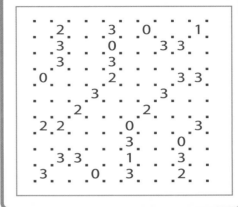

# 40 DOTTY DILEMMA

Connect adjacent dots with vertical or horizontal lines so that a single loop is formed with no crossings or branches. Each number indicates how many lines surround it, while empty cells may be surrounded by any number of lines.

| | 2 | | 3 | 0 | | 1 |
|---|---|---|---|---|---|---|
| | 3 | | 0 | | 3 | 3 |
| | 3 | | 3 | | | |
| 0 | | | 2 | | 3 | 3 |
| | | | | 3 | | |
| | | 2 | | 2 | | |
| 2 | 2 | | | 0 | | 3 |
| | | | 3 | | 0 | |
| | 3 | 3 | | 1 | | 3 |
| 3 | | 0 | | 3 | | 2 |

# 41 COLOUR BLIND

Police Officer Friendly's informer, Slippery Sid, is none too helpful when it comes to pointing out which of various colourful characters keeps their car behind which coloured garage door. The only thing that we do know is that no garage has either a door, car or an owner's name with the same colour in it. From Sid's statement see if you can fill in the form correctly.

| LEFT | | | | | |
|---|---|---|---|---|---|
| Owner | | | | | |
| Car Make | | | | | |
| Car Colour | | | | | |

Mr Brown's car, which is next to both the BMW and the black one, is not the Fiat, which is next to both the brown car and Mr White's. The Volvo is two places to the right of the grey car and the Audi which is not Mr White's is two places to the left of Mr Grey's car. There are also both a red and green car, Mr Black and Mr Green are the other two owners and the final make of car is a Ford.

# 42 WHERE THE L?

Twelve L shapes like the ones below have been fitted into a rectangular shape. Each L has one hole, and there are three of each type in the rectangle. No two pieces of the same type are adjacent, even at a corner. They fit together so well that the spaces between pieces do not show. From the locations of the holes, can you tell where each L is?

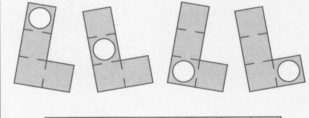

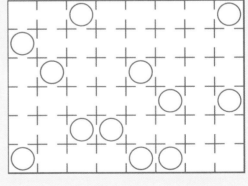

## 43 PATTERN MAKER

Can you place the numbered blocks into the grid to form the pattern shown? The blocks may be placed horizontally or vertically, and may be turned round.

| 4 | 6 | 4 | 3 |
|---|---|---|---|
| 3 | 3 | 2 | 2 |
| 5 | 5 | 5 | 4 |
| 6 | 4 | 2 | 6 |
| 5 | 6 | 3 | 2 |

| 5 | 6 |
|---|---|

| 4 | 2 |
|---|---|

| 3 | 2 |
|---|---|

| 6 | 4 |
|---|---|

| 3 | 6 |
|---|---|

| 5 | 4 |
|---|---|

| 3 | 4 |
|---|---|

| 5 | 3 |
|---|---|

| 2 | 5 |
|---|---|

| 2 | 6 |
|---|---|

## 44 IT FIGURES

Place a number from 1 to 9 in each empty cell so that the sum of each vertical or horizontal block equals the number at the top or on the left of that block. Numbers may only be used once in each block.

## 45 BLACK AND WHITE

In a negative, everything which is really black appears white and everything which is really white appears black.

Can you see which one of the three boots A, B and C is shown as a negative?

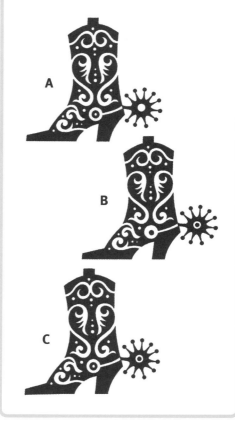

A

B

C

## 46 POKER PLACES

These seven regulars of a weekly poker school have developed a ritual for deciding where each man will sit. They form a line, host at the front. He selects a seat and sits down. The others move clockwise around the table in line, passing three empty chairs and sitting at the next empty chair. This continues until all are sat down. For tonight's game, we can tell you that: Malcolm was directly in front of the doctor and directly behind Lionel in the line. Jerry who was next in line after the mail man is sat with Keith on his right hand and the financier on his left hand. The jockey was the third man in the line. He sat next door to neither the salesman or Gus who were next to each other in the line and are next to each other at the table. The bookmaker sat down next after Syd. The baker who was two places earlier in the line than Wilf is seated two places clockwise from him. Can you work out the occupation of each man and place him at the table?

HINT: Number the men in the line 1 to 7 and work out first where each 'number' is sat. Then work out who can't be in each seat.

## 47 HAT CHECK

Which silhouette exactly matches the cowboy with the air-conditioned stetson?

## 48 CRAZY MAZE

Can you find your way through this mad scientist's smoky maze?

## 49 TOGA PARTY

Each figure differs from the other three by one extra detail. Can you spot all four extra details?

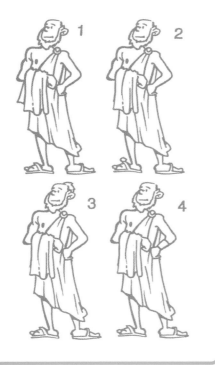

## 50 TAKING STEPS

During their vacation at Pantings (with reduced rates for the anniversarily challenged), three couples became close friends. In the two dances recorded here, nobody danced with his/her spouse and each had a different partner for each dance.
The couples were:

FOXTROT
Andrew and the lady from New York.
Floe's husband and Mrs Gould.
Mr Hedges and Colin's wife.

WALTZ
Brian and the lady from Kansas City.
Dolly's husband and the lady from New Orleans.
Mr Jacobs and Edna.

Can you name each married couple and say where they came from?

## 51 DOMINO SEARCH

A set of dominoes has been laid out, using numbers instead of dots for clarity, but the lines which separate the dominoes have been left out. Can you show where each domino in the set has been placed? You may find the check grid useful as each domino is identified by its number pair and the appropriate box can be ticked when the domino has been located. To give you a start 6*4 has been marked in.

| 0 | 0 | 1 | 5 | 4 | 5 | 2 | 6 |
|---|---|---|---|---|---|---|---|
| 1 | 0 | 5 | 3 | 6 | 1 | 4 | 2 |
| 3 | 5 | 0 | 4 | 5 | 3 | 4 | 1 |
| 2 | 5 | 6 | 5 | 6 | 1 | 3 | 6 |
| 2 | 3 | 2 | 3 | 2 | 4 | 3 | 6 |
| 0 | 0 | 5 | 0 | 2 | 1 | 0 | 6 |
| 4 | 3 | 6 | 1 | 1 | 4 | 2 | 4 |

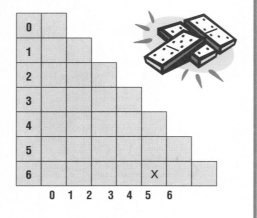

## 52 CODE MASTER

Just follow the rules of that classic puzzle, Master Mind, to crack the colour code. The first number tells you how many of the pegs are exactly correct – the right colour in the right place(✓✓). The second number tells you how many pegs are the correct colour but are not in the right place(✓). Colours may be repeated in the answer. By comparing the information given by each line, can you work out which colour goes in which place?

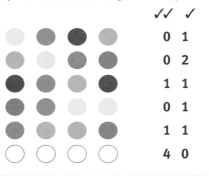

|  | ✓✓ | ✓ |
|---|---|---|
|  | 0 | 1 |
|  | 0 | 2 |
|  | 1 | 1 |
|  | 0 | 1 |
|  | 1 | 1 |
|  | 4 | 0 |

## 53 CELL STRUCTURE

The object is to create white areas surrounded by black walls, so that:
• Each white area contains only one number
• The number of cells in a white area is equal to the number in it
• The white areas are separated from each other with a black wall
• Cells containing numbers must not be filled in
• The black cells must be linked into a continuous wall
• Black cells cannot form a square of 2 x 2 or larger

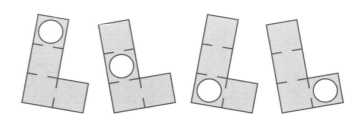

## 54 WHERE THE L?

Twelve L shapes like the ones below have been fitted into an oblong shape. Each L has one hole, and there are three of each type in the square. No two pieces of the same type are adjacent, even at a corner. They fit together so well that the spaces between pieces do not show. From the locations of the holes, can you tell where each L is?

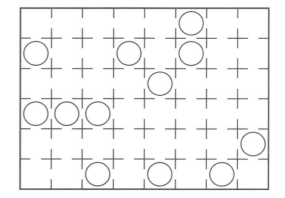

## 55 STICKY TIME

There are 30 squares here of various sizes. Remove nine matchsticks, so that *no squares exist at all*.

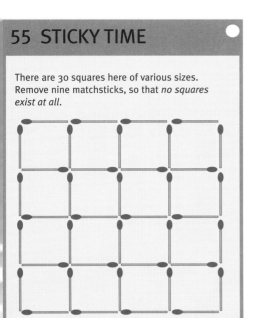

## 56 I ON U!

Nanotec, launchers of such great software as Peephole2001, have hired IonU Surveillance Ltd to report on members of staff making illegal use of company facilities. Within hours, four hapless souls were on the carpet. Sean de Lear sent the fax but not to Burnley. The phone call was to Canada. Mother was contacted in Accrington and Wilf Hickset contacted Denmark. Neither the connection to the bookmaker in Burnley nor the one via the Internet was made by Rhoda Luck. Tania Hyde's e-mail was not the message to the car salesman as a man sent that.

| CONTACT | EMPLOYEE | METHOD | PLACE |
|---|---|---|---|
| Bookmaker | | | |
| Car Sales | | | |
| Mother | | | |
| Partner | | | |

## 57 SIX-PACK

By packing numbers in the empty spaces, can you make the numbers in each of the 16 hexagons add up to 25? No two numbers in each hexagon may be the same and you can't use zero. We've started you off.

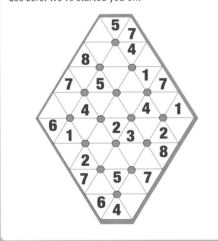

## 58 LIFE ON THE OCEAN WAVE

Which one of the numbered prints did the stamp create?

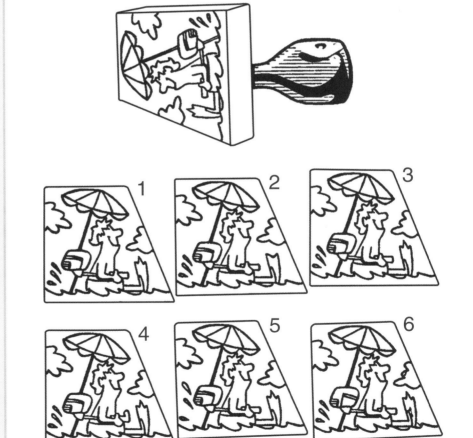

23

## 59 CUT BACK

The first three pictures A, B, C form a sequence. Which of the pictures D, E and F is the correct one to continue the pattern?

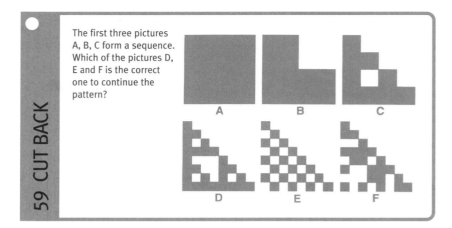

## 61 BOOK BORROWING

The top shelf shows books at the start of the day, when Puzzleton Library opened. The bottom shelf shows books at the end of the day, when Puzzleton Library closed. During the day the books were all studied by various people who replaced them in different positions and one was borrowed and taken home. Can you discover which is missing?

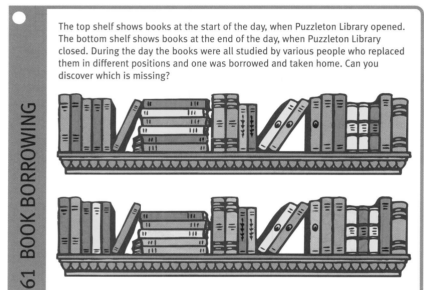

## 60 NUMBER JIG

Fit the numbers into the grid. One has been done for you.

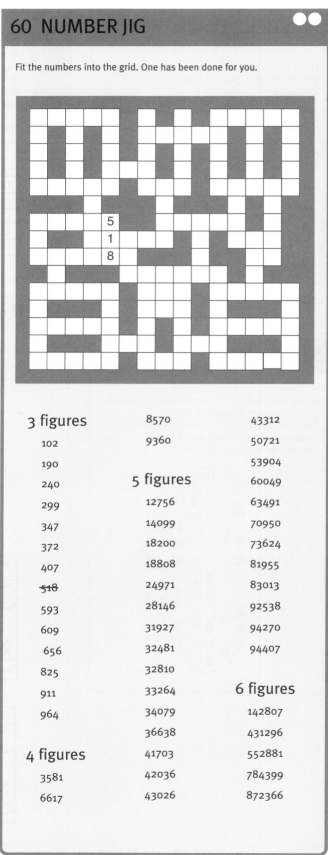

| 3 figures | 8570 | 43312 |
|---|---|---|
| 102 | 9360 | 50721 |
| 190 | | 53904 |
| 240 | 5 figures | 60049 |
| 299 | 12756 | 63491 |
| 347 | 14099 | 70950 |
| 372 | 18200 | 73624 |
| 407 | 18808 | 81955 |
| ~~518~~ | 24971 | 83013 |
| 593 | 28146 | 92538 |
| 609 | 31927 | 94270 |
| 656 | 32481 | 94407 |
| 825 | 32810 | |
| 911 | 33264 | 6 figures |
| 964 | 34079 | 142807 |
| | 36638 | 431296 |
| 4 figures | 41703 | 552881 |
| 3581 | 42036 | 784399 |
| 6617 | 43026 | 872366 |

## 62 SUDOKU

Place a number from 1 to 9 in each empty cell so that each row, each column and each 3 x 3 block contains all the numbers from 1 to 9.

|   | 6 | 3 |   |   | 2 | 4 | 1 |   |
|---|---|---|---|---|---|---|---|---|
| 4 |   |   | 5 |   | 8 |   |   | 7 |
| 8 |   |   | 1 |   | 3 |   |   | 6 |
| 9 | 8 | 7 |   |   |   | 1 | 4 |   |
|   |   |   |   | 3 |   |   |   |   |
|   | 2 | 4 |   |   |   | 6 | 9 | 5 |
| 7 |   |   | 2 |   | 1 |   |   | 4 |
| 6 |   |   | 3 |   | 9 |   |   | 1 |
|   | 1 | 8 | 4 |   |   | 7 | 3 |   |

# 63 MAZE MYSTERY

Travel from the entrance to the exit of the maze, filling the path completely to create a picture.

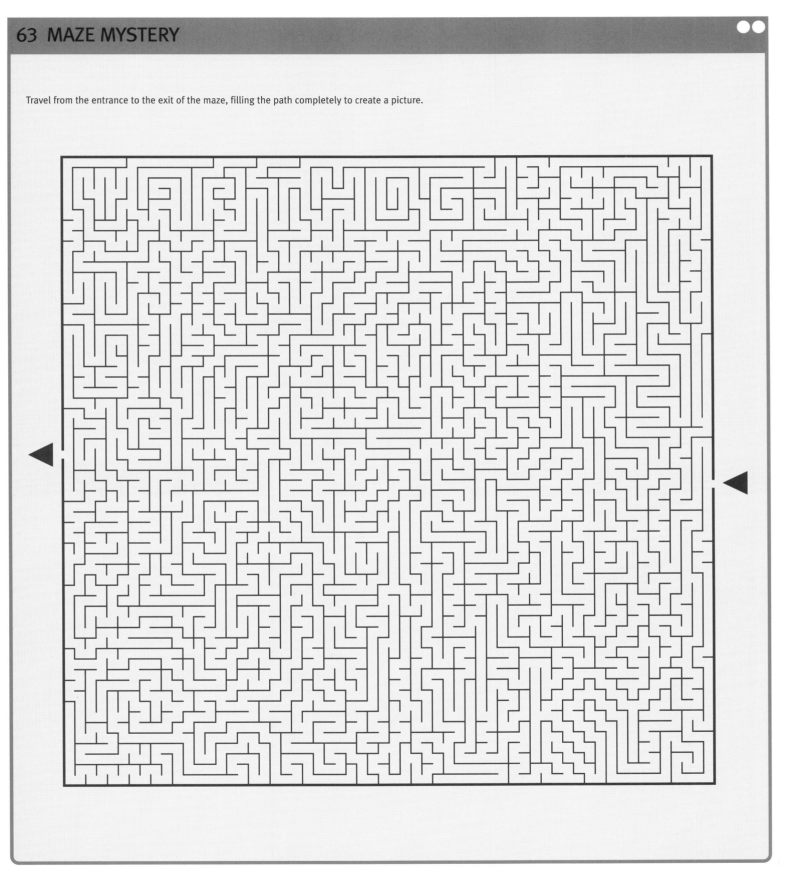

## 64 BOXES

Pattern A when cut out and folded along the straight lines will make a cube-shaped box. This folded box is shown in figures 1 and 2 but in each case one face is left blank. Can you fill in the missing symbols which should appear on the blank faces? When you have done this, repeat the same procedure with pattern B and figures 3 and 4.

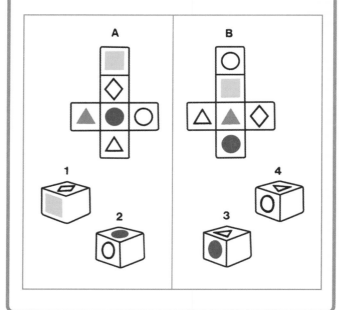

## 65 ONE TO TEN

In this tangle of numbers, can you find a path which passes through all the numbers from 1 to 10? The numbers must run consecutively.

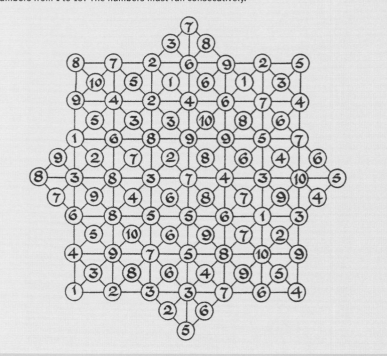

## 66 DOMINO SEARCH

A set of dominoes has been laid out, using numbers instead of dots for clarity, but the lines which separate the dominoes have been left out. Can you show where each domino in the set has been placed? You may find the check grid useful as each domino is identified by its number pair and the appropriate box can be ticked when the domino has been located. To give you a start 0*9 has been marked in.

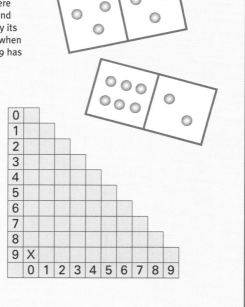

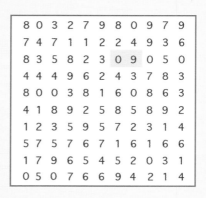

## 67 CELL STRUCTURE

The object is to create white areas surrounded by black walls, so that:
• Each white area contains only one number
• The number of cells in a white area is equal to the number in it
• The white areas are separated from each other with a black wall
• Cells containing numbers must not be filled in
• The black cells must be linked into a continuous wall
• Black cells cannot form a square of 2 x 2 or larger

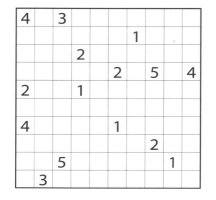

# 68 SHORT ORDER

These six souls are happy couples – can you put a name to each and match up the pairs?

1 Art is heavier than Alice's date.
2 Bill's date is taller than Chuck's date.
3 Chuck is heavier than Beth's date.
4 Chuck's date is taller than Cathy.

# 70 IT FIGURES

Place a number from 1 to 9 in each empty cell so that the sum of each vertical or horizontal block equals the number at the top or on the left of that block. Numbers may only be used once in each block.

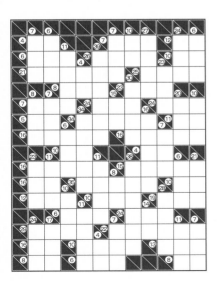

## 69 BOX CLEVER

Using just two straight lines, can you divide this box into three segments, each containing six differently coloured crayons?

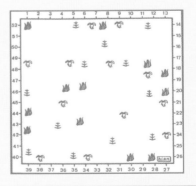

# 71 BIG BREAK

A snooker break is made up by potting red balls (maximum 15) which are each followed by one of six different colours. The point values of the balls are:-

 RED 1

 YELLOW 2

 GREEN 3

 BROWN 4

 BLUE 5

 PINK 6

 BLACK 7

Snooker player Bob Basher made a break of 74, which ended when he failed to pot a red. In the break he potted more blacks than browns and more blues than pinks, potting all four colours in the break, each a different number of times.

How many of each colour ball were potted?

# 72 21s

Obeying the normal rules of arithmetic, with the numbers given, using only where necessary +, –, x, or ÷, make the resulting calculations equal 21.

$$6 \quad 3 \quad 9 \quad 6 = 21$$
$$4 \quad 4 \quad 2 \quad 3 = 21$$
$$3 \quad 5 \quad 10 \quad 4 = 21$$

# 73 TRILINES

Can you divide this square into six sections, each containing three pairs of different symbols, by drawing three straight lines? The lines must run from one reference number to another on the other side of the square.

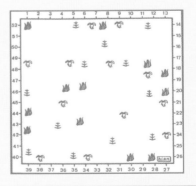

## 74 TEA FOR TWO

Which two teapots are exactly identical?

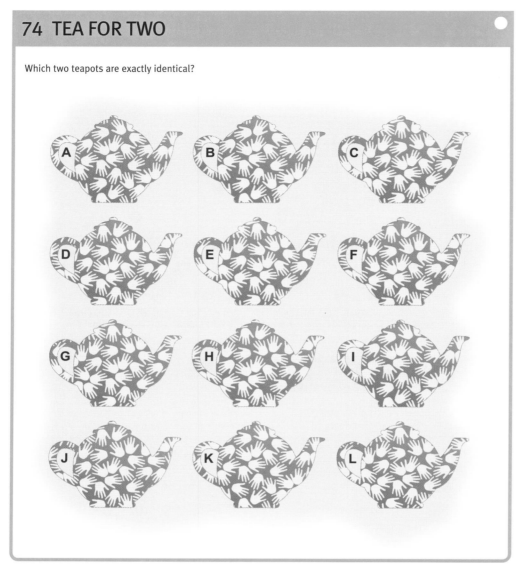

## 75 LOGI-5

Each line, across and down, is to have each of the letters A, B, C, D and E, appearing once each. Also, every shape – shown by the thick lines, must also have each of the letters in it. Can you fill in the grid?

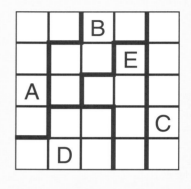

## 76 ABC

Each line, across and down, is to have each of the letters A. B and C, and two empty squares. The letter outside the grid shows the first or second letter in the direction of the arrow. Can you fill in the grid?

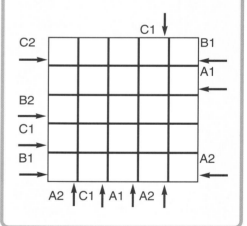

## 77 LOGI-TILES

Following the first diagram, there is a logical rule that determines how the next block is to be filled in. Given these three blocks, can you colour in the fourth?

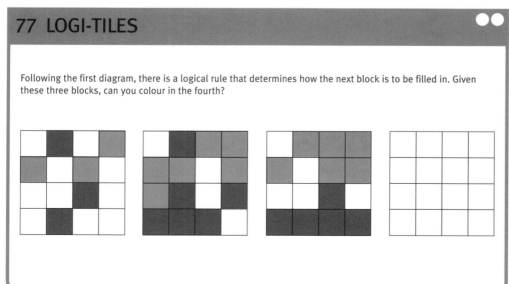

## 78 NUMBER JIG

Fit the numbers into the grid. One has been done for you.

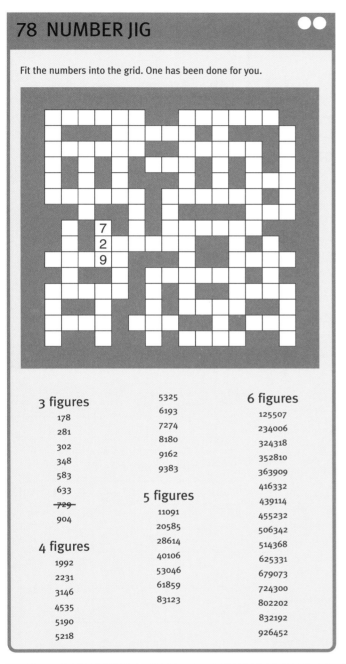

**3 figures**
178
281
302
348
583
633
~~729~~
904

**4 figures**
1992
2231
3146
4535
5190
5218

5325
6193
7274
8180
9162
9383

**5 figures**
11091
20585
28614
40106
53046
61859
83123

**6 figures**
125507
234006
324318
352810
363909
416332
439114
455232
506342
514368
625331
679073
724300
802202
832192
926452

## 79 WHERE THE L?

Twelve L shapes like the ones below have been fitted into a square shape. Each L has one hole, and there are three of each type in the square. No two pieces of the same type are adjacent, even at a corner. They fit together so well that the spaces between pieces do not show. From the locations of the holes, can you tell where each L is?

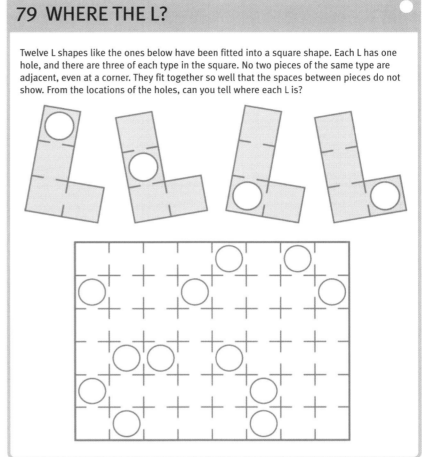

**?**

## 80 SUDOKU

Place a number from 1 to 9 in each empty cell so that each row, each column and each 3 x 3 block contains all the numbers from 1 to 9.

| 2 | 5 |   |   | 4 |   |   | 7 | 1 |
|---|---|---|---|---|---|---|---|---|
| 7 |   |   | 9 | 1 |   |   |   | 2 |
|   |   | 6 |   | 7 |   | 5 |   |   |
|   | 6 |   | 2 |   | 4 |   | 1 |   |
| 4 |   | 1 |   |   |   | 2 |   | 3 |
|   | 9 |   | 6 |   | 8 |   | 5 |   |
|   |   | 5 |   | 2 |   | 8 |   |   |
| 9 |   |   | 7 |   | 5 |   |   | 4 |
| 6 | 3 |   |   | 8 |   |   | 2 | 5 |

## 81 SET SQUARE

All the digits from 1 to 9 are used in this grid, but only once. Can you work out their positions in the grid and make the sums work? We've given two numbers to start you off.

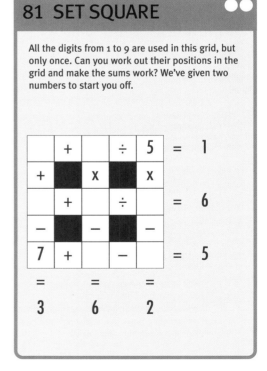

## 82 TAKING STEPS

At Come Prancing's Annual Dance Gala, four couples reprised the Latin-American section from the previous week's Amateur Finals. As the gala was a fancy dress affair, at least the ladies could now wear more each than they had between them in the competition and the men could remove the rose stems from between their punctured gums. This time round, nobody danced with his/her spouse and each had a different partner in each dance. From these pairings, hastily made as the couples twirled faster than a cheerleader's baton, can you identify each married couple and the costume each is sporting?

| CHA-CHA | RUMBA | TANGO |
|---|---|---|
| Pirate & Ann | Jester & Mark's wife | Fairy's husband & Rose |
| Mr Turner & Mrs Young | Steve & Ballerina | Eskimo & King's wife |
| Rose's husband & Leila | Mr Turner & Nurse | Jester & Norman's wife |
| John & Mrs Downs | Norman & Cowgirl | Mr West & Zoe |

## 85 HIGH CARDS

Five cards have been laid out, all are between Ace and Ten. All four suits are represented. No three of the cards form a consecutive sequence of numbers.

The total value of Red cards is the same as the total value of Black cards.
The total value of Hearts is 12.
The even-value cards have a total four higher than the sum of the odd-value cards.
The Club has a lower value than the Spade. The lowest card is a Diamond.
Which five cards have been dealt?

## 83 EASY AS ABC

Each row and column originally contained one A, one B, one C, one D and two blank squares. Each letter and number refers to the first or second of the four letters encountered when travelling in the direction of the arrow. Can you complete the original grid?

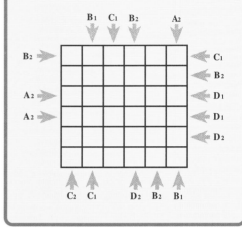

## 84 SUDOKU

Place a number from 1 to 9 in each empty cell so that each row, each column and each 3 x 3 block contains all the numbers from 1 to 9.

|   |   |   | 9 | 5 | 6 | 4 |   |   |
|---|---|---|---|---|---|---|---|---|
|   |   | 6 |   |   |   |   | 8 | 2 |
|   |   | 8 |   | 4 | 9 |   |   | 5 |
|   | 4 | 6 | 1 |   | 3 | 5 |   | 7 |
| 2 |   |   |   | 5 |   |   |   | 8 |
| 3 |   | 5 | 7 |   | 9 | 2 | 6 |   |
| 4 |   | 8 | 9 |   | 7 |   |   |   |
| 1 | 2 |   |   |   | 8 |   |   |   |
|   | 6 | 7 | 3 | 4 |   |   |   |   |

## 86 COG-ITATION

In which direction will each of the lettered weights move when the figure pulls the rope?

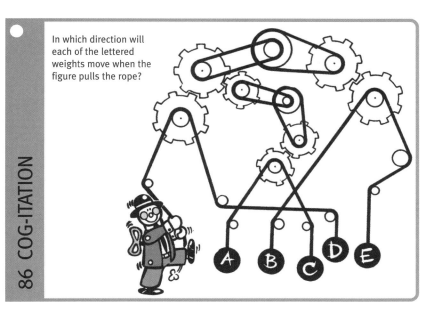

## 88 ALL FALL DOWN

Which of the falling girls are identical?

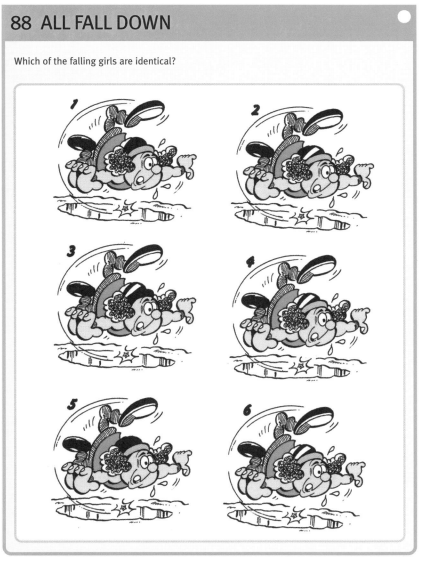

## 87 NUMBER JIG

Fit the numbers into the grid. One has been done for you.

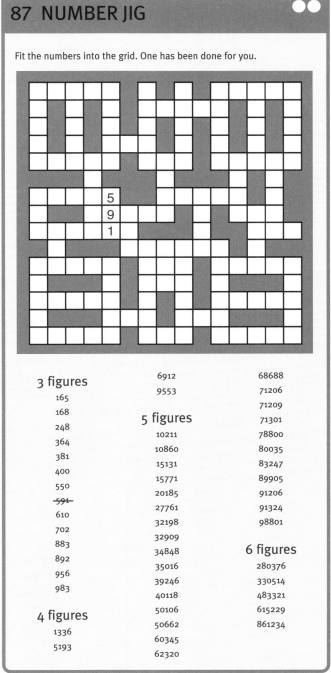

**3 figures**
165
168
248
364
381
400
550
591
610
702
883
892
956
983

**4 figures**
1336
5193

6912
9553

**5 figures**
10211
10860
15131
15771
20185
27761
32198
32909
34848
35016
39246
40118
50106
50662
60345
62320

68688
71206
71209
71301
78800
80035
83247
89905
91206
91324
98801

**6 figures**
280376
330514
483321
615229
861234

## 89 MAZE MYSTERY

Travel from the entrance to the exit of the maze, filling the path completely to create a picture.

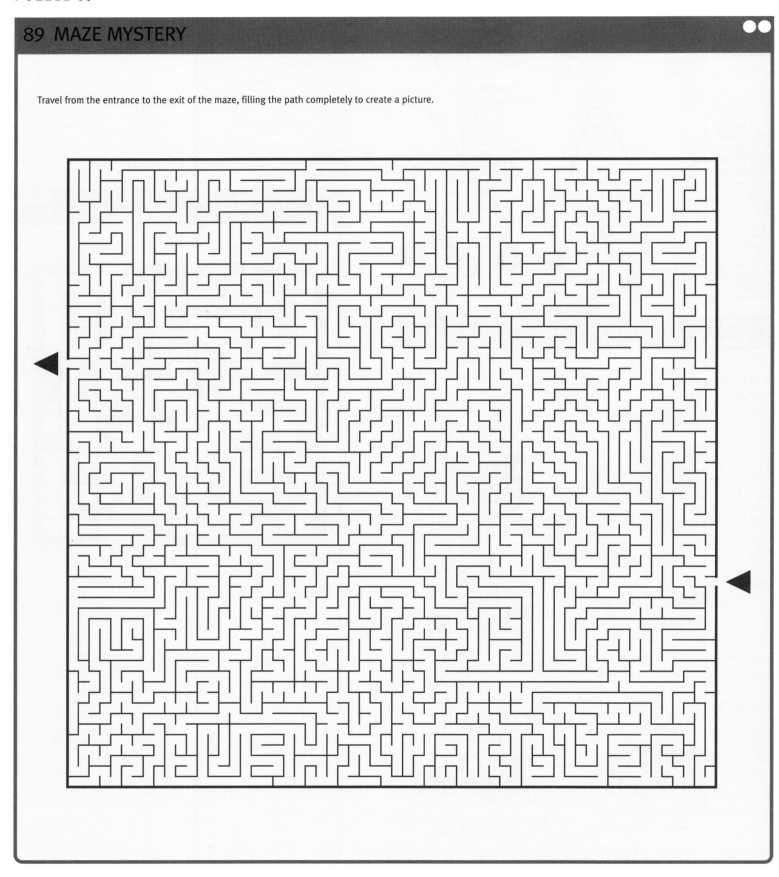

# 90 DOMINO SEARCH

A set of dominoes has been laid out, using numbers instead of dots for clarity, but the lines which separate the dominoes have been left out. Can you show where each domino in the set has been placed? You may find the check grid useful as each domino is identified by its number pair and the appropriate box can be ticked when the domino has been located. To give you a start, 0*9 has been marked in.

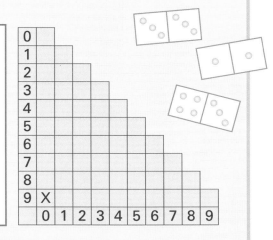

| 5 | 8 | 0 | 1 | 0 | 3 | 4 | 0 | 1 | 6 | 3 |
|---|---|---|---|---|---|---|---|---|---|---|
| 6 | 7 | 4 | 5 | 2 | 0 | 8 | 5 | 8 | 9 | 0 |
| 6 | 9 | 4 | 6 | 0 | 6 | 2 | 1 | 2 | 4 | 7 |
| 4 | 7 | 4 | 2 | 3 | 1 | 4 | 0 | 8 | 7 | 5 |
| 4 | 8 | 5 | 9 | 6 | 8 | 0 | 3 | 9 | 7 | 2 |
| 4 | 3 | 7 | 4 | 7 | 1 | 9 | 2 | 1 | 3 | 2 |
| 6 | 2 | 5 | 1 | 0 | 6 | 1 | 6 | 1 | 3 | 6 |
| 7 | 8 | 9 | 7 | 0 | 2 | 7 | 8 | 3 | 8 | 3 |
| 0 | 9 | 1 | 2 | 3 | 5 | 5 | 3 | 9 | 8 | 5 |
| 7 | 9 | 4 | 2 | 9 | 6 | 5 | 8 | 1 | 5 | 9 |

# 91 LOGI-5

Each line, across and down, is to have each of the five colours appearing once each. Each colour must also appear just once in each shape, shown by thick lines. Can you colour in this crazy quilt, or mark each square with its correct letter B, G, R, V or Y?

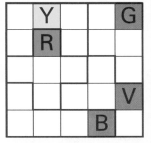

# 92 TAKE NOTE

Something's gone wrong with Tony's saxophone. He wants to play a tune but can't produce a note. Can you find ten musical notes hidden somewhere in this picture so that Tony can start to play?

# 93 ON THE SPOT

Can you place the dominoes into the grid so that the four vertical, four horizontal and both diagonal rows each have a spot total of eleven?

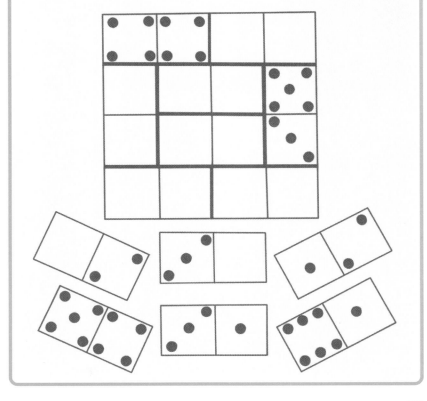

## 94 DOTTY DILEMMA

Connect adjacent dots with vertical or horizontal lines so that a single loop is formed with no crossings or branches. Each number indicates how many lines surround it, while empty cells may be surrounded by any number of lines.

```
.  . 3. 3.  .   .  .  . 0.  .   .
.  .   .   . 1. 3.  . 3.  . 1
. 0. 2.  .   .   .   .   .   . 2.
.  .   .   . 1. 0.  . 2.  .   .
. 3.  .   .   .  . 3.  . 3.  .
.  . 2.  . 3.  .   .   . 0.  .
.  .   .   . 0.  . 3. 2.  .   .
. 2.  .   .   .   .   .  . 2. 3.
. 3.  . 2.  . 3. 0.  .   .   .
.  .   . 0.  .   .   .  . 0. 2.
```

## 96 NUMBER JIG

Fit the numbers into the grid. One has been done for you.

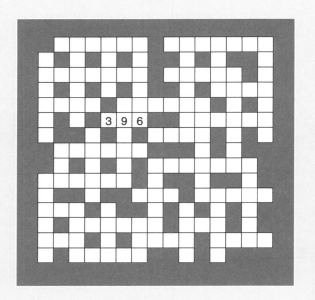

(grid with 3 9 6 filled in)

| 3 figures | | |
|---|---|---|
| 128 | 6233 | 411074 |
| 285 | 8139 | 525008 |
| ~~396~~ | 9303 | 606340 |
| 586 | | 726493 |
| 793 | **5 figures** | 783914 |
| 861 | 25510 | 803103 |
| 950 | 32165 | 895105 |
| | 51995 | 938118 |
| **4 figures** | 78163 | |
| 1218 | 92851 | **7 figures** |
| 1809 | | 1438116 |
| 2237 | **6 figures** | 2117055 |
| 3354 | 108392 | 3248813 |
| 4026 | 122589 | 5246319 |
| 5302 | 210101 | 5360241 |
| 6195 | 329406 | 8302269 |
| | 403625 | 9372688 |

## 95 DOMINO DEAL

A standard set (0–0 to 6–6) is laid out below. Each domino is placed so that the larger number will be on the bottom: i.e.
```
3        not      6
6                 3
```

Those TOP NUMBERS show the four numbers which form the top half of each domino in that column. The BOTTOM NUMBERS, below the grid, give the four bottom numbers for that column. The seven numbers on the left show the numbers which belong in that row. Can you cross-reference the facts and deduce where each domino has been placed? 3*6 is given as a start.

**'TOP' NUMBERS**

| | 00 03 | 00 26 | 11 ⅓4 | 12 24 | 00 15 | 22 34 | 11 35 |
|---|---|---|---|---|---|---|---|
| 0 0 1 1 2 2 3 / 1 2 4 5 5 5 6 | | | | | | | |
| 0 1 1 1 1 2 6 / 0 2 3 4 5 6 6 | | | | | | | |
| 0 0 2 3 4 4 5 / 2 3 4 4 6 6 6 | | | | | | | |
| 0 0 2 3 ⅘ 4 5 / 1 3 3 4 5 5 ⅚ | | | | 3 / 6 | | | |

| | 02 44 | 13 46 | 14 5⅘ | 24 55 | 35 56 | 35 66 | 23 66 |
|---|---|---|---|---|---|---|---|

**'BOTTOM' NUMBERS**

## 97 SIX GEESE-A-LAYING

When the six geese were finally trapped and boxed they settled down and began laying eggs, in nests numbered 1 to 6. Next morning, Miss T Hyde discovered that:

1 Only two of the birds laid the same number of eggs as the number of the box each was in.
2 Twenty-one eggs were laid altogether, no two birds laying the same number. No bird failed to lay any.
3 Clarissa, who was on one end, laid half as many eggs as were laid by both Brenda and the goose in box 5 added together.
4 Deirdre laid twice as many eggs as her box number. Her neighbour on one side, Felicity, laid two less eggs than Edwina who was Deirdre's neighbour on the other side.
5 The goose to the right of Abigail laid 3 eggs which was less than were laid in box 1.

Naturally, that golden egg was the only one laid by that remarkably gifted bird. Can you name her, and say in which box Miss Hyde will find her fortune? (Right is as you face the nests.)

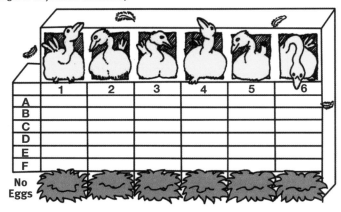

| | 1 | 2 | 3 | 4 | 5 | 6 |
|---|---|---|---|---|---|---|
| A | | | | | | |
| B | | | | | | |
| C | | | | | | |
| D | | | | | | |
| E | | | | | | |
| F | | | | | | |
| No Eggs | | | | | | |

## 98 POLYGON POSER

Which are the only two pieces that will fit together perfectly, to form a blue copy of this white shape?

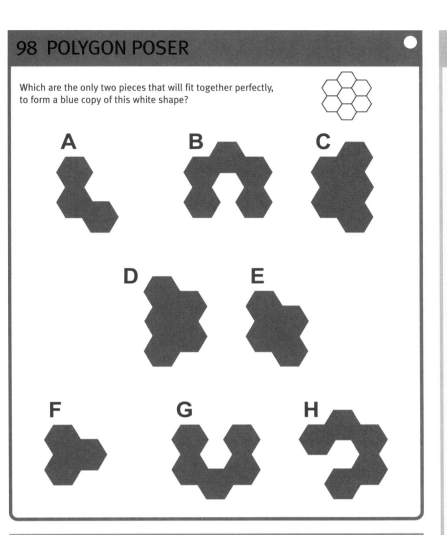

## 99 NUMBER JIG

Fit the numbers into the grid. One has been done for you.

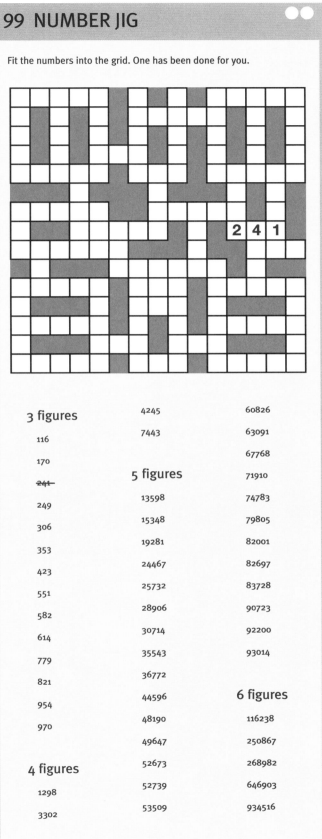

| 3 figures | | |
| --- | --- | --- |
| 116 | 4245 | 60826 |
| 170 | 7443 | 63091 |
| 241 | | 67768 |
| 249 | **5 figures** | 71910 |
| 306 | 13598 | 74783 |
| 353 | 15348 | 79805 |
| 423 | 19281 | 82001 |
| 551 | 24467 | 82697 |
| 582 | 25732 | 83728 |
| 614 | 28906 | 90723 |
| 779 | 30714 | 92200 |
| 821 | 35543 | 93014 |
| 954 | 36772 | |
| 970 | 44596 | **6 figures** |
| | 48190 | 116238 |
| | 49647 | 250867 |
| **4 figures** | 52673 | 268982 |
| 1298 | 52739 | 646903 |
| 3302 | 53509 | 934516 |

## 100 SUDOKU

Place a number from 1 to 9 in each empty cell so that each row, each column and each 3 x 3 block contains all the numbers from 1 to 9.

| 2 | 6 |   |   |   | 3 |   |   | 1 |
|---|---|---|---|---|---|---|---|---|
|   |   |   | 8 |   |   | 4 |   | 7 |
|   | 8 | 3 | 7 |   |   | 9 |   |   |
| 1 |   |   |   |   |   | 5 |   |   |
|   | 9 |   |   | 4 |   |   | 8 |   |
|   |   | 2 |   |   |   |   |   | 3 |
|   |   | 8 |   |   | 2 | 6 | 9 |   |
| 6 |   | 4 |   | 1 |   |   |   |   |
| 5 |   |   | 6 |   |   |   | 2 | 8 |

## 101 PATTERN MAKER

Can you place the numbered blocks into the grid to form the pattern shown? The blocks may be placed horizontally or vertically, and can be turned round.

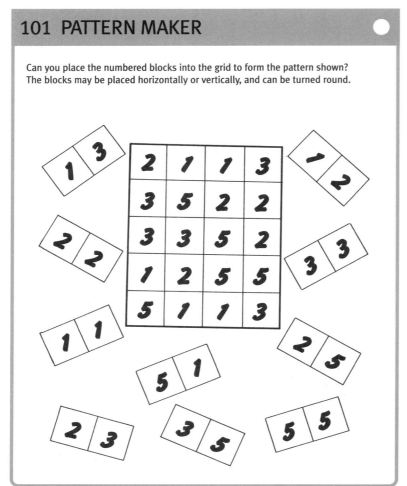

## 103 ROPED INTO IT!

When the man pulls the rope which weights will go down and which will go up?

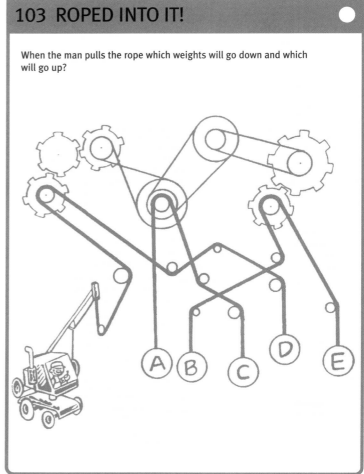

## 102 METEOR MUDDLE

In the picture on the left there are seven flying saucers flying through a meteorite storm. When they returned one was missing. Can you work out which one?

## 104 LONELY VIGILS

In the later years of the Roman occupation of Britain, the garrisons in the legionary fortresses were much depleted. In Deva, for example, they could spare only one man at a time to guard each of the four walls. From the clues given, can you indicate in the diagram the name of the soldier on each wall, his home country and the number of years he had served in his legion?

### Clues

1 The wall patrolled by Blunderbuss was opposite the one whose guard had twelve years' service; he was not Rictus.
2 The man on the south wall was neither Voluminus nor the one from Syria.
3 The man from Gallia had been assigned to the west wall; the one from Africa had eleven years' service behind him; and the man on the north wall had served for nine years.
4 The duty centurion making a clockwise tour of the walls would have come across Hiatus next after the man from Germania; neither of these was the longest serving legionary.

Names: Blunderbuss; Hiatus; Rictus; Voluminus
Countries: Africa; Gallia; Germania; Syria
Years' service: 9, 10, 11, 12

Starting tip: Work out who has served for twelve years.

Name: _____
Country: _____
Years: _____

N

Name: _____
Country: _____
Years: _____

W          E

Name: _____
Country: _____
Years: _____

S

Name: _____
Country: _____
Years: _____

## 105 LOGI-5

Each line, across and down, is to have each of the letters A, B, C, D and E, appearing once each. Also, every shape – shown by the thick lines – must also have each of the letters in it. Can you fill in the grid?

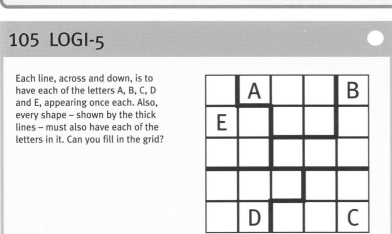

## 106 NUMBER SQUARES

Find the following numbers in the grid in a square formation. The first set has been found for you. Take care, some digits may be mixed up within the square.

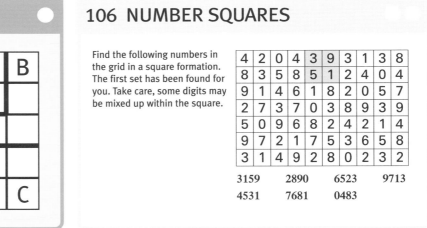

| 4 | 2 | 0 | 4 | 3 | 9 | 3 | 1 | 3 | 8 |
|---|---|---|---|---|---|---|---|---|---|
| 8 | 3 | 5 | 8 | 5 | 1 | 2 | 4 | 0 | 4 |
| 9 | 1 | 4 | 6 | 1 | 8 | 2 | 0 | 5 | 7 |
| 2 | 7 | 3 | 7 | 0 | 3 | 8 | 9 | 3 | 9 |
| 5 | 0 | 9 | 6 | 8 | 2 | 4 | 2 | 1 | 4 |
| 9 | 7 | 2 | 1 | 7 | 5 | 3 | 6 | 5 | 8 |
| 3 | 1 | 4 | 9 | 2 | 8 | 0 | 2 | 3 | 2 |

3159     2890     6523     9713
4531     7681     0483

## 107 SET SQUARE

All the digits from 1 to 9 are used in this grid, but only once each. Can you work out their positions in the grid and make the sums work? We've given two numbers to start you off.

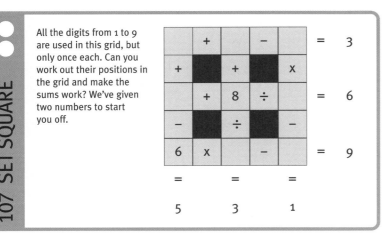

## 108 SUDOKU

Place a number from 1 to 9 in each empty cell so that each row, each column and each 3 x 3 block contains all the numbers from 1 to 9.

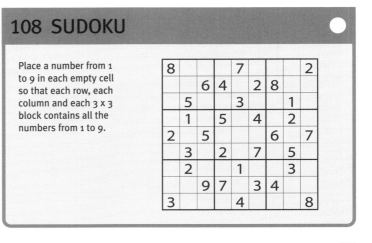

## 109 MAZE MYSTERY

Travel from the entrance to the exit of the maze, filling the path completely to create a picture.

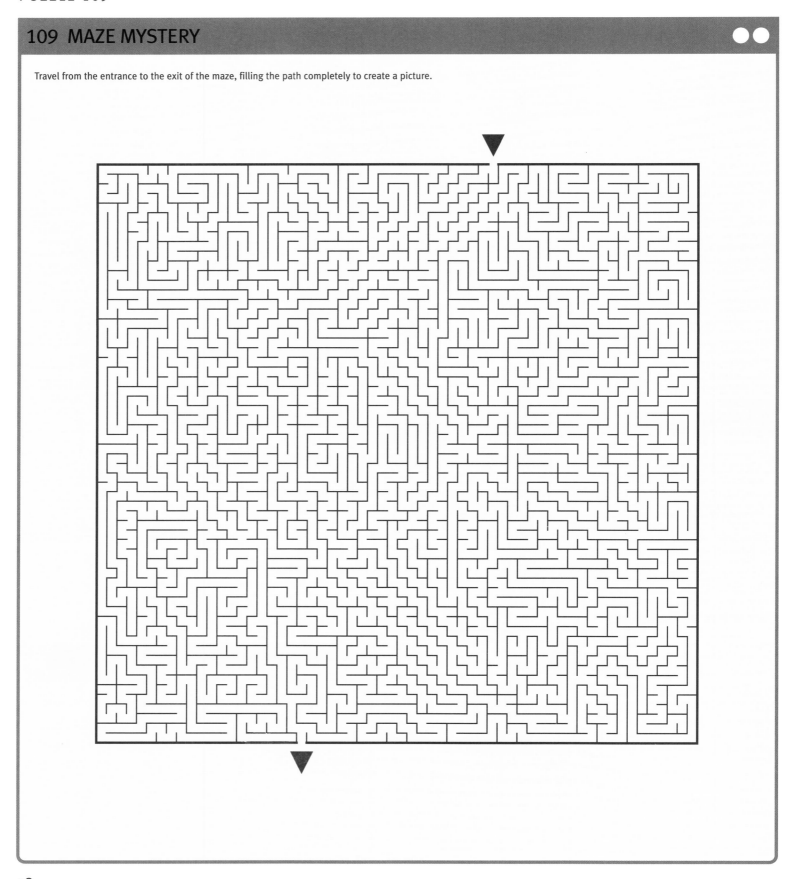

# 110 LOGI-5

Each line, across and down, is to have each of the five colours appearing once each. Each colour must also appear just once in each shape, shown by thick lines. Can you colour in this crazy quilt, or mark each square with its correct letter B, G, R, V or Y?

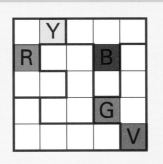

## 112 WHERE THE L?

Twelve L-shapes like the ones shown have been inserted in the grid. Each L has one hole in it. There are three pieces of each of the four kinds shown below and any piece might be turned or flipped over before being put into the grid. No two pieces of the same kind touch, even at a corner. The pieces fit together so well that you cannot see the spaces between them; only the holes show. Can you tell where the Ls are?

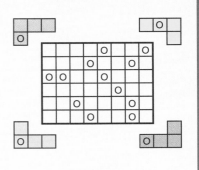

# 111 MISTLING OUT

Letting down the company's structural barriers at Amalgamated Scrufflinks office party last week produced predictable results. Five males, armed with alcohol and mistletoe, set out for closer contact with a lady than ever is possible at departmental meetings. Experience, though, has also armed each lady…

1 The director pursued the personnel officer who is not I Noah who invited her mistletoe waver to meet her husband who was just looming large in the doorway. H Bee-Pensill is not the general manager.

2 The secretary suggested to her pursuer that he listen to a tape recording she had made at last year's party but this was to neither D Veeus nor the driver.

3 E Stender was offered a look at the file reporting his inflated expenses but by neither J Beecy nor the typist.

4 F Ishent is a director but was not the lady pursued by the salesman or the one who stopped A Hound in his tracks by getting him drunk.

5 C Nutting is the clerk who was after neither the general manager nor G Purrs who was harrassed by the accountant who is not A Hound or E Stender.

6 It was the salesman who had his picture taken just as he leered into action but he is not B Pushie who is not the driver.

|  | ACCOUNTANT | CLERK | DIRECTOR | DRIVER | SALESMAN | F ISHENT | G PURRS | H BEE-PENSILL | I NOAH | J BEECY | DIRECTOR | GEN. MANAGER | PERSONNEL OFF. | SECRETARY | TYPIST | GET DRUNK | MEET HUSBAND | PLAY TAPE | SHOW FILE | TAKE PICTURE |
|---|---|---|---|---|---|---|---|---|---|---|---|---|---|---|---|---|---|---|---|---|
| A HOUND | | | | | | | | | | | | | | | | | | | | |
| B PUSHIE | | | | | | | | | | | | | | | | | | | | |
| C NUTTING | | | | | | | | | | | | | | | | | | | | |
| D VEEUS | | | | | | | | | | | | | | | | | | | | |
| E STENDER | | | | | | | | | | | | | | | | | | | | |
| GET DRUNK | | | | | | | | | | | | | | | | | | | | |
| MEET HUSBAND | | | | | | | | | | | | | | | | | | | | |
| PLAY TAPE | | | | | | | | | | | | | | | | | | | | |
| SHOW FILE | | | | | | | | | | | | | | | | | | | | |
| TAKE PICTURE | | | | | | | | | | | | | | | | | | | | |
| DIRECTOR | | | | | | | | | | | | | | | | | | | | |
| GEN. MANAGER | | | | | | | | | | | | | | | | | | | | |
| PERSONNEL | | | | | | | | | | | | | | | | | | | | |
| SECRETARY | | | | | | | | | | | | | | | | | | | | |
| TYPIST | | | | | | | | | | | | | | | | | | | | |
| F ISHENT | | | | | | | | | | | | | | | | | | | | |
| G PURRS | | | | | | | | | | | | | | | | | | | | |
| H BEE-PENSILL | | | | | | | | | | | | | | | | | | | | |
| I NOAH | | | | | | | | | | | | | | | | | | | | |
| J BEECY | | | | | | | | | | | | | | | | | | | | |

| HE | JOB | SHE | JOB | PLOY |
|---|---|---|---|---|
| | | | | |
| | | | | |
| | | | | |
| | | | | |
| | | | | |

## 113 TAKE FIVE

Can you complete the 5 x 5 block so that each of the following symbols appears in all vertical and horizontal lines?

Symbols:

◆ ■ ✚ ● ▲

## 114 ISLAND HOPPING

Each circle containing a number represents an island. The object is to connect each island with vertical or horizontal bridges so that:
* The number of bridges is the same as the number inside the island.
* There can be up to two bridges between two islands.
* Bridges cannot cross islands or other bridges.
* There is a continuous path connecting all the islands.

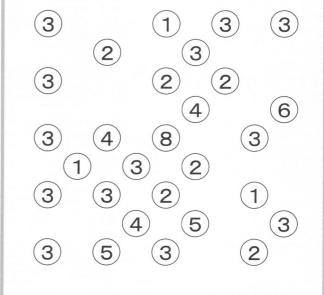

## 115 NUMBER JIG

Fit the numbers into the grid. One has been done for you.

**3 figures**
172
296
317
366
413
541
552
622
673
707
745
818
820
914

**4 figures**
2933
3461
6514
9943

**5 figures**
11903
14712
15704
21014
26817
29306
29317
30115

37304
39610
39792
40013
42618
48887
49980
50468
52789
67158
72422
72431
73538
75368
77213

86261
92065
93371
93770

**6 figures**
493918
763081
876421
933016
946152

## 116 FIT TOGETHER

Which are the only two pieces which will fit together perfectly, to form a complete circle?

## 117 ON THE SPOT

Can you place the dominoes into the grid so that the four vertical, four horizontal and both diagonal rows each have a spot total of ten?

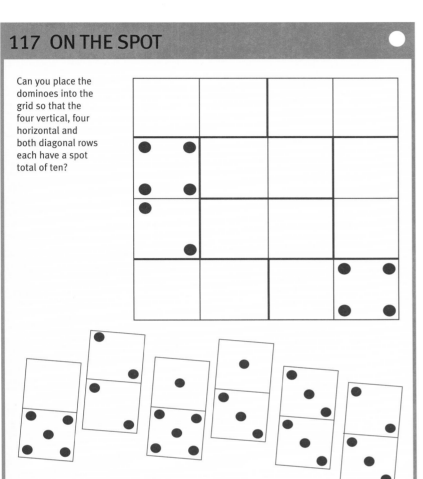

## 118 LOGI-5

Can you place the letters A, B, C, D, E, one to each square so that every line across and down contains each letter once and every shape made from five squares also has each letter once?

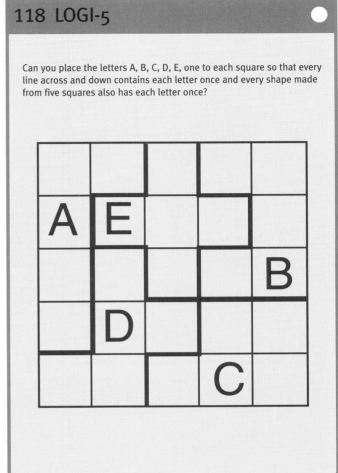

## 119 STOCKING FILLER

Three friends have been shopping in Weale and each bought three little presents to put in their children's Christmas stockings. Between them they bought three oranges, costing a penny each, three boxes of dates, costing twopence each, and three wooden tops costing threepence each. They did not make identical purchases; Mrs Featherbed spent exactly twice as much as Mrs Greengage and Mrs Flowerpot did not buy all three wooden tops. Who bought what?

| LADY | ORANGES | DATES | TOPS |
|------|---------|-------|------|
|      |         |       |      |
|      |         |       |      |
|      |         |       |      |

## 120 ABC

Each line, across and down, is to have each of the letters A, B and C, and two empty squares. The letter outside the grid shows the first or second letter in the direction of the arrow. Can you fill in the grid?

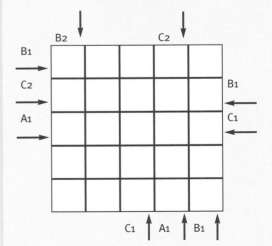

## 121 FIT TOGETHER

Which are the only three pieces which will fit together perfectly, to form a complete polygon?

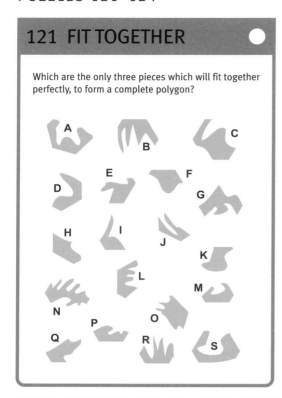

## 122 CAROUSEL

The merry-go-round at the fair, turning clockwise, has 16 single seats, all occupied – they too are numbered clockwise.

1 is opposite 9, 2 is opposite 10 etc. Christine is directly opposite Alice, whose one-digit seat is not no. 1 or 9; Mary's number is three lower than Joan's, and Enid's is two lower than George's.

As they turn, Peter is immediately behind Jerry, whose number is two lower than Daisy's. Bernard is one place ahead of Tom and directly opposite Kate, whose number is higher.

Freddy is one place behind Jack, whose one-digit number (not no. 1) is three lower than Charley's.

Lottie's number is divisible by three, and is one higher than Kate's.

The initial of the name of the child in seat 1 comes earlier in the alphabet than that of the child in seat 16, while the names of the children in seats 3, 10 and 14 do not begin with J.

George's seat number is prime, and is higher than Charley's, which is not prime. 1 is considered prime.

Can you locate each child?

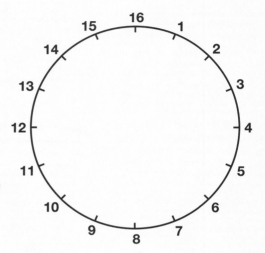

## 123 IT FIGURES

Place a number from 1 to 9 in each empty cell so that the sum of each vertical or horizontal block equals the number at the top or on the left of that block. Numbers may only be used once in each block.

## 124 DOUBLE DUTCH

Theo Versteylan, a tulip grower from Zuidelijk, was found murdered. He had been hit on the head with one of his own clogs. Commissaris Van Drijver of the Amsterdam police was despatched to investigate. Five suspects are discovered but they all claim alibis from each other. The facts listed may sound like so much double Dutch, but from them Van Drijver was able to deduce that one suspect did not have an alibi. Can you?

1 Hein was not with Roel or Rudig unless Jan was with Wouter.

2 Jan was not with Roel or Wouter unless Hein was with Rudig.

3 Roel was not with Jan or Rudig unless Hein was with Wouter.

4 Rudig was not with Jan or Wouter unless Hein was with Roel.

5 Wouter was not with Hein or Roel unless Jan was with Rudig.

# 125 LOGI-PATH

Use your deductive reasoning to form a pathway from the box marked START to the box marked FINISH moving in either direction horizontally or vertically (but not diagonally). The number at the beginning of every row or column indicates exactly how many boxes in that row or column your pathway must pass through. The small diagram is given as an example of how it works.

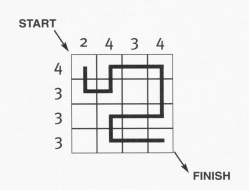

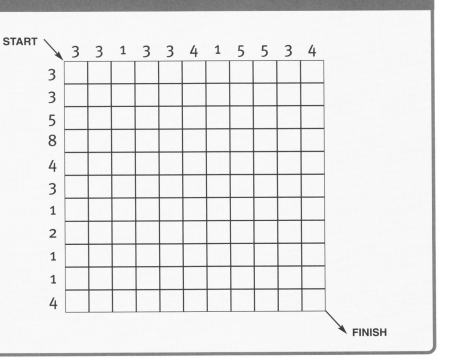

# 126 AROUND THE CLOCK

Tick, tock! Starting from picture 9, can you put these pictures in time order?

# 127 MARATHON MAN

Can you help this long-distance runner find his way to the flag?

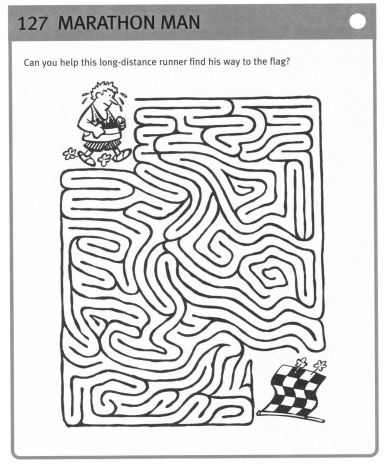

43

## 128 DOTTY DILEMMA

Connect adjacent dots with vertical or horizontal lines so that a single loop is formed with no crossings or branches. Each number indicates how many lines surround it, while empty cells may be surrounded by any number of lines.

```
0 1   3   0 2     2
2         3     0 3
      3 2
    0 2     2 2   3
        3   3   3 1
  2 0   2   1
    2   2 0     0 1
      3   1
  0 1     2       3
  1     1 3   3   0 1
```

## 129 ISLAND HOPPING

Each circle containing a number represents an island. The object is to connect each island with vertical or horizontal bridges so that:
* The number of bridges is the same as the number inside the island.
* There can be up to two bridges between two islands.
* Bridges cannot cross islands or other bridges.
* There is a continuous path connecting all the islands.

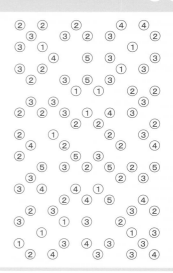

## 130 BIG BREAK

A pool break is made up by potting red balls (maximum 15) which are each followed by one of six different colours. The point values of the balls are:

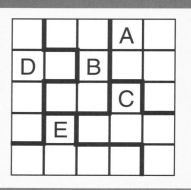

RED 1    BROWN 4    BLUE 5
YELLOW 2    PINK 6
GREEN 3    BLACK 7

Pool player Bob Basher, otherwise known as the Bristol Breeze, made a break of 69, which ended when he failed to pot a red. In the break he potted one less black than blue and one more brown than yellow, potting only these four colours in the break. Can you work out how the break was compiled?

## 131 LOGI-5

Each line, across and down, is to have each of the letters A, B, C, D and E, appearing once each. Also, every shape – shown by the thick lines – must also have each of the letters in it. Can you fill in the grid?

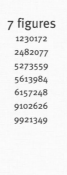

## 132 NUMBER JIG

Fit the numbers into the grid. One has been done for you.

**3 figures**
150
344
391
629
782
888
943

**4 figures**
1622
2191
3160
3731
4570

5768
5921
7726
8273
9801

**5 figures**
13804
14630
27403
28135
78836

**6 figures**
187332
228433
314517
341712
410355
435127
467169
637901
643115
729362
862561
910266
955925

**7 figures**
1230172
2482077
5273559
5613984
6157248
9102626
9921349

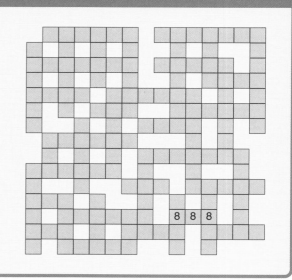

## 133 MAZE MYSTERY

Travel from the entrance to the exit of the maze, filling the path completely to create a picture.

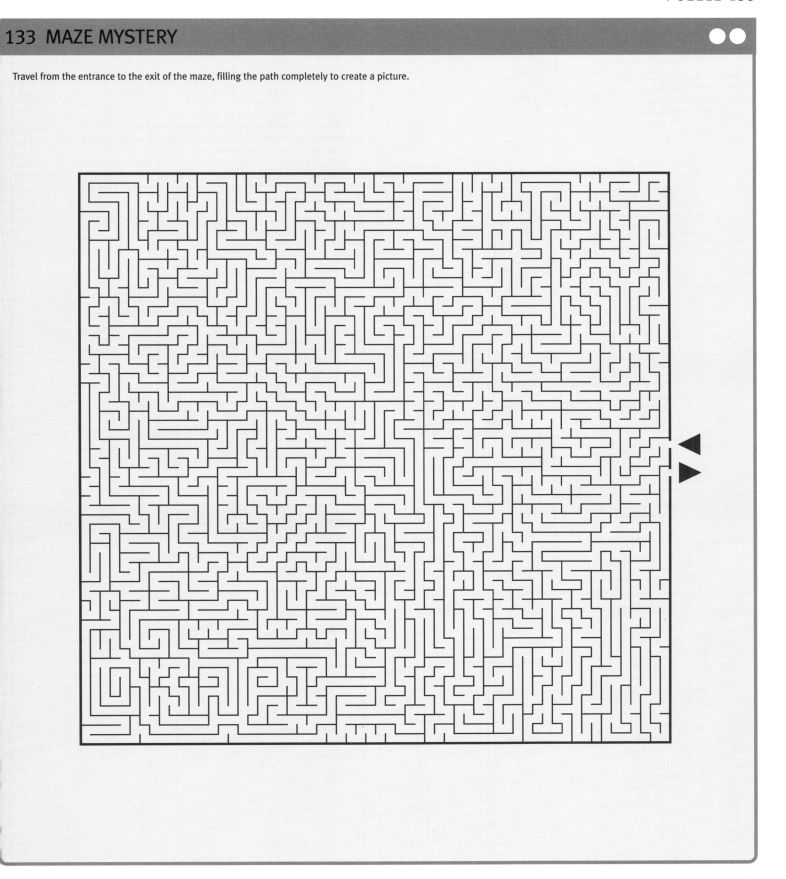

## 134 ON THE SPOT

Can you place the dominoes into the grid so that the four vertical, four horizontal and both diagonal rows each have a spot total of nine?

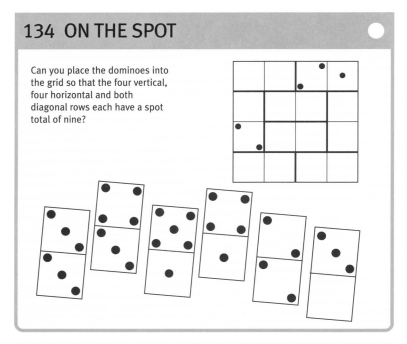

## 135 LOGI-5

Each line, across and down, is to have each of the five colours appearing once each. Each colour must also appear just once in each shape, shown by thick lines. Can you colour in this crazy quilt, or mark each square with a letter by which the colour can be identified?

## 136 ABC

Each line, across and down, is to have each of the letters A, B and C, and two empty squares. The letter outside the grid shows the first or second letter in the direction of the arrow. Can you fill in the grid?

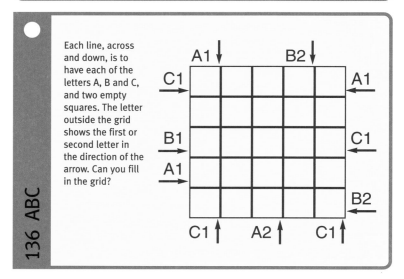

## 137 BEARED RIDDEN

Goldie Locks was not alone in wreaking havoc at the Bears' semi-detached pad in Dingley Dell. Four companions helped her cause devastation by sampling a different cereal each, breaking an item of furniture and crashing out in each of the family's beds. Goldie Locks was not the one who broke the table and slept in Papa Bear's bed; nor did Cilla Field who ate Bran Bits. The one who broke the chair ate Chafflakes but neither she nor Cilla slept in Fred Bear's bed which was claimed by the one who smashed the sideboard. Cher Noble slept in Mama Bear's bed but is not the one who flattened the desk. Wyn Frith did not eat the Ricypops but Dawn Ray did try the Weetybricks. Neither slept in Teddy Bear's bed. The one who ate Muesli Munch broke the bookcase but did not sleep in Carmen Bear's cot or Teddy Bear's bed.

Who slept in each bed, what did he/she eat for breakfast and what did he/she break?

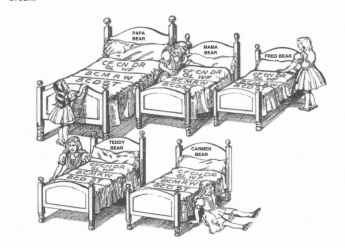

## 138 POCKET LOGIC

Three girls in class 2ZZ at Grabham High have received Valentine cards from three boys. Can you post the details into the summary grid?

### Clues

1 Marian did not receive a card from Gary.
2 Alan and Ian sent cards to the same girl who was not Ava.
3 David and Henry sent cards to the same girl who was not Marian.
4 Brian and Eric sent cards to the same girl who was not Gladys.

| | ALAN | BRIAN | COLIN | DAVID | ERIC | FRANK | GARY | HENRY | IAN |
|---|---|---|---|---|---|---|---|---|---|
| AVA CRUSH | | | | | | | | | |
| GLADYS MIGN | | | | | | | | | |
| MARIAN KYND | | | | | | | | | |
| GARY | | | | | | | | | |
| HENRY | | | | | | | | | |
| IAN | | | | | | | | | |
| DAVID | | | | | | | | | |
| ERIC | | | | | | | | | |
| FRANK | | | | | | | | | |

| GIRL | BOY | BOY | BOY |
|---|---|---|---|
| | | | |
| | | | |

# 140 SAFE BET

This is a strange safe. Answer all the questions and the combination will appear in the shaded boxes.

## ACROSS

1   Multiply *24 down* by 3
5   Add 1,000 to *1 across*
7   Square *4 down*
8   Multiply *23 down* by 3
12  Add 3 to *4 down*
14  Square *1 across*
18  Square *5 across*
19  Anagram of digits of *8 across*
21  Add *3 down* to *4 down*
26  Subtract 24,142 from *8 down*
27  Next in series 4,267, 4,317, 4,367,…
28  Subtract *4 down* from *27 across*, then subtract 5

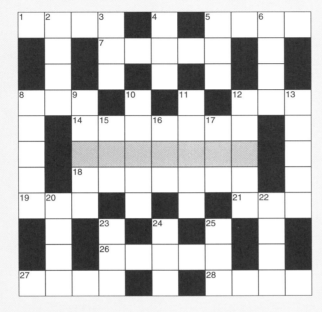

## DOWN

2   Square the last two digits of *8 down*
3   Square root of 44,100
4   Second, third and fourth digits of *26 across*
5   Subtract 1 from *3 down*
6   Multiply *23 down* by 10
8   Add 45 to *13 down*
9   Subtract 2,802 from *12 down*
10  3 per cent of 1,229,700
11  Add 23,000 to *10 down*
12  Add 4,043 to *7 across*
13  Multiply *8 across* by *23 down* and subtract 5,967
15  Subtract 314 from *16 down*
16  Add 318 to *17 down*
17  Square root of 244,036
20  Add *1 across* to *5 across*
22  Next in series 1,611, 1,701, 1,791,…
23  Divide *20 down* by 32, then add 10
24  Square root of 163,216
25  Twice *23 down*

---

# 139 SUDOKU

Place a number from 1 to 9 in each empty cell so that each row, each column and each 3 x 3 block contains all the numbers from 1 to 9.

| 1 |   |   | 4 |   | 6 |   | 2 |   |
|---|---|---|---|---|---|---|---|---|
|   | 4 | 3 |   | 8 | 9 |   |   | 2 |
|   | 7 |   |   | 1 |   |   | 3 |   |
|   | 1 |   | 7 |   | 5 |   | 4 |   |
| 6 |   |   |   | 2 |   |   |   | 3 |
|   | 3 |   | 1 |   | 9 |   | 5 |   |
|   | 2 |   |   | 8 |   |   |   | 9 |
|   |   | 8 | 9 |   | 7 | 2 |   |   |
|   | 4 |   | 2 |   | 1 |   |   | 6 |

---

# 141 DOMINO SEARCH

A set of dominoes has been laid out, using numbers instead of dots for clarity, but the lines which separate the dominoes have been left out. Can you, armed with a sharp pencil and keen brain, show where each domino in the set has been placed? You may find the check grid useful as each domino is identified by its number pair and the appropriate box can be ticked when the domino has been located.

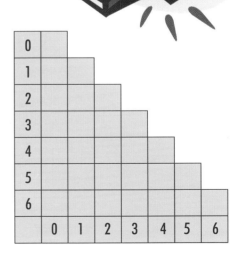

| 3 | 1 | 3 | 4 | 1 | 3 | 1 | 4 |
|---|---|---|---|---|---|---|---|
| 1 | 4 | 1 | 4 | 5 | 6 | 0 | 6 |
| 1 | 3 | 5 | 0 | 5 | 2 | 6 | 5 |
| 6 | 5 | 2 | 4 | 2 | 3 | 2 | 4 |
| 0 | 0 | 0 | 2 | 0 | 5 | 6 | 5 |
| 6 | 4 | 0 | 6 | 2 | 5 | 6 | 0 |
| 1 | 4 | 2 | 1 | 2 | 3 | 3 | 3 |

Check grid:

|   |   |   |   |   |   |   |
|---|---|---|---|---|---|---|
| **0** |   |   |   |   |   |   |
| **1** |   |   |   |   |   |   |
| **2** |   |   |   |   |   |   |
| **3** |   |   |   |   |   |   |
| **4** |   |   |   |   |   |   |
| **5** |   |   |   |   |   |   |
| **6** |   |   |   |   |   |   |
|   | **0** | **1** | **2** | **3** | **4** | **5** | **6** |

## 142 ON THE SPOT

Can you place the dominoes into the grid so that the four vertical, four horizontal and both diagonal rows each have a spot total of eight?

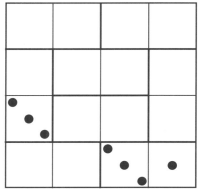

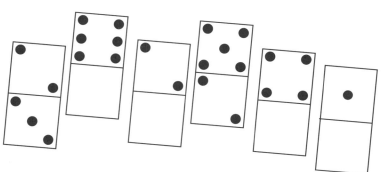

## 143 PUPPY POWER

When the dog pulls the rope which weights will go down and which will go up?

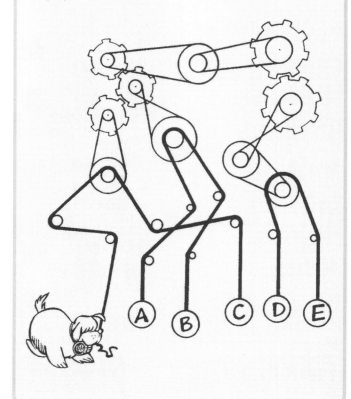

## 144 FLOWER POWER

Patriotic Pete sells bunches of red, white and blue flowers in the market. Some bunches have just a single colour, some have two and some a mixture of all three. If he brings along a total of 80 bunches, can you work out how many bunches have flowers of all three colours?

Half the bunches contain red flowers and a quarter of the bunches have both blue and white. There is one more bunch with red flowers only than there are with both blue and white but no red. The total number of those with both red and white but no blue and red and blue but no white is five greater than the number containing red only. How many bunches have all three colours?

## 145 BIG BREAK

A pool break is made up by potting red balls (maximum 15) which are each followed by one of six different colours. The point values of the balls are:

- RED 1
- YELLOW 2
- GREEN 3
- BROWN 4
- PINK 6
- BLUE 5
- BLACK 7

Pool player Bob Basher, otherwise known as the Bristol Breeze, made a break of 71, which ended when he failed to pot a red. In the break he potted two more pinks than greens and two more yellows than blues, potting only these four colours in the break. Can you work out how the break was compiled?

# 146 PATTERN MAKER

Can you place the numbered blocks into the grid to form the pattern shown?
The blocks may be placed horizontally or vertically, and may be turned around.

| 0 | 1 | 3 | 2 |
|---|---|---|---|
| 1 | 2 | 3 | 2 |
| 2 | 2 | 0 | 0 |
| 1 | 1 | 1 | 0 |
| 3 | 3 | 0 | 3 |

| 0 1 |  | | 0 3 |
| 2 2 | 1 3 | 3 3 |
| 0 2 | 1 2 | 0 0 |
| 1 1 |  | | 3 2 |

# 147 SPOT THE DIFFERENCE

Can you tell which one of these pictures is different from the others?

# 148 ACROSS THE BOARD

Can you place the numbered blocks into the grid to form the pattern shown? The blocks may be placed horizontally or vertically, and can be turned round.

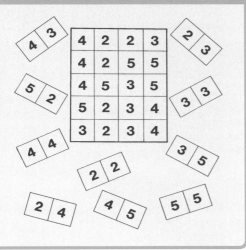

# 149 TEE TIME

Three old-timers play a weekly game of golf on the Golden Lawns 18-hole, par 72, course. Each score at every hole falls into one of five categories. Each golfer gets a different result, greater than zero in each category. Also, no category has the same result for another player, i.e., if a player has two eagles, he has a different number in the other four and no other player has two eagles. With the score details below and the information given can you fill in their card? Nick's bogeys were the same as Barry's pars and Parnell's double bogeys and together they totalled the same as Parnell's pars which were one more than Nick's birdies which were one more than Barry's double bogeys which were the same as Parnell's eagles and these last two together totalled Barry's birdies. The total number of eagles was more than the double bogeys but less than the bogeys.

| | Eagle −2 | Birdie −1 | Par 0 | Bogey +1 | Double Bogey +2 | FINAL SCORE |
|---|---|---|---|---|---|---|
| Parnell Darma | | | | | | |
| Nick Jackliss | | | | | | |
| Barry Clayer | | | | | | |

## 150 ABC

Each line, across and down, is to have each of the letters A, B and C, and two empty squares. The letter outside the grid shows the first or second letter in the direction of the arrow. Can you fill in the grid?

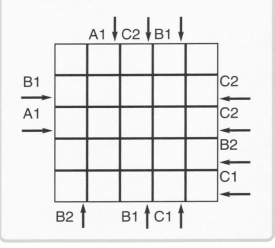

## 151 21S

Obeying the normal rules of arithmetic, with the numbers given, using only where necessary +, −, x, or ÷, make the resulting calculations equal 21.

9 (3 2) 6 = 21    7 4 9 9 = 21
(3 5 8) 3 = 21

## 152 FILLING IN

Each of the nine empty boxes contains a different digit from 1 to 9. Each calculation is to be treated sequentially rather than according to the 'multiplication first' system. Can you fill in the empty boxes?

|   | + |   | ÷ |   | = 2 |
|---|---|---|---|---|-----|
| ÷ |   | + |   | x |     |
|   | + |   | − |   | = 5 |
| + |   | − |   | − |     |
|   | x |   | ÷ |   | = 6 |
| = 6 |   | = 6 |   | = 9 |   |

## 153 DOMINO SEARCH

A set of dominoes has been laid out, using numbers instead of dots for clarity, but the lines which separate the dominoes have been left out. Can you, armed with a sharp pencil and keen brain, show where each domino in the set has been placed? You may find the check grid useful as each domino is identified by its number pair and the appropriate box can be ticked when the domino has been located.

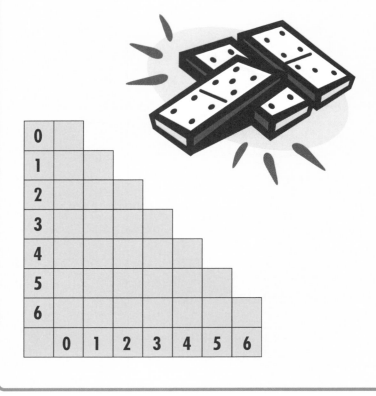

| 2 | 4 | 3 | 3 | 0 | 3 | 3 | 1 |
|---|---|---|---|---|---|---|---|
| 4 | 1 | 1 | 6 | 1 | 6 | 4 | 3 |
| 5 | 2 | 4 | 5 | 4 | 4 | 1 | 5 |
| 4 | 2 | 0 | 1 | 5 | 3 | 5 | 2 |
| 3 | 6 | 2 | 0 | 4 | 6 | 0 | 1 |
| 3 | 2 | 1 | 0 | 0 | 5 | 5 | 2 |
| 6 | 6 | 2 | 6 | 5 | 0 | 6 | 0 |

## 154 MAZE MYSTERY

Travel from the entrance to the exit of the maze, filling the path completely to create a picture.

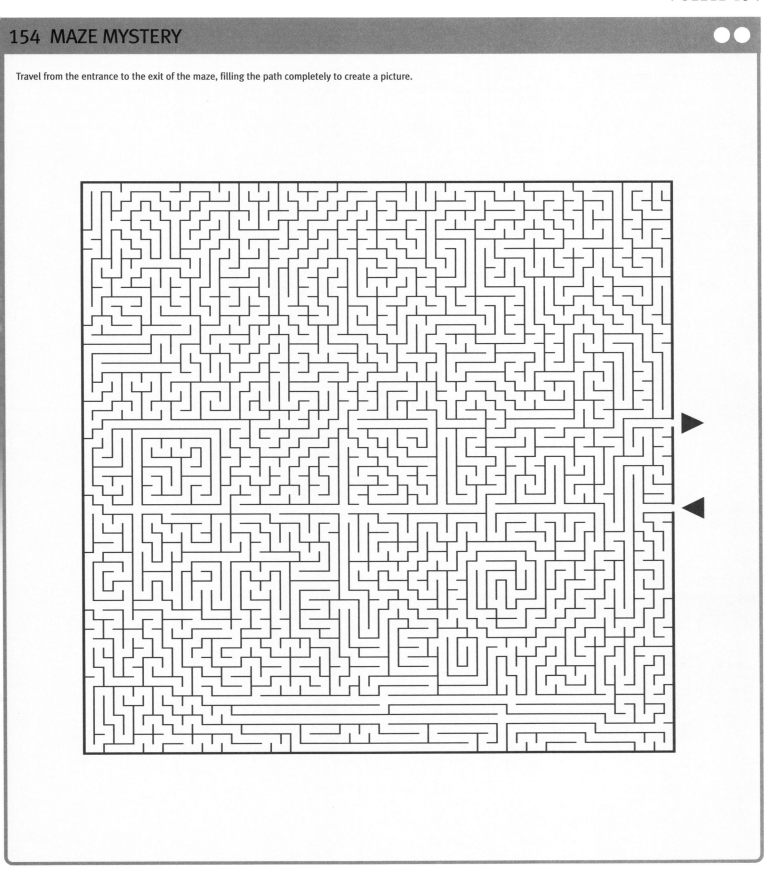

## 155 MAIL MAN'S PROBLEM ●●

The old houses in the community have always caused a problem for mail men – the house numbers seem to bear no relationship to their positions around a central square. So to help all new mail men on that round learn where each number is, the following puzzle is given to them.

The houses are numbered from 1 to 24, and the position of each letter in the diagram indicates the front of its respective house. P, Q and R – along with S, T and U – are all odd numbers; both of these sets of three add up to the same total, which is two more than the total of F's and G's numbers – F's being twice G's. The total of numbers J, K, L, M and N is ten more than that of A, B, C, D and E. W, X and Y add up to twenty more than the total of S, T and U.

House B is No. 20. Nos. 5 and 7 have west-facing frontages, but they're not adjacent. C's number is half that of D's, which is half that of E's. C and D add up to A's number. X's number is four times W's, V's is nineteen less than Z's, which is twice H's. N's number is one more than Z's and two more than K's, which is one-and-a-half times that of J.

E's number is four more than A's, and T's is greater than U's, which is greater than S's. No. 2 is somewhere due west of No. 10, and No. 7 is somewhere due north of No. 5. Where is each number?

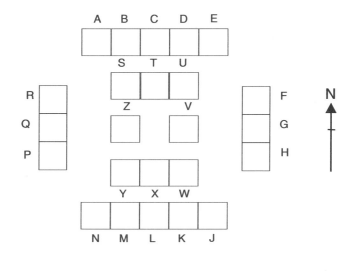

## 156 AGE GROUP ●●

Can you calculate the age of each of these men from the following information? B is twice as old as D. The difference in age of A and B is the same as the difference in age between C and D, while the difference in age between A and C is half the difference in age between B and D. None of the men is older than forty or younger than twenty, and A is older than C.

## 157 ON THE SPOT ●

Can you place the dominoes into the grid so that the four vertical, four horizontal and both diagonal rows each have a spot value of nine?

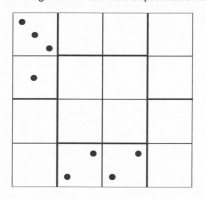

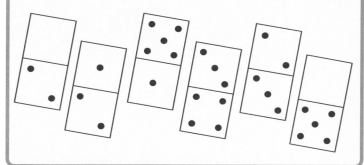

## 158 ISLAND HOPPING ●

Each circle containing a number represents an island. The object is to connect each island with vertical or horizontal bridges so that:
* The number of bridges is the same as the number inside the island.
* There can be up to two bridges between two islands.
* Bridges cannot cross islands or other bridges.
* There is a continuous path connecting all the islands.

# 159 BLOOMERS

Charlie Dimwit's garden centre, Bloomers, has a fine display of pot plants for sale. Four gardeners each took ten pots from the stand. Each gardener took a different number of pots of the colours they selected. After they had taken their pots there were an equal number of each colour left over. From the information given can you work out what each gardener selected?

Mary bought two more green than yellow and together this was twice Dawn's red, which were the same as John's yellow. Neither man bought any green but Dawn bought twice as many green as John bought red. John who bought no violet bought two more blue than yellow. Alan bought no red and Mary bought no blue. Dawn bought one more yellow than blue.

# 160 SIX-PACK

By packing numbers in the empty spaces, can you make the numbers in each of the sixteen hexagons add up to 25? No two numbers in each hexagon may be the same and you can't use zero. We've started you off.

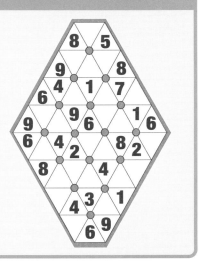

# 161 IT'S MAGIC

This magic square can be completed using the numbers from 61 to 85 inclusive. To give you a start, in each square with a black corner dot, all the even digits have been entered. In a plain square all the odd digits have been entered. Can you complete the square so that the five numbers in each row, column and diagonal add up to the magic total? The total—and close your eyes now if you don't want to be told—is 365.

|   | 6 |   |   |   |
|---|---|---|---|---|
|   |   |   | 8 2 |   |
| 8 |   | 6 | 7 1 | 8 |
| 7 | 6 | 3 | 6 | 7 |
| 6 | 7 | 2 | 7 9 | 8 |

# 163 ENGINE DRIVER

There are eight differences between these two pictures – can you discover them all?

# 162 SET SQUARE

All the digits from 1 to 9 are used in this grid, but only once. Can you work out their positions in the grid and make the sums work? We've given two numbers to start you off.

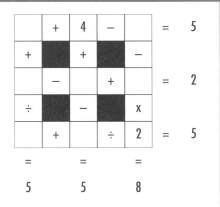

## 164 DOUBLE PUZZLE

Roll up folks, for our special sale offer—two puzzles for the price of one!

Puzzle One: Each colour has been given a value from 1 to 7. Given the totals at the end of each line, can you work out the value of each colour?

Puzzle Two: The picture is a layout of a set of colour dominoes—just like ordinary dominoes but with colours instead of spots. Can you draw in the lines to show each separate domino?

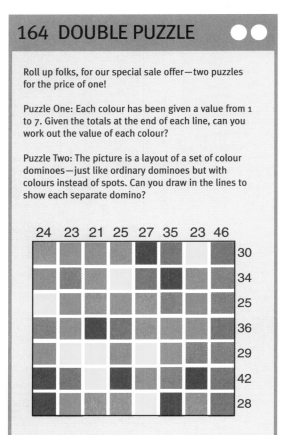

## 165 WELL SPOTTED

The number in each circle tells you how many of it and its touching neighbours are to be filled in.

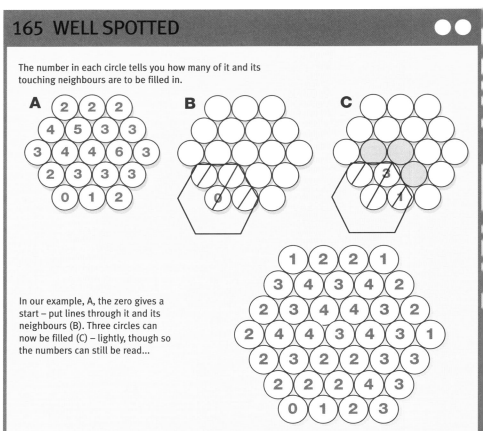

In our example, A, the zero gives a start – put lines through it and its neighbours (B). Three circles can now be filled (C) – lightly, though so the numbers can still be read...

## 166 NUMBER JIG

Fit the numbers into the grid. One has been done for you.

**3 figures**
109
388
460
472
699
702
980

**4 figures**
1372
1626
3019
3491
4590
6395
7424
7677
8118
9103

**5 figures**
32094
36125
39942
60841
82160

**6 figures**
100341
122074
335642
382772
412979

420799
430216
543748
710327
786243

793612
813730
918622

**7 figures**
1505213
2188663
4623963
4956134
7026471
8146072
9783288

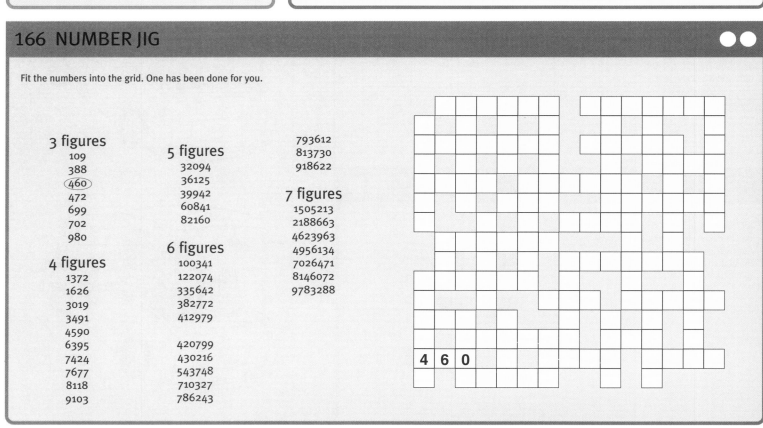

## 167 DOMINO SEARCH

A set of dominoes has been laid out, using numbers instead of dots for clarity, but the lines which separate the dominoes have been left out. Can you, armed with a sharp pencil and keen brain, show where each domino in the set has been placed? You may find the check grid useful as each domino is identified by its number pair and the appropriate box can be ticked when the domino has been located. To give you a start 7*9 is given.

Hint: Look near the bottom left corner – which is the only domino that goes there?

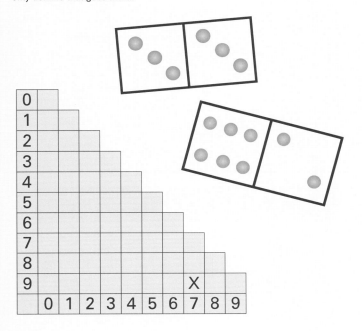

| 8 | 2 | 8 | 1 | 0 | 5 | 2 | 8 | 5 | 0 | 1 |
|---|---|---|---|---|---|---|---|---|---|---|
| 8 | 7 | 3 | 7 | 4 | 4 | 6 | 3 | 3 | 9 | 3 |
| 0 | 4 | 4 | 2 | 7 | 3 | 8 | 9 | 2 | 7 | 0 |
| 3 | 5 | 1 | 6 | 8 | 4 | 0 | 9 | 2 | 3 | 4 |
| 1 | 8 | 3 | 8 | 0 | 6 | 0 | 5 | 8 | 1 | 4 |
| 1 | 6 | 0 | 9 | 1 | 3 | 6 | 5 | 6 | 6 | 7 |
| 9 | 7 | 5 | 6 | 6 | 2 | 0 | 2 | 5 | 0 | 7 |
| 0 | 4 | 5 | 9 | 9 | 6 | 7 | 1 | 5 | 1 | 4 |
| 1 | 7 | 3 | 2 | 7 | 9 | 6 | 5 | 7 | 2 | 9 |
| 4 | 1 | 5 | 9 | 9 | 4 | 8 | 3 | 2 | 8 | 2 |

## 168 KARL KRACK'S CIRCUS ●●

Karl Krack, who owns a small travelling circus, believes that variety is the spice of life and for each show he alters the order of his eight acts. Can you work out what the order will be for tonight's performance?

No act is next to another with the same initials. The Clever Clowns come two acts after Fred the Fire-eater and two acts before Senor Pedro's Poodles. Jim the Juggler comes three acts before the Agilles Acrobats but he does not open the show. The Flying Fortresses come four acts after Madame Poll's Parrots, but not immediately before the Poodles. The Crazy Carvellos are not the final act.

| 1 | 2 | 3 | 4 |
|---|---|---|---|
| 5 | 6 | 7 | 8 |

## 169 DOUBLE PUZZLE ●●

Roll up folks, for our special sale offer – two puzzles for the price of one!

Puzzle One: Each colour has been given a value from 1 to 7. Given the totals at the end of each line, can you work out the value of each colour?

Puzzle Two: The picture is a layout of a set of colour dominoes – just like ordinary dominoes but with colours instead of spots. Can you draw in the lines to show each separate domino?

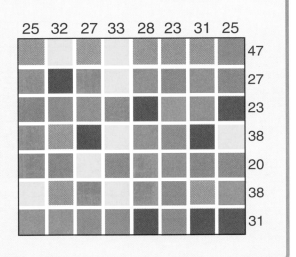

25 32 27 33 28 23 31 25

47
27
23
38
20
38
31

## 170 FLOWER POWER

Patriotic Pete sells bunches of red, white and blue flowers in the market. Some bunches have just a single colour, some two and some a mixture of all three. If he brings along a total of 80 bunches, can you work out how many bunches have flowers of all three colours? The number of bunches with both red and blue but no white is the same as that with blue only and together they total the number with both red and white but no blue. The number with white only is double that with all three, which is one less than red only, which is the same as that with both blue and white but no red. Fifty-five bunches had white flowers in them.

## 171 BATTLESHIPS

Do you remember the old game of battleships? These puzzles are based on that idea. Your task is to find the vessels in the diagram. Some parts of boats or sea squares have already been filled in, and a number next to a row or column refers to the number of occupied squares in that row or column. The boats may be positioned horizontally or vertically, but no two boats or parts of boats are in adjacent squares – horizontally, vertically or diagonally.

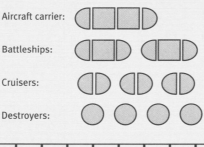

Aircraft carrier:

Battleships:

Cruisers:

Destroyers:

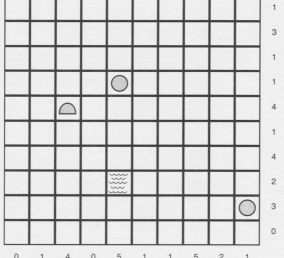

## 172 ON THE SPOT

Can you place the dominoes into the grid so that the four vertical, four horizontal and both diagonal rows have a spot total of eight?

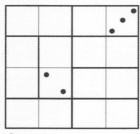

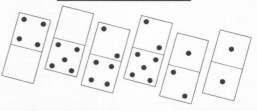

## 173 PAINT BOXES

In each of the pictures on the right, there is a different amount of paint dripping from the brush. Starting with picture F, can you put these pictures in order, so that in each new picture the paint drip is larger than before?

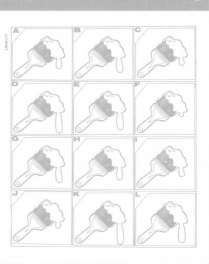

## 174 SUDOKU

Place a number from 1 to 9 in each empty cell so that each row, each column and each 3 x 3 block contains all the numbers from 1 to 9.

|   |   |   | 5 |   | 4 |   | 1 |   |
|---|---|---|---|---|---|---|---|---|
| 6 | 8 |   |   |   | 9 |   | 7 |   |
|   |   | 9 |   |   |   | 3 |   |   |
| 3 | 5 |   |   | 7 |   |   |   | 8 |
|   |   |   | 2 |   | 1 |   |   |   |
| 1 |   |   |   | 4 |   |   | 5 | 9 |
|   |   | 2 |   |   |   | 5 |   |   |
|   | 9 |   | 3 |   |   |   | 4 | 2 |
|   | 4 |   | 6 |   | 8 |   |   |   |

# 175 NUMBER JIG

Fit the numbers into the grid. One has been done for you.

**3 figures**
106
204
301
567
605
723
818
(919)

**4 figures**
1010
1853
2380
3123
4017
4190

5111
6037
7283
8093
8866
9171

**5 figures**
41528
43150
55073
60523
71375
81797
90173

**6 figures**
105921
166927
224466
299102
337473
344353
403044
413013
513397
523149
620732
668896
723378
789121
836343
977027

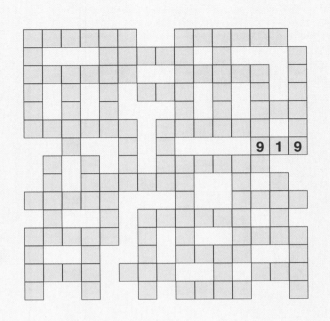

# 176 DOMINO SEARCH

A set of dominoes has been laid out, using numbers instead of dots for clarity, but the lines which separate the dominoes have been left out. Can you, armed with a sharp pencil and keen brain, show where each domino in the set has been placed? You may find the check grid useful as each domino is identified by its number pair and the appropriate box can be ticked when the domino has been located. To give you a start 2*9 is given.

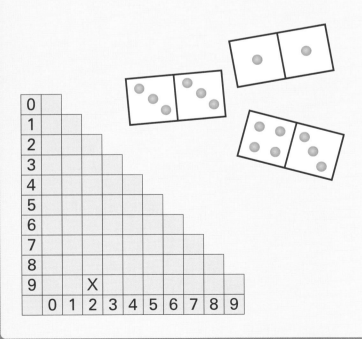

| | 0 | 1 | 2 | 3 | 4 | 5 | 6 | 7 | 8 | 9 |
|---|---|---|---|---|---|---|---|---|---|---|
| 0 | | | | | | | | | | |
| 1 | | | | | | | | | | |
| 2 | | | | | | | | | | |
| 3 | | | | | | | | | | |
| 4 | | | | | | | | | | |
| 5 | | | | | | | | | | |
| 6 | | | | | | | | | | |
| 7 | | | | | | | | | | |
| 8 | | | | | | | | | | |
| 9 | | | X | | | | | | | |

| 4 | 7 | 2 | 9 | 9 | 2 | 5 | 6 | 3 | 7 | 2 |
|---|---|---|---|---|---|---|---|---|---|---|
| 4 | 3 | 7 | 0 | 4 | 1 | 2 | 2 | 0 | 4 | 7 |
| 0 | 9 | 8 | 5 | 9 | 3 | 8 | 3 | 1 | 9 |
| 0 | 5 | 3 | 6 | 4 | 6 | 1 | 4 | 6 | 8 | 8 |
| 6 | 6 | 3 | 0 | 7 | 7 | 5 | 5 | 2 | 6 | 0 |
| 7 | 5 | 1 | 9 | 3 | 4 | 1 | 1 | 4 | 1 | 9 |
| 9 | 0 | 6 | 6 | 1 | 0 | 0 | 1 | 5 | 8 | 3 |
| 8 | 1 | 2 | 5 | 8 | 7 | 2 | 7 | 3 | 1 | 2 |
| 4 | 0 | 8 | 5 | 9 | 4 | 5 | 2 | 7 | 8 | 6 |
| 3 | 4 | 3 | 9 | 5 | 8 | 0 | 7 | 6 | 8 | 2 |

## 177 IT FIGURES

Place a number from 1 to 9 in each empty cell so that the sum of each vertical or horizontal block equals the number at the top or on the left of that block. Numbers may only be used once in each block.

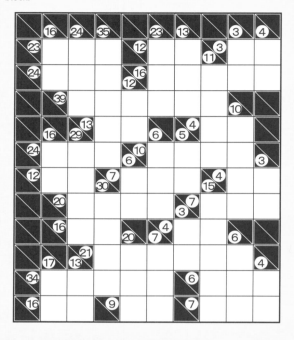

## 178 FLOWER POWER

Patriotic Pete sells bunches of red, white and blue flowers in the market. Some bunches have just a single colour, some two and some a mixture of all three. If he brings along a total of 80 bunches, can you work out how many bunches have flowers of all three colours?

There are 16 bunches with both blue and red and of these the number with no white is the same as that with white only, which is one less than the number with blue only and the total of the blue only and white only is the same as that of the ones with both red and white but no blue. Of the 47 bunches containing red flowers only 12 had just the one colour.

## 179 LOGI-TILES

Following the first diagram, there is a logical rule that determines how the next block is to be filled in. Given these three blocks, can you colour in the fourth?

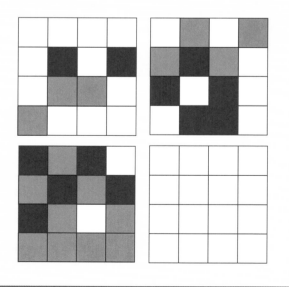

## 180 CAKE RACE

These joggers are so pleased with themselves for doing some exercise over Christmas that they've decided to treat themselves to extra helpings of cake when they get back. Follow the trails to discover which runner is after each cake.

# 181 OUT WEST

Towards the end of the last century in Wichita USA, the main street was becoming quite well established, as our drawing of the first five buildings in that street shows. From the following clues, can you discover the name of each establishment and the name of the proprietor? By eliminating with an X any initial letter in the Answer Block, which does not apply, you will eventually arrive at the full answer.

1 Frank Foster is at No. 2 but he does not run the Trading Post.
2 Jesse Jones is not the proprietor of No. 3.
3 The number of Jesse Jones's building is smaller than the number allocated to Chuck Carson's Saloon which is not No. 5.
4 The Bank is at No. 4 but the Trading Post is not No. 1.
5 Rocky Rawlings is not the manager of the Bank. The Wells Fargo office is not No. 2.
6 The Jail is one of the buildings but is Dave Dalton the Sheriff?

| NUMBER | PROPRIETOR | BUILDING |
|---|---|---|
| 1 | C D F J R | B J S T W |
| 2 | C D F J R | B J S T W |
| 3 | C D F J R | B J S T W |
| 4 | C D F J R | B J S T W |
| 5 | C D F J R | B J S T W |

# 182 SUDOKU

Place a number from 1 to 9 in each empty cell so that each row, each column and each 3 x 3 block contains all the numbers from 1 to 9.

| 5 | 7 |   |   |   |   |   | 2 | 4 |
|---|---|---|---|---|---|---|---|---|
|   | 9 | 8 |   |   |   |   | 1 | 3 |
|   |   |   |   | 3 | 7 |   |   |   |
| 2 | 3 |   |   | 8 | 9 |   |   |   |
| 7 | 6 |   |   |   |   |   | 8 | 5 |
|   |   |   | 4 | 6 |   |   | 3 | 7 |
|   |   |   | 9 | 2 |   |   |   |   |
| 8 | 1 |   |   |   |   |   | 4 | 6 |
| 5 | 2 |   |   |   |   | 1 | 7 |   |

# 183 EASY AS ABC

Each row and column originally contained one A, one B, one C, one D and two blank squares. Each letter and number refers to the first or second of the four letters encountered when travelling in the direction of the arrow. Can you complete the original grid?

Top arrows: A2 B1 A1 — A1 C1
Left: D1, C1, A2, B1
Right: C1, C2, B1
Bottom arrows: B1 — B2 A1 D1

# 184 SIX-PACK

By packing numbers in the empty spaces, can you make the numbers in each of the 16 hexagons add up to 25? No two numbers in each hexagon may be the same and you can't use zero. We've started you off.

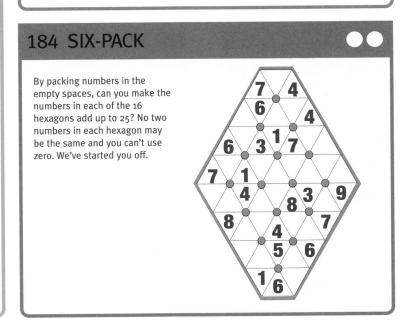

## 185 SET SQUARE

All the digits from 1 to 9 are used in this grid, but only once. Can you work out their positions in the grid and make the sums work? We've given two numbers to start you off.

| | + | 7 | – | | = | 2 |
|---|---|---|---|---|---|---|
| + | ■ | + | ■ | – | | |
| | + | | – | | = | 1 |
| – | ■ | ÷ | ■ | + | | |
| 1 | x | | – | | = | 3 |
| = | | = | | = | | |
| 9 | | 2 | | 3 | | |

## 186 EASY AS ABC

Each row and column originally contained one A, one B, one C, one D and two blank squares. Each letter and number refers to the first or second of the four letters encountered when travelling in the direction of the arrow. Can you complete the original grid?

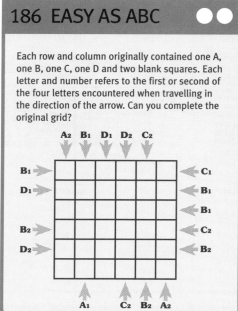

## 187 KNOT SO

Can you work out which tangles will form a knot, and which will not?

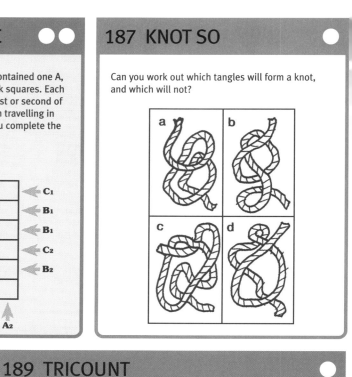

## 188 DOLLY THE CLONE

Which two of the pictures form a matching pair?

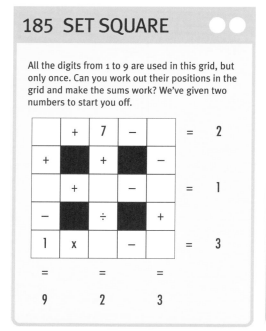

## 189 TRICOUNT

How many triangles can you find in this figure?

## 190 TEACUP TWINS

Can you match up the teacups into identical pairs?

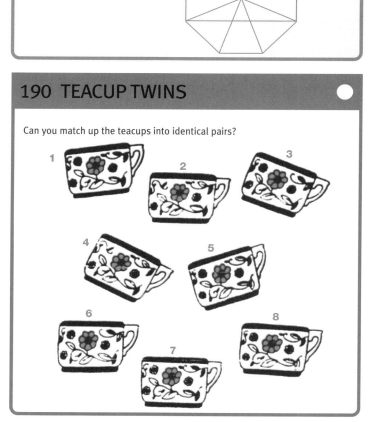

# 191 BIG BREAK

A snooker break is made up by potting red balls (maximum 15) which are each followed by one of six different colours. The point values of the balls are:

- 🔴 RED 1
- 🟡 YELLOW 2
- 🟢 GREEN 3
- 🟤 BROWN 4
- 🔵 BLUE 5
- 🩷 PINK 6
- ⚫ BLACK 7

In this next frame, Bob made a break of 85, which ended when he failed to pot a red. In the break he potted one more black than green and two more pink than blue, potting all four colours in the break and no other colours. How many of each colour ball were potted?

# 192 PATTERN MAKER

Can you place the numbered blocks below into the grid on the right to form the pattern shown? The blocks may be placed horizontally or vertically, and may be turned around.

| 6 5 | | 4 5 |
| 6 3 | 5 3 | 4 6 |
| 3 4 | 3 0 | 5 0 |
| 6 0 | | 4 0 |

| 3 | 6 | 6 | 5 |
|---|---|---|---|
| 4 | 4 | 3 | 4 |
| 0 | 0 | 0 | 5 |
| 6 | 5 | 3 | 3 |
| 0 | 6 | 4 | 5 |

# 193 GIVING IT THE BOOT

Four boys were fishing in a shallow stream, each wearing a different coloured pair of boots. From the clues given below, can you identify the boys in positions 1 to 4, and work out the colour of the boots each was wearing?

**Clues**

1  The boy in the red boots is somewhere to the left of Shaun, whose surname is not Brook.
2  Darren Poole is somewhere to the right of the youth in the brown boots.
3  Wader number 3 is Johnny, but the surname of the boy in position 2 is not Burne.
4  The green boots are worn by a boy wading alongside Garry, while Waters is standing next to his friend whose boots are black.

First name: _____

Surname: _____

Boots: _____

First names: Darren; Garry; Johnny; Shaun
Surnames: Brook; Burne; Poole; Waters
Boots: black; brown; green; red

Starting tip: Start by working out the first name of the boy in position 1.

# 194 NUMBER JIG

Fit the numbers into the grid. One has been done for you.

**3 figures**
161
358
444
(483)
560
809
942

**4 figures**
1108
2921
3250

4230
6307
6323
6519
8243
8313
9054

**5 figures**
27328
39902
48326
71166

73014

**6 figures**
103600
175050
235798
326419
384104
403647
409214
524939
538018
640882

713648
810123
932100

**7 figures**
1638425
2152260
4236909
5990304
6539112
6603299
9013302

## 195 HORSE SHOW

Which one of the happy horses cast this shadow?

## 196 ON THE SPOT

Can you place the dominoes in the grid so that the four vertical, four horizontal and both diagonal rows each have a spot total of eight?

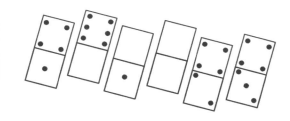

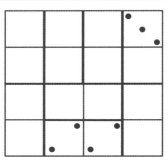

## 197 BLOOMERS

Charlie Dimwit's garden centre, Bloomers, has a fine display of pot plants for sale. Four gardeners each took ten pots from the stand. Each gardener took a different number of pots of the colours they selected. After they had taken their pots there were an equal number of each colour left over. From the information given can you work out what each gardener selected?

The two 'A' gardeners bought seven blues between them. George bought twice as many yellows as reds. The two ladies each bought the same number of yellows. Barbara bought no blues or violets. The two men bought half the sold number of blues but neither bought any greens. Anne bought one more green than violets and the total of the two was one more than Barbara's reds. Albert also bought some fertilizer.

## 198 ISLAND HOPPING

Each circle containing a number represents an island. The object is to connect each island with vertical or horizontal bridges so that:
* The number of bridges is the same as the number inside the island.
* There can be up to two bridges between two islands.
* Bridges cannot cross islands or other bridges.
* There is a continuous path connecting all the islands.

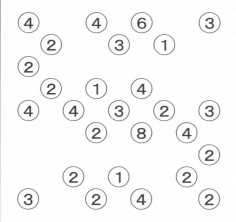

## 199 DOMINO SEARCH

A standard set of dominoes has been laid out, using numbers instead of dots for clarity. Using a sharp pencil and a keen brain, can you draw in the lines to show where each domino has been placed? You may find the check grid useful – crossing off each domino as you find it.

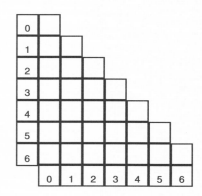

| 1 | 2 | 4 | 5 | 2 | 3 | 2 | 3 |
|---|---|---|---|---|---|---|---|
| 1 | 5 | 6 | 4 | 4 | 2 | 3 | 1 |
| 1 | 4 | 2 | 2 | 1 | 0 | 3 | 4 |
| 2 | 5 | 1 | 6 | 5 | 6 | 3 | 3 |
| 3 | 5 | 4 | 6 | 6 | 2 | 5 | 1 |
| 0 | 5 | 3 | 6 | 4 | 6 | 1 | 0 |
| 0 | 4 | 5 | 0 | 6 | 0 | 0 | 0 |

## 200 MAZE MYSTERY

Travel from the entrance to the exit of the maze, filling the path completely to create a picture.

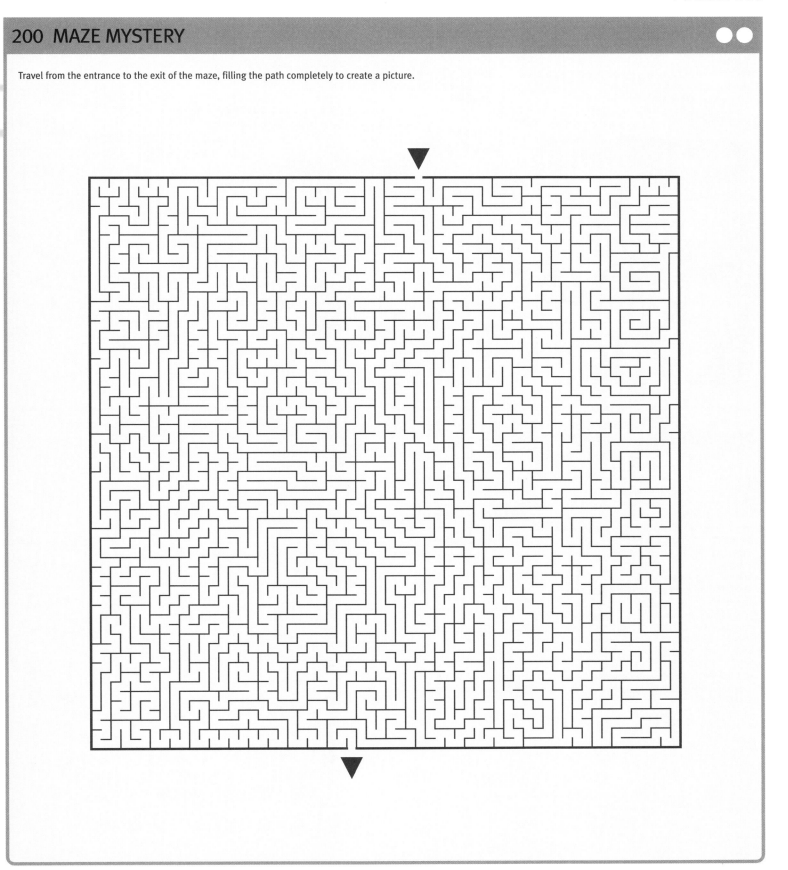

## 201 IT FIGURES

Place a number from 1 to 9 in each empty cell so that the sum of each vertical or horizontal block equals the number at the top or on the left of that block. Numbers may only be used once in each block.

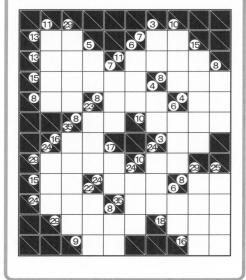

## 202 KNOT SO

Can you work out which of these ropes will form a knot when their ends are pulled, and which will not?

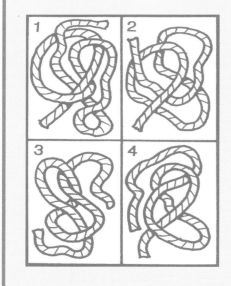

## 203 MATCH THAT

Rearrange these matches to make 14 squares.

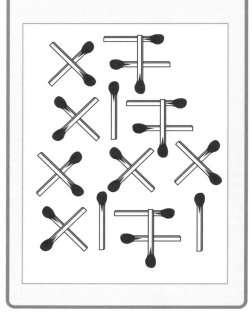

## 204 ALPHABET ECHO

In the grid, each letter of the alphabet appears twice and there are four blanks. Neither the same or any two consecutive letters of the alphabet appear in the same row, column or diagonal. A and Z are not treated as consecutive in this puzzle. Beside each row and column appear two numbers; the black number shows how many vowels appear in that row or column and the blue number shows how many of the letters are in the first half of the alphabet i.e. A–M. Using the additional clues below, can you fill in the grid?

Letters which are repeated:
| | |
|---|---|
| In the first four rows | D, F, M, P, S, U, Y |
| In the last four rows | A, C, L, O, Q, T |
| In the first four columns | B, D, G, K, N, Q, R, V |
| In the last four columns | C, E, H, I, M, O, P, S, U, X, Z |
| In successive rows | D, F, M, O, P, Q, S, U, Y |
| In successive columns | B, H, I, K, X, Z |

JRY and FIR read diagonally downwards. One column contains three blanks but there are none in the left-hand column. One G is in the top row but there are no Bs in row 6.

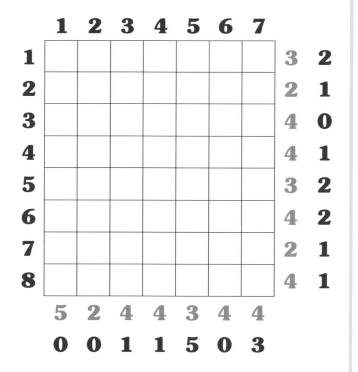

# 205 CELL STRUCTURE

The object is to create white areas surrounded by black walls, so that:
• Each white area contains only one number
• The number of cells in a white area is equal to the number in it
• The white areas are separated from each other with a black wall
• Cells containing numbers must not be filled in
• The black cells must be linked into a continuous wall
• Black cells cannot form a square of 2 x 2 or larger

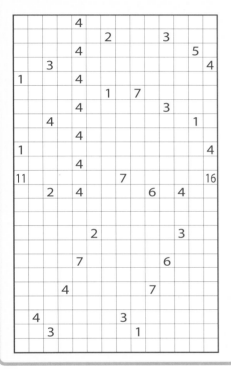

# 206 STAR STUDENTS

In a magazine article, three popular Albion-TV personalities talk about their time at university, studying for careers which they never pursued after getting into television. From the clues given below, can you work out each woman's full name, what she does on Albion-TV and what she trained to be originally?

## Clues

1 It wasn't Donna who was trained as a teacher.
2 Miss Knight is host of Albion-TV's popular Saturday evening quiz show Go For It!
3 Laura is a newsreader, presenting Albion-TV's flagship 9.00pm summary every weekday.
4 Susan Niven never had any ambition to be a nurse.
5 It isn't the one-time student teacher who now presents current affairs programmes for Albion-TV.

|  | Knight | Niven | Robins | Newsreader | Presenter | Quiz host | Nurse | Lawyer | Teacher |
|---|---|---|---|---|---|---|---|---|---|
| Donna |  |  |  |  |  |  |  |  |  |
| Laura |  |  |  |  |  |  |  |  |  |
| Susan |  |  |  |  |  |  |  |  |  |
| Nurse |  |  |  |  |  |  |  |  |  |
| Lawyer |  |  |  |  |  |  |  |  |  |
| Teacher |  |  |  |  |  |  |  |  |  |
| Newsreader |  |  |  |  |  |  |  |  |  |
| Presenter |  |  |  |  |  |  |  |  |  |
| Quiz host |  |  |  |  |  |  |  |  |  |

| FIRST NAME | SURNAME | TV CAREER | STUDIED AS |
|---|---|---|---|
|  |  |  |  |
|  |  |  |  |
|  |  |  |  |

# 207 TOP APARTMENT

The brass number plate for the apartments in Leakey Towers was bought from the Nutting-Fitz Hardware Store. This place never has exactly what anyone wants, so the locals have to make do with what they get. Young vandals have already ensured that one apartment number needs replacing. What should it be?

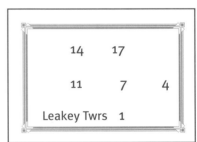

# 208 BLACK AND WHITE

A question frequently asked is – "How many squares are there on a chessboard?" It's a pretty old question as well, so if you're young enough not to have heard it before, it is worth finding out now! (No, it isn't 64, is it?)

What isn't asked quite so often is – "How many squares are there on a chessboard which are more black than white?" Can you work that out?

## 209 DOTTY DILEMMA

Connect adjacent dots with vertical or horizontal lines so that a single loop is formed with no crossings or branches. Each number indicates how many lines surround it, while empty cells may be surrounded by any number of lines.

```
    0       2 1         1
 3     3         2         0
    3           2
    0     1 3       2
 1     0       3       2
 1     3       1       0
    1     2 1       3
    1           1
 3     2       1       2
    3       3 3       3
```

## 210 HEDGE YOUR BETS

Can you draw the boundary lines on this estate so that each plot is the same size as each of the others and each contains a house, a cat, a dog and a tree?

## 211 STRAWBERRY SHARES

Can you carve up this ornate cake, cutting along the intersecting lines only, to produce eight equal sized portions? Each portion is to be decorated with 1 piece of chocolate, 1 iced star, a blob of cream and 1 strawberry.

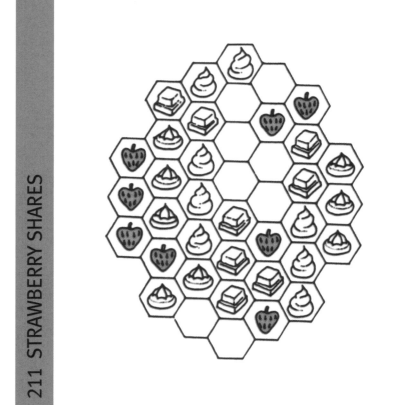

## 212 PYROTECHNIC PAIRS

Find the matching pair of fireworks?

# 213 SQUARE THE CIRCLE

Divide the 6 x 6 square into four identical pieces so that one circle appears on each piece.

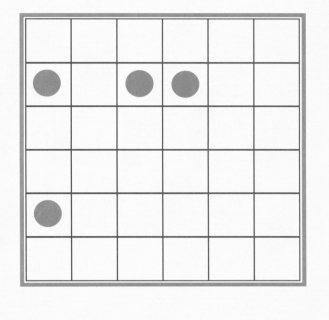

# 214 TENTACKLE

Eight children are camping out, two to each tent, and some have given us a couple of clues as to how to find them. The trouble is their directions are as bad as their cooking and in each case only one direction is true whilst the other is an exact opposite, so that East should read West, etc. Directions are not necessarily exact so North could be North, Northeast or Northwest. To help you one child is already tucked into a sleeping bag.

Owen says:  I'm West of Rob and South of Pete
Sam says:  I'm East of Vince and North of Nick
Vince says:  I'm West of Nick and South of Tom
Will says:  I'm East of Vince and North of Rob

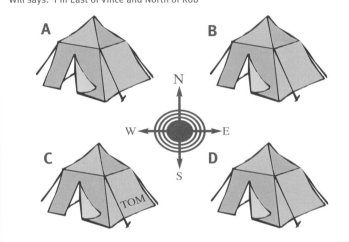

215 FACE VALUES

There are three faces hidden somewhere in this picture – can you find them?

## 216 SIX PACK

By packing numbers in the empty spaces, can you make the numbers in each of the 16 hexagons add up to 25? No two numbers in each hexagon may be the same and you can't use zero. We've started you off.

## 217 TIME PLEASE

Look at the three clocks, then work out what the last clock should say to continue the sequence. Can you draw in the hands correctly?

## 218 DOMINO SEARCH

A standard set of dominoes has been laid out, using numbers instead of dots for clarity. Using a sharp pencil and a keen brain, can you draw in the lines to show where each domino has been placed? You may find the check grid useful – crossing off each domino as you find it.

| 1 | 2 | 4 | 5 | 1 | 1 | 1 | 3 |
|---|---|---|---|---|---|---|---|
| 6 | 2 | 2 | 5 | 6 | 2 | 5 | 3 |
| 2 | 1 | 2 | 5 | 6 | 3 | 6 | 3 |
| 2 | 6 | 4 | 5 | 0 | 4 | 0 | 4 |
| 0 | 3 | 0 | 5 | 6 | 0 | 0 | 0 |
| 5 | 3 | 6 | 5 | 4 | 4 | 6 | 3 |
| 3 | 1 | 4 | 1 | 4 | 0 | 1 | 2 |

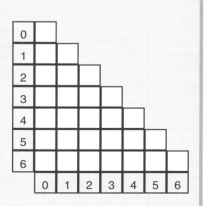

## 219 SET SQUARE

All the digits from 1 to 9 are used in this grid, but only once. Can you work out their positions in the grid and make the sums work? We've given two numbers to start you off.

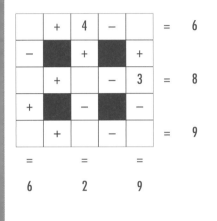

|   | + | 4 | − |   | = | 6 |
|---|---|---|---|---|---|---|
| − |   | + |   | + |   |   |
|   | + |   | − | 3 | = | 8 |
| + |   | − |   | − |   |   |
|   | + |   | − |   | = | 9 |
| = |   | = |   | = |   |   |
| 6 |   | 2 |   | 9 |   |   |

## 220 COMMUNITY VIEWS

Three friends who were artists each produced a work showing a different feature of the community they all lived in. From the clues given below, can you identify the three, say which view each chose to depict, and work out the medium in which each worked?

### Clues

1 Ms Frame chose the local church as her subject.
2 Rosalind, whose surname is not Canvass, produced the oil painting.
3 The windmill was the subject of the watercolour painting, which was not the work of Nadine.
4 The pond was not the view selected by the artist who favoured pen and ink for her picture.

|             | Canvass | Frame | Pallett | Pond | Local church | Windmill | Oils | Pen and ink | Watercolour |
|-------------|---------|-------|---------|------|--------------|----------|------|-------------|-------------|
| Josephine   |         |       |         |      |              |          |      |             |             |
| Nadine      |         |       |         |      |              |          |      |             |             |
| Rosalind    |         |       |         |      |              |          |      |             |             |
| Oils        |         |       |         |      |              |          |      |             |             |
| Pen and ink |         |       |         |      |              |          |      |             |             |
| Watercolour |         |       |         |      |              |          |      |             |             |
| Pond        |         |       |         |      |              |          |      |             |             |
| Local church|         |       |         |      |              |          |      |             |             |
| Windmill    |         |       |         |      |              |          |      |             |             |

| FIRST NAME | SURNAME | VIEW | MEDIUM |
|------------|---------|------|--------|
|            |         |      |        |
|            |         |      |        |
|            |         |      |        |

## 221 FLOWER POWER

Patriotic Pete sells bunches of red, white and blue flowers in the market. Some bunches have just a single colour, some two and some a mixture of all three. If he brings along a total of 80 bunches, can you work out how many bunches have flowers of all three colours?

The number of bunches with both red and white flowers is the same as that with both blue and white but no red. The number of bunches with only white flowers is the same as that with only red and the number of bunches with only blue flowers is the same as that with both red and blue but no white. Forty bunches contain red flowers, 49 bunches contain white and 44 contain blue. There are 38 bunches with just one colour in them.

## 222 SUDOKU

Place a number from 1 to 9 in each empty cell so that each row, each column and each 3 x 3 block contains all the numbers from 1 to 9.

|   |   |   | 9 | 7 | 4 |   |   |   |
|---|---|---|---|---|---|---|---|---|
|   |   | 2 |   |   |   |   | 5 |   |
|   |   |   | 3 | 6 |   |   |   | 1 |
|   | 7 |   |   |   | 1 | 9 |   | 3 |
| 3 |   | 6 |   |   |   | 5 |   | 7 |
| 4 |   | 2 | 3 |   |   |   | 8 |   |
| 9 |   |   | 4 | 5 |   |   |   |   |
|   | 5 |   |   |   | 3 |   |   |   |
|   |   | 4 | 1 | 2 |   |   |   |   |

## 223 WHERE THE L?

Sixteen L shapes like the ones below have been fitted into a square shape. Each L has one hole, and there are four of each type in the square. No two pieces of the same type are adjacent, even at a corner. They fit together so well that the spaces between pieces do not show. From the locations of the holes, can you tell where each L is?

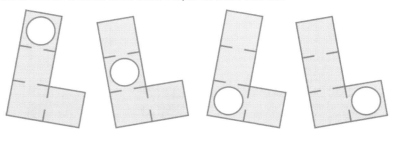

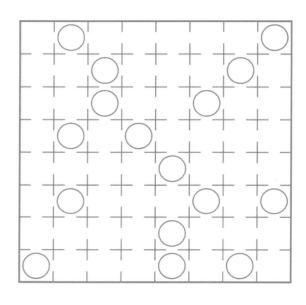

## 224 IN THE PICTURE

Only two of the lettered dogs match the portrait. Which are they?

## 225 ROUND TRIP

We have made a round trip through the dots in the grid, visiting each dot once and returning to the start. Part of our path is shown; can you deduce the rest?

HINT: Once a dot has two lines leaving it, it can't have any more. Show this by hash lines xxxx.

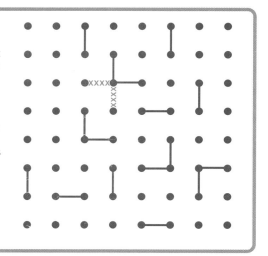

## 226 ISLAND HOPPING

Each circle containing a number represents an island. The object is to connect each island with vertical or horizontal bridges so that:
•The number of bridges is the same as the number inside the island.
•There can be up to two bridges between two islands.
•Bridges cannot cross islands or other bridges.
•There is a continuous path connecting all the islands.

# 227 ARTIST'S PALETTE

Which one of the numbered boxes has been removed from this culinary scene?

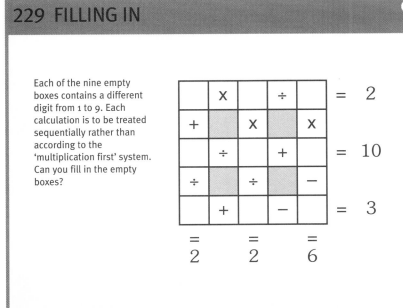

# 228 NUMBER JIG

Fit the numbers into the grid. We have done one for you.

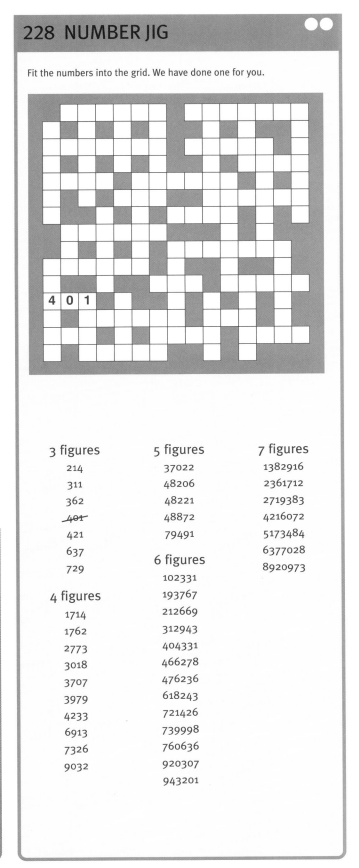

| 3 figures | 5 figures | 7 figures |
|---|---|---|
| 214 | 37022 | 1382916 |
| 311 | 48206 | 2361712 |
| 362 | 48221 | 2719383 |
| ~~401~~ | 48872 | 4216072 |
| 421 | 79491 | 5173484 |
| 637 | | 6377028 |
| 729 | **6 figures** | 8920973 |
| | 102331 | |
| **4 figures** | 193767 | |
| 1714 | 212669 | |
| 1762 | 312943 | |
| 2773 | 404331 | |
| 3018 | 466278 | |
| 3707 | 476236 | |
| 3979 | 618243 | |
| 4233 | 721426 | |
| 6913 | 739998 | |
| 7326 | 760636 | |
| 9032 | 920307 | |
| | 943201 | |

# 229 FILLING IN

Each of the nine empty boxes contains a different digit from 1 to 9. Each calculation is to be treated sequentially rather than according to the 'multiplication first' system. Can you fill in the empty boxes?

|   | × |   | ÷ |   | = 2 |
|---|---|---|---|---|---|
| + |   | × |   | × |   |
|   | ÷ |   | + |   | = 10 |
| ÷ |   | ÷ |   | − |   |
|   | + |   | − |   | = 3 |
| = 2 |   | = 2 |   | = 6 |   |

## 230 BLOOMERS

Charlie Dimwit's garden centre, Bloomers, has a fine display of pot plants for sale, an equal number of each colour. Four gardeners each took ten pots from the stand. Each gardener took a different number of pots of the colours they selected. After they had taken their pots there were an equal number of each colour left over. From the information given can you work out what each gardener selected?

Brian who bought no yellows, bought the same number of reds as Pete did violets and this was double Gloria's yellows. Green was the only colour bought by all four; all the other colours were bought by three gardeners. The two 'B' gardeners bought the same number of green pots and together these were one more than Gloria's red pots which was the same as Beth's violet pots. Brian bought the same number of violets as Gloria did greens and this was two less than Brian's blues. Pete bought no reds.

## 231 STICKY TIME

These 16 sticks make five squares. Can you work out how to move *just two sticks* to leave four squares? The squares you leave must all be the same size and we said move not throw away. Don't leave any loose ends either.

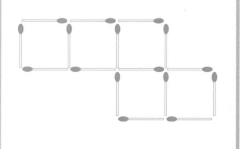

## 232 PATTERN MAKER

Can you place the numbered blocks into the grid to form the pattern shown? The blocks may be placed horizontally or vertically, and can be turned round.

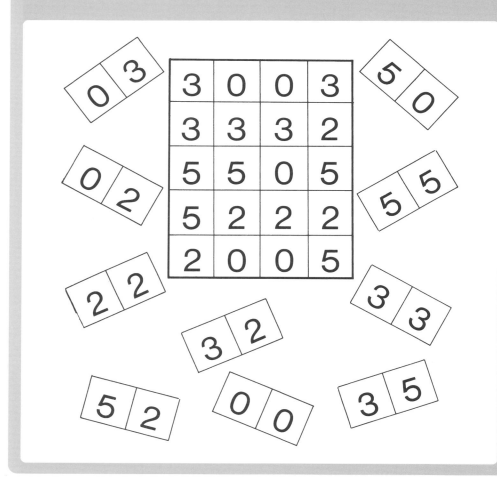

## 233 END OF THE LINE

There are eight differences between these two pictures – can you find them all?

# 234 SKI MAZE

Soppy Sally has let her skis slide down the ski slope (try saying that fast!). Can you find the way through the maze from Sally to the skis?

## 235 COG-ITATE

Which one of the two contacts will be touched when the mechanic turns the handle as shown?

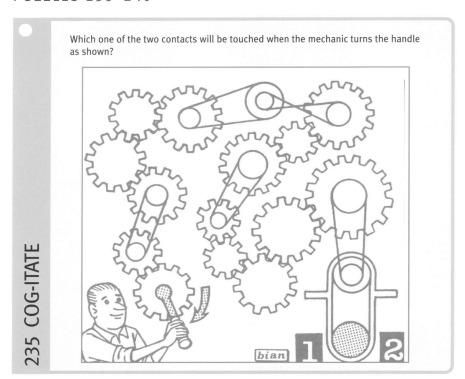

## 236 EASY AS ABC

Each row and column originally contained one A, one B, one C, one D and two blank squares. Each letter and number refers to the first or second of the four letters encountered when travelling in the direction of the arrow. Can you complete the original grid?

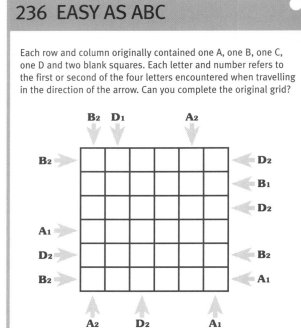

## 237 FILLING IN

Each of the nine empty boxes contains a different digit from 1 to 9. Each calculation is to be treated sequentially rather than according to the 'multiplication first' system. Can you fill in the empty boxes?

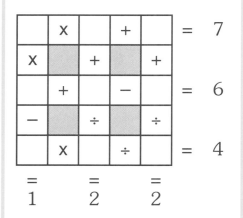

## 238 DOMINO SEARCH

A standard set of dominoes has been laid out, using numbers instead of dots for clarity. Using a sharp pencil and a keen brain, can you draw in the lines to show where each domino has been placed? You may find the check grid useful – crossing off each domino as you find it.

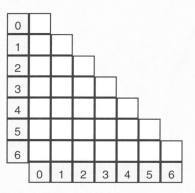

## 239 SQUARE FILL

How many squares, of all sizes, are more black than white in this picture?

## 240 RIGHT NUMBER

How many rectangles are there in this picture? (Remember, squares count as rectangles.)

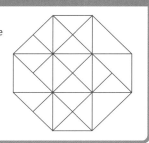

# 241 BLOOMERS

Charlie Dimwit's garden centre, Bloomers, has a fine display of pot plants for sale. Four gardeners each took ten pots from the stand. Each gardener took a different number of pots of the plants they selected. After they had taken their pots there was an equal number of each plant left over. From the information give below can you work out what each gardener selected? In case you are tempted to rush along to Bloomers, the gardenias are now sold out!

Connie bought twice as many African violets as begonias and the same number of begonias as Debbie who bought two less African violets than begonias. Arthur bought half the number of begonias as Barry bought cyclamens and Barry bought no begonias. Debbie was the only one not to buy cyclamens and Arthur bought no African violets but twice as many jasmines as Barry.

# 242 FLOWER POWER

Mucky Mouse has got a new camera and he's been busy snapping some flowers. Can you sort his photos into five matching pairs?

# 243 FRAME UP

It's that time of year again and the Mail Office has taken on extra staff for the forthcoming rush, John has persuaded his fellow recruits at Kimbledown to appear in a photo before exhaustion sets in and he himself is in position G. Left and right are as you look at the photo, and in front and behind are not necessarily directly so unless stated, i.e., it is true to say that A is behind K.

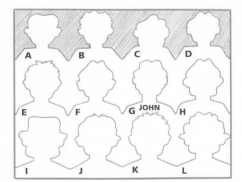

1 Fred is not next to Cleo and is not in an end position.
2 Gwen is in an end position and is behind Karl.
3 Edna is to the left of Lucy and to the right of Babs.
4 Alan is behind Dave and next to Fred.
5 Hugh is to the right of Irma and immediately in front of Edna.
6 Dave is to the right of Karl and in front of Irma.
7 Cleo is next to Lucy and they are behind John.

## 244 MOSTLY GHOSTS

Can you see which one of the four shadows belongs to the rabbit in the top left-hand corner?

## 245 NUMBER JIG

Fit the numbers into the grid. One has been done for you.

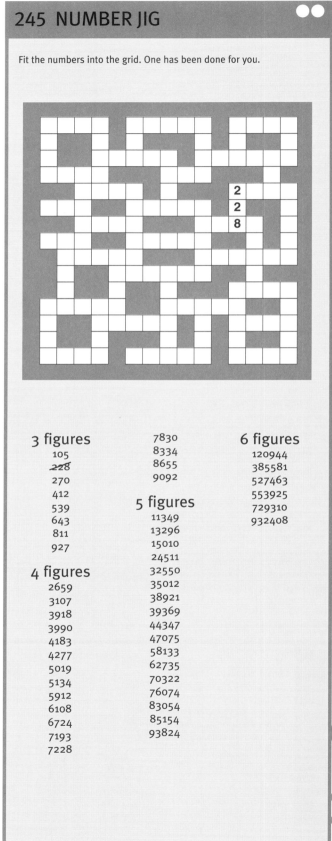

| 3 figures | 7830 | 6 figures |
|---|---|---|
| 105 | 8334 | 120944 |
| 228 | 8655 | 385581 |
| 270 | 9092 | 527463 |
| 412 | | 553925 |
| 539 | 5 figures | 729310 |
| 643 | 11349 | 932408 |
| 811 | 13296 | |
| 927 | 15010 | |
| | 24511 | |
| 4 figures | 32550 | |
| 2659 | 35012 | |
| 3107 | 38921 | |
| 3918 | 39369 | |
| 3990 | 44347 | |
| 4183 | 47075 | |
| 4277 | 58133 | |
| 5019 | 62735 | |
| 5134 | 70322 | |
| 5912 | 76074 | |
| 6108 | 83054 | |
| 6724 | 85154 | |
| 7193 | 93824 | |
| 7228 | | |

## 246 DOTTY DILEMMA

Connect adjacent dots with vertical or horizontal lines so that a single loop is formed with no crossings or branches. Each number indicates how many lines surround it, while empty cells may be surrounded by any number of lines.

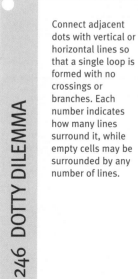

# 247 CELL STRUCTURE

The object is to create white areas surrounded by black walls, so that:
* Each white area contains only one number
* The number of cells in a white area is equal to the number in it
* The white areas are separated from each other with a black wall
* Cells containing numbers must not be filled in
* The black cells must be linked into a continuous wall
* Black cells cannot form a square of 2x2 or larger

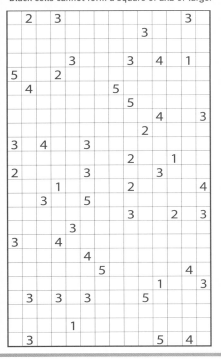

# 248 WHAT A CRACKER

Four celebratory souls are about to pull arms from sockets, wait in vain for the non-existent crack and see what expensive luxury lies hidden in each 50 cent cracker. Can you pull apart the clues, cross off the impossible and leave each cracker displaying the name of the owner, gift, motif and colour?

**1** Paul has the cracker numbered two higher than Yapp's whose silver cracker is decorated with reindeer.

**2** Jock has cracker No. 2 which does not have the knife in it. The gold cracker is neither No. 1 nor the one with the tinsel decoration which was given to a lady.

**3** Cracker No. 3 has stars on it but is not ruby in colour. Cole was not given this one but the one with the picture in it.

**4** The cracker decorated with cakes has the scarf in it which is for neither Tricia nor Williams.

**5** Audrey is not Lewis and neither has the cracker with the biro nor No. 4 which is bronze in colour.

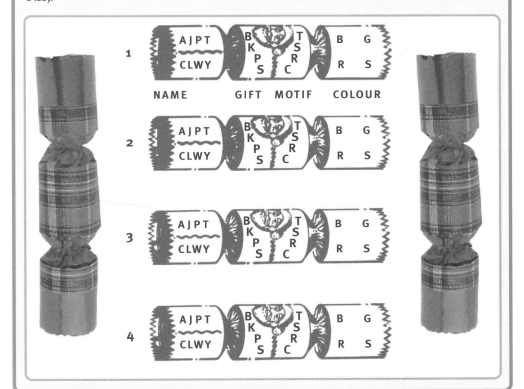

# 249 COG-ITATE

Which of the four weights will rise and which will fall when the handle is turned as shown?

# 250 FLOWER POWER

Patriotic Pete sells bunches of red, white and blue flowers in the market. Some bunches have just a single colour, some two and some a mixture of all three. If he brings along a total of 80 bunches, can you work out how many bunches have flowers of all three colours?

The number of bunches with both red and blue flowers but no white is the same as the number with red only and the number of bunches with both blue and white but no red is the same as the number with blue only and this is equal to the total number of bunches with red only and with both red and white but no blue. Three times as many bunches have white flowers only as have all three colours. Twenty-nine bunches contained red flowers and 41 bunches contained blue.

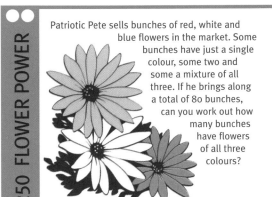

## 251 IN DEEP WATER

Which one of these numbered prints has been developed from the negative?

## 252 WHERE THE L?

Sixteen L shapes like the ones below have been fitted into a square shape. Each L has one hole, and there are four of each type in the square. No two pieces of the same type are adjacent, even at a corner. They fit together so well that the spaces between pieces do not show. From the locations of the holes, can you tell where each L is?

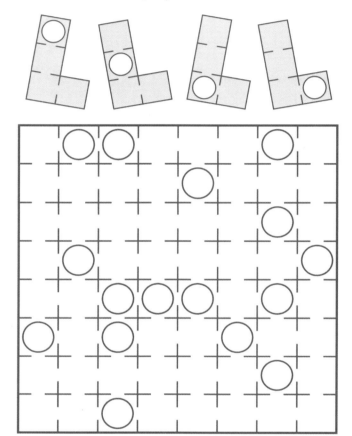

## 253 FILLING IN

Each of the nine empty boxes contains a different digit from 1 to 9. Each calculation is to be treated sequentially rather than according to the 'multiplication first' system. Can you fill in the empty boxes?

|   | ÷ |   | + |   | = | 7 |
|---|---|---|---|---|---|---|
| x |   | + |   | + |   |   |
|   | x |   | ÷ |   | = | 12 |
| − |   | ÷ |   | ÷ |   |   |
|   | + |   | − |   | = | 1 |
| = |   | = |   | = |   |   |
| 5 |   | 3 |   | 1 |   |   |

## 254 BIRD BOXES

Can you see which one of the four boxes contains the pieces of the bird shown below?

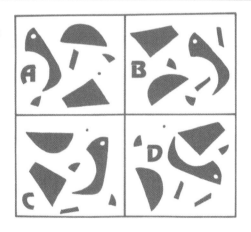

# 255 WELL SPOTTED

The number in each circle tells you how many of it and its touching neighbours are to be filled in.

In our example, A, the zero gives a start – put lines through it and its neighbours (B). Three circles can now be filled (C) – lightly, though so the numbers can still be read...

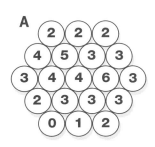

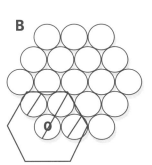

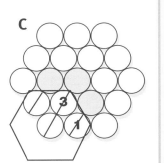

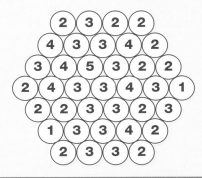

# 256 PIXELATED PICS

| 1 | 2 | 3 |
|---|---|---|
| 8 | X | 4 |
| 7 | 6 | 5 |

The numbers in the squares tell you how many of it and its neighbours are to be filled in. A square can have up to eight neighbours. Using logic alone, can you fill in the pixels and create an admirable portrait?

| 0 | | 0 | 2 | 5 | 5 | 2 | 0 | | 0 |
|---|---|---|---|---|---|---|---|---|---|
| | 1 | | 4 | 6 | 6 | 6 | 3 | 0 | |
| 0 | | 4 | 7 | 5 | 7 | 8 | 2 | | 0 |
| | 4 | | 8 | 4 | 5 | 8 | 7 | 2 | |
| 2 | | 7 | 4 | 6 | 7 | 7 | 7 | | 3 |
| | 7 | | 6 | 6 | 6 | 3 | 6 | 8 | |
| 3 | | 6 | 7 | 6 | 3 | 3 | 6 | | 4 |
| | 3 | | 5 | 6 | 2 | 2 | 2 | 3 | |
| 0 | | 1 | 5 | 3 | 2 | 3 | 1 | | 0 |
| | 0 | | 0 | 3 | 2 | 1 | 2 | 0 | |
| 0 | | 0 | 1 | 3 | 3 | 4 | 1 | | 0 |
| | 0 | | 0 | 1 | 3 | 5 | 3 | 0 | |
| 0 | | 2 | 3 | 3 | 5 | 6 | 3 | | 2 |
| | 4 | | 6 | 6 | 4 | 4 | 5 | 5 | |
| 4 | | 8 | 9 | 8 | 5 | 6 | 7 | | 6 |
| | 8 | | 8 | 9 | 6 | 5 | 4 | 6 | |
| 4 | | 7 | 7 | 8 | 8 | 8 | 6 | | 6 |
| | 4 | | 4 | 8 | 7 | 7 | 4 | 6 | |
| 1 | | 2 | 4 | 8 | 8 | 8 | 6 | | 6 |
| | 0 | | 0 | 4 | 5 | 5 | 3 | 4 | |

# 257 STAR LINES

With one continuous line, join up all the circles (starting from Pisces) and, with another continuous line, join up all the triangles (starting from Gemini). The lines must not cross!

# 258 21s

Obeying the normal rules of arithmetic, with the numbers given, using only where necessary +, –, x, or ÷, make the resulting calculations equal 21.

2　(12　3)　9 = 21　　2　11　11　10 = 21

5　3　8　2 = 21

## 259 SPOT THE DIFFERENCE

Can you spot the ten differences between these two pictures?

## 260 NUMBER SQUARES

Can you complete the grids with the aid of the numbers given, so that all sums, whether horizontal or vertical, are correct? (Please note that each sum should be treated separately.)

| 64 | ÷ | | = | | + | | = | 56 |
|---|---|---|---|---|---|---|---|---|
| − | | + | | − | | ÷ | | − |
| | ÷ | | = | | + | 4 | = | |
| = | | = | | = | | = | | = |
| | ÷ | | = | 4 | × | | = | |
| + | | × | | + | | + | | − |
| | − | 4 | = | | + | | = | |
| = | | = | | = | | = | | = |
| 41 | − | | = | | + | | = | 27 |

## 261 SUDOKU

Place a number from 1 to 9 in each empty cell so that each row, each column and each 3 x 3 block contains all the numbers from 1 to 9.

| | | | | | | | 5 | 4 |
|---|---|---|---|---|---|---|---|---|
| | 5 | 4 | | | | 6 | | |
| 3 | | | 2 | | | 7 | | |
| | | | 1 | 7 | | | 4 | 8 |
| 7 | 3 | | | 4 | 9 | | | |
| | | 1 | | | 7 | | | 9 |
| | 5 | | | | | 3 | 2 | |
| 2 | 9 | | | | | | | |

## 262 RINGING IN THE CHANGES

Karl Krack, who owns a small travelling circus, believes that variety is the spice of life and for each show he alters the order of his eight acts. Can you work out what the order will be for tonight's performance? The Flying Fortresses will perform immediately after Jim the Juggler and Fred the Fire-eater is immediately before the Crazy Carvellos. The Clever Clowns are in action three acts after Senor Pedro's Poodles and three acts before the Agilles Acrobats. Madame Poll's Parrots are two acts after the Flying Fortresses.

| 1 | 2 | 3 | 4 |
|---|---|---|---|
| 5 | 6 | 7 | 8 |

# 263 HARE PLAY

Which two of the pictures below form a matching pair?

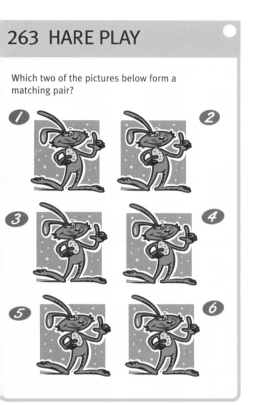

# 264 ACE IN PLACE

The cards Eight to King of each suit, together with the Ace of Hearts, have been placed in a five by five square. Figures and letters to the values – 8, 9, T, Q, K and suits – C, D, H, S have been placed at the end of each line across and down. With the Ace in place and the fact that the two cards shown at the top left belong in the shaded squares, can you work out the unique place for each card?

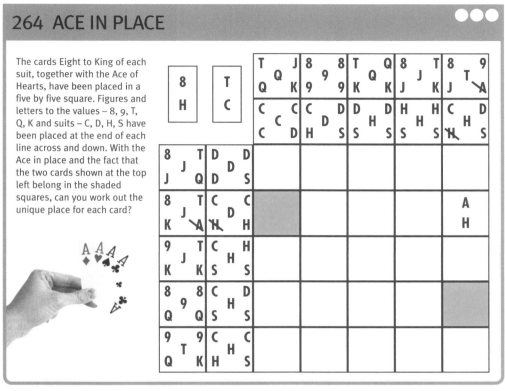

# 265 STICKY TIME

Using just these six matchsticks, can you make 12 right-angled triangles?

# 266 DOTTY DILEMMA

Connect adjacent dots with vertical or horizontal lines so that a single loop is formed with no crossings or branches. Each number indicates how many lines surround it, while empty cells may be surrounded by any number of lines.

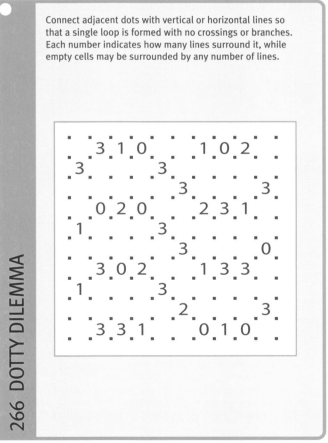

## 267 ROOM TO MANOEUVRE

Inspector Drayne of The Yard pulled up in his car at the door of Whartson Hall, home of Lord and Lady Mole.

He entered the Hall. Swiftly his eyes travelled round the interior. Not waiting for them to come back, he stepped blindly forward and tripped over a scullery maid.

A large butler helped him to his feet.

"This way, sir. The body is waiting for you in the library."

Passing through another door, Drayne stopped in horror. He had seen death before many times – but never like this. The body of Lord Mole lay on a Persian rug – his head was caked in a thick, glutinous yellow liquid. It was obvious he had been battered to death.

Drayne turned to the local detective who was leaning against a Constable.

"Where was each person at the time of the murder?"

The detective cleared his throat, cleaned his glass eye and varnished his nails.

"Lady Mole says she was in the card room; the Hon. Reginald Ackney in the billiard room; Reverend Rash, the lounge; Lance O'Boyle, the morning room. Miss Felicity Bytes was in the study. Spott, the butler, and Wicklow, the maid, were in the cloak room."

"Thank you. Now it's obvious that...."

A sobbing interrupted his train of thought which went off into a siding.

The maid he had tripped over was having her arm set in plaster but Drayne was sure her tears were not for that. He looked at her, stern but kindly.

"Please, sir. I was told to say we were together by Mr Spott. But we wasn't."

"Were you alone?"

"If you please, sir, yes, sir."

An inner light in Drayne's mind signalled green and his train of thought shunted back into consciousness.

"Not only was Wicklow here, lying" he said, "but I know for a fact that not one of you was in the room you claimed to be in. And each of you was alone – except one – the murderer!"

Seven heads fell.

"I shall now take a statement from each of you and it had better be the truth this time."

It was.

Lady Mole recalled that Reverend Rash was in a room next to hers but Wicklow was not.

The Honourable Reginald, who thought himself frightfully good with numbers, was in a room with fewer doors than the one Her Ladyship was in but more than the one occupied by Lance O'Boyle.

Reverend Rash seem flustered. "Well, yes. I'm sure there was a lady in one room next to mine and a man in another. But I don't know who was in the third – you see, the door to that room was shut at the time."

Felicity Bytes stated candidly that Reverend Rash had not been in the lounge as she had been in a room next to it.

Spott declared that he had not been in a room adjacent to either Wicklow or the Honourable Reginald. He also confirmed that there was no door between the billiard room and the study.

Wicklow sobbed out between her tears that Mr O'Boyle had been in a room next to hers.

Drayne was stumped. The security camera replay showed him well out of his crease. He wrung his hands and then his wife. She agreed to warm his dinner in the oven – it was a ham salad.

To the assembled suspects he had but one thing to say. "I haven't a clue who was in the library – will somebody please confess?"

No one did, so-whodunnit?

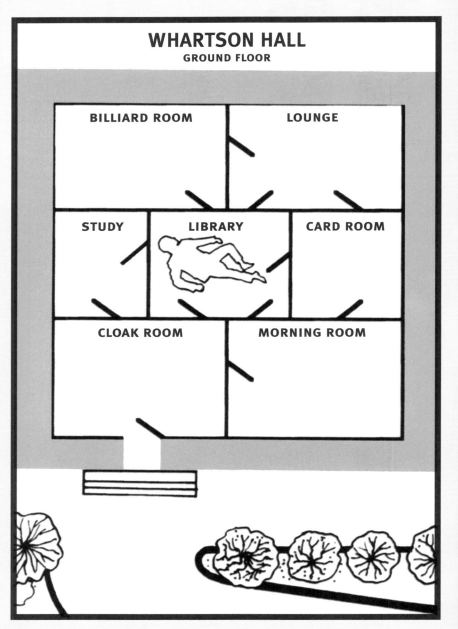

# 268 ISLAND HOPPING

Each circle containing a number represents an island. The object is to connect each island with vertical or horizontal bridges so that:
* The number of bridges is the same as the number inside the island
* There can be up to two bridges between two islands
* Bridges cannot cross islands or other bridges
* There is a continuous path connecting all the islands.

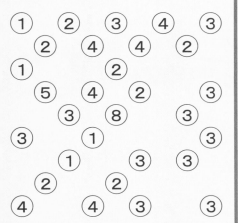

# 269 ILLOGI-5

Clever Trevor is trying to compile a little logical puzzle – the idea is that each line across and down has each letter A, B, C, D, E once only. Also, each shape of five squares also has the letters A to E once only. After hours of effort and wasted paper, he still hasn't managed to find a suitable arrangement. Can you end the misery by proving, quite simply, that the task is impossible?

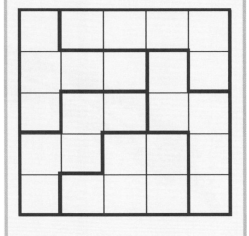

# 270 LOGIQUATIONS

In the following problems the digits 0 to 9 are represented by letters. Within each separate puzzle the same letter always represents the same digit. Can you find the correct values each time so that all sums, both horizontal and vertical, are correct? There is a clue to help start you off.

$$ABC \times DE = EFCE$$
$$+ \qquad +$$
$$GHJG - EDH = GKGF$$
$$\overline{FDEB - EFJ = GGDA}$$

| A | B | C | D | E | F | G | H | J | K |
|---|---|---|---|---|---|---|---|---|---|
|   |   |   |   |   |   |   |   |   |   |

**Clue: AC is a square**

# 271 GAME SET AND MATCH

Which two of the pictures below form a matching pair?

# 272 SET PIECES

Which one of these broken televisions used to look exactly like the complete one?

## 273 BRICK UP

The numbers on the bottom row of bricks are random. Above that, every number on each brick is made up – following some simple rule – from the TWO numbers on the bricks directly below it. Can you work out what the rule is and put the right number on the top brick?

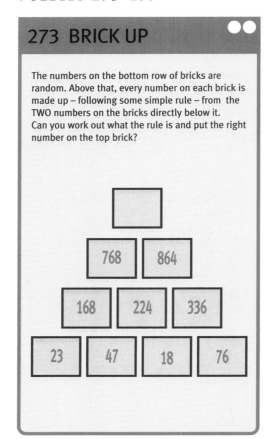

## 274 DEAR DEER

As usual Rudolph is in the lead as Santa's sleigh speeds down the M1. From the patrolling policeman's notes, can you name the reindeer in each of the other eight positions?

1  Cupid is Cornet's right-hand partner but Donner is further forward than, and on the opposite side to, Dasher.

2  Blitzen is further back than Dancer who, in turn, is further back than Prancer and directly in front of Vixen.

3  Cornet is directly in front of Dasher who is on the opposite side to the one both Vixen and Donner are on.

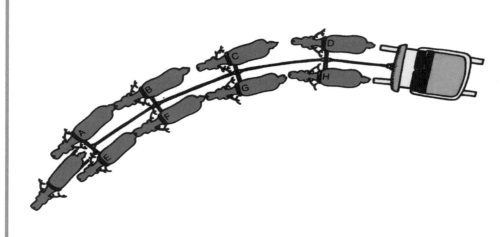

## 275 COG-ITATE

When the handle is turned in the direction shown, which two of the four weights will rise and which two will fall?

## 276 EASY AS ABC

Each row and column originally contained one A, one B, one C, one D and two blank squares. Each letter and number refers to the first or second of the four letters encountered when travelling in the direction of the arrow. Can you complete the original grid?

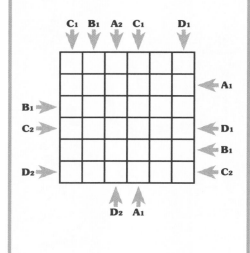

## 277 DOUBLE DUCKS

Can you spot three pairs of identical ducks and say which two are totally different from the others?

# 278 NUMBER JIG

Fit the numbers into the grid. One has been done for you.

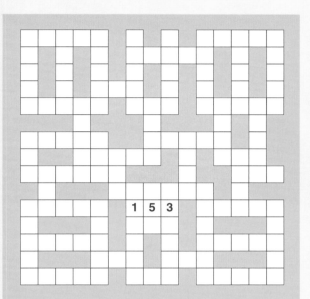

The grid contains: 1 5 3

## 3 figures
~~153~~
247
285
318
396
407
562
564
628
630
741
779
856
962

## 4 figures
1578
1646
2108
3704

## 5 figures
10123
12101
13452
24539
26908
28930
31243
34074
38620
41773
46789
47504
51234
51848
58907
61953
65678
67768
71234
72062
77678
82129
83103
86115
95422
97324
99283

## 6 figures
293492
615454
734537
868789
918466

# 279 TENTACKLE

Eight children are camping, two to each tent, and some have given us a couple of clues as to how to find them. The trouble is their directions are as bad as their cooking and in each case only one direction is true whilst the other is an exact opposite, so that East should read West etc. Directions are not necessarily exact so North could be North, Northeast or Northwest. To help you, one child is already tucked into a sleeping bag.

**Kate says:** I'm West of Jenny and South of Sally.
**Megan says:** I'm East of Lisa and South of Naomi.
**Rita says:** I'm West of Megan and South of Kate.
**Sally says:** I'm West of Paula and North of Lisa.

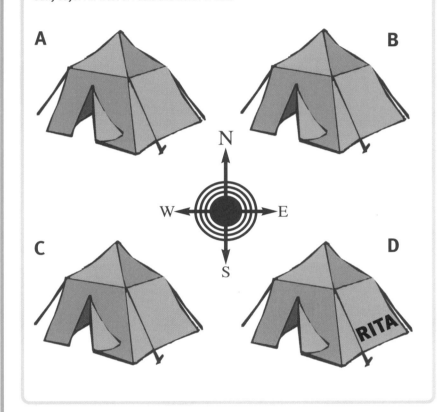

# 280 STICKY TIME

These 13 sticks have been placed to form four squares. Can you remove three sticks then move two of those left to form just *two* squares?

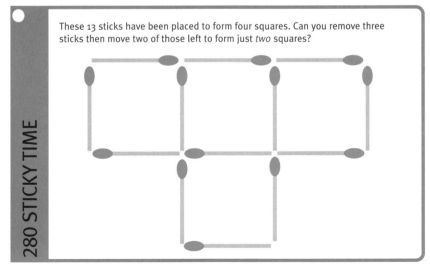

## 281 FIDDLEHAM APARTMENTS

The super of these notorious apartments continues to confuse visitors with his addiction to Invicta's game Master Mind. Instead of 'Smith's in Apartment X, buddy.' he hands the visitor a list of current residents and asks him to make guesses as to who is in each apartment. He then marks the line of guesses with two numbers:

First: how many are exactly right – the correct name on the right door.
Second: how many of the names are correct for that floor but are on the wrong door.
The only other information he gives is that each surname can only occur on one floor – if Smith is on the ground floor, that name can't be on either of the other two floors. However, the same name can occur more than once on the same floor.
From the 12 guesses below and the list of names on the right, can you work out the correct name for each flat?

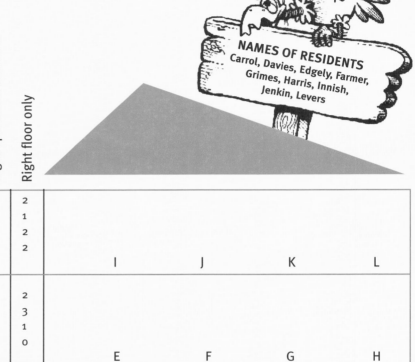

**NAMES OF RESIDENTS**
Carrol, Davies, Edgely, Farmer, Grimes, Harris, Innish, Jenkin, Levers

| # | | | | | Right apartment and floor | Right floor only |
|---|---|---|---|---|---|---|
| 1 | Grimes | Jenkin | Farmer | Farmer | 0 | 2 |
| 2 | Carrol | Levers | Farmer | Edgely | 1 | 1 |
| 3 | Innish | Harris | Carrol | Davies | 0 | 2 |
| 4 | Grimes | Edgely | Farmer | Jenkin | 0 | 2 |
| | I | J | K | L | | |

| # | | | | | | |
|---|---|---|---|---|---|---|
| 5 | Levers | Levers | Grimes | Grimes | 0 | 2 |
| 6 | Grimes | Harris | Grimes | Davies | 1 | 3 |
| 7 | Innish | Grimes | Grimes | Levers | 1 | 1 |
| 8 | Grimes | Carrol | Jenkin | Innish | 1 | 0 |
| | E | F | G | H | | |

| # | | | | | | |
|---|---|---|---|---|---|---|
| 9 | Edgely | Levers | Edgely | Levers | 2 | 2 |
| 10 | Innish | Davies | Innish | Levers | 1 | 0 |
| 11 | Jenkin | Edgely | Levers | Davies | 1 | 1 |
| 12 | Grimes | Davies | Levers | Grimes | 0 | 1 |
| | A | B | C | D | | |

(Answer grid letters: I J K L / E F G H / A B C D)

## 282 ROUND TRIP

We have made a round trip through the dots in the grid, visiting each dot once and returning to the start. Part of our path is shown. Can you deduce the rest?

HINT: Once a dot has two lines leaving it, it can't have any more. Show this by hash lines xxxx.

## 283 DOTTY DILEMMA

Connect adjacent dots with vertical or horizontal lines so that a single loop is formed with no crossings or branches. Each number indicates how many lines surround it, while empty cells may be surrounded by any number of lines.

```
                        2 0
  2 3 0 2   1     3
                2       2
    2 1 3     3
  0         2       1 3
    3 0       2         2
      3       2 1 2
    3       1
  1       2   3 2 3 3
      3 1
```

## 284 HEART ON HIS SLEEVE

Can you spot the eight differences between these two pictures?

Each circle containing a number represents an island. The object is to connect each island with vertical or horizontal bridges so that:
• The number of bridges is the same as the number inside the island
• There can be up to two bridges between two islands
• Bridges cannot cross islands or other bridges
• There is a continuous path connecting all the islands.

```
2       3   4   4
3   4     2   2
2   5     4
5   4         3
      2   3
2         2   4
    3     3   2
  4   3     2   2
3   2   2     2
```

There are six differences in the pictures below. Can you spot them?

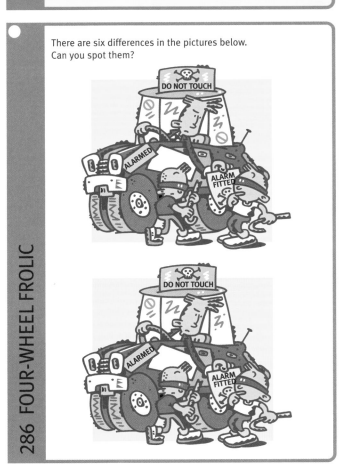

## 287 BLOOMIN' MARVELLOUS

There are six differences between these two pictures.
Can you find them all?

## 289 CUBE IT

Inside the circle are three views of the same cube.
Which of the lettered shapes can be folded up to make this cube?

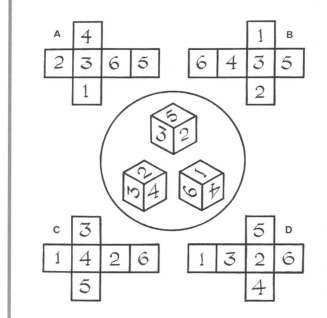

## 288 SUDOKU

Place a number from 1 to 9 in each empty cell so that each row, each column and each 3 x 3 block contains all the numbers from 1 to 9.

|   |   |   |   |   | 9 | 1 |   |   |
|---|---|---|---|---|---|---|---|---|
|   | 4 | 2 | 1 |   |   |   | 7 |   |
| 3 |   |   | 5 |   |   |   | 6 |   |
| 2 |   |   |   |   |   | 4 |   |   |
|   |   | 1 |   |   | 9 |   |   |   |
|   | 6 |   |   |   |   |   |   | 5 |
|   | 5 |   |   | 6 |   |   |   | 1 |
|   | 7 |   |   |   | 3 | 5 | 2 |   |
|   |   | 8 | 9 |   |   |   |   |   |

## 290 ROUND TRIP

We have made a round trip through the dots in the grid, visiting each dot once and returning to the start. Part of our path is shown; can you deduce the rest?

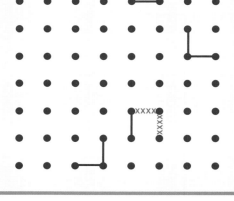

## 291 DOTTY DILEMMA

Connect adjacent dots with vertical or horizontal lines so that a single loop is formed with no crossings or branches. Each number indicates how many lines surround it, while empty cells may be surrounded by any number of lines.

## 292  MAZE MYSTERY

Travel from the entrance to the exit of the maze, filling the path completely to create a picture.

## 293 SPOT THE DIFFERENCE

How quickly can you discover the ten differences between these two pictures?

## 294 FIGUREWORK

Just fit these numbers into the grid.

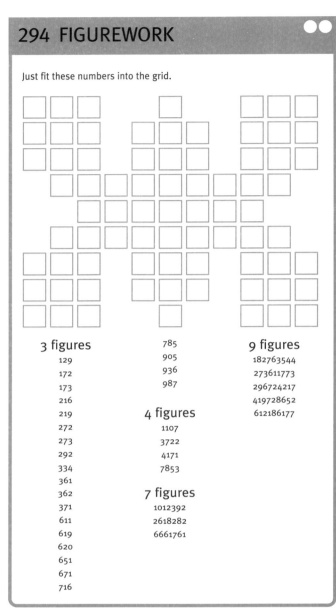

**3 figures**
129
172
173
216
219
272
273
292
334
361
362
371
611
619
620
651
671
716

785
905
936
987

**4 figures**
1107
3722
4171
7853

**7 figures**
1012392
2618282
6661761

**9 figures**
182763544
273611773
296724217
419728652
612186177

## 295 ROUND TRIP

We have made a round trip through the dots in the grid below, visiting each dot once and returning to the start. Part of our path is shown; Can you deduce the rest?

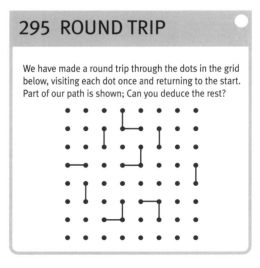

## 296 ACE IN PLACE

The cards Eight to King of each suit, together with the Ace of Hearts, have been placed in a 5 x 5 square. Figures and letters showing the values – 8, 9, T, J, Q, K and suits – C, D, H, S have been placed at the end of each line across and down. With the Ace in place and the fact that the two cards shown at the top left belong in the shaded squares, can you work out the unique place for each card?

# 297 SPOT THE DIFFERENCE

One of these footballers looks different from all the others. Can you spot the odd one out?

# 298 CUBE IT

Which two of the numbered pieces will fit together to make cube A?

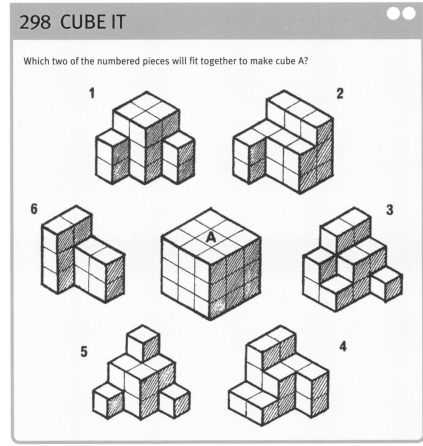

# 299 IT FIGURES

Place a number from 1 to 9 in each empty cell so that the sum of each vertical or horizontal block equals the number at the top or on the left of that block. Numbers may only be used once in each block.

## 300 DOMINO DEAL

A standard set (0 – 0) to (6 – 6) is laid out below. Each domino is placed so that the larger number will be on the bottom:

i.e.    3         not         6
        6                     3

Those top numbers show the four numbers which form the top half of each domino in that column. The bottom numbers, below the grid, give the four bottom numbers for that column. The seven numbers on the left show the numbers which belong in that row. Can you cross-reference the facts and deduce where each domino had been placed?

3*6 is given as a start.

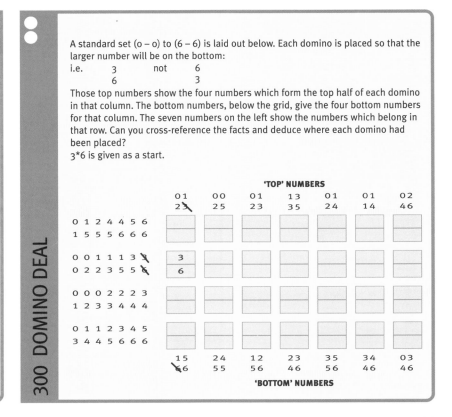

## 301 PROFESSIONAL PARTNERS

Each of the six persons mentioned has at least one sibling in the group and has exactly one spouse in the group. Each person is a member of one of the professions mentioned. No one shares a profession with a sibling or a spouse.

Here are the names with some other facts:

1 Neither Alice nor Dave is a surgeon.
2 Betty's sister's husband is an accountant.
3 Carol's husband's brother is an accountant.
4 Ed's wife is a surgeon, and so is Ed's sibling's spouse.
5 Frank's wife's brother is a lawyer.

You are now invited to identify the pre-marriage family groups, the marriages, and the profession of each person.

## 302 TRILINES

Can you draw three straight lines, each one drawn from one edge to another, so that it divides the box into five plots each containing two different fruits?

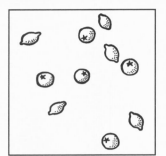

## 303 WHERE THE L?

Sixteen L-shapes like the ones on the right have been inserted into a square shape. Each L has one hole, and there are four of each type in the square. No two pieces of the same type are adjacent, even at a corner. They fit together so well that the spaces between pieces do not show. From the locations of the holes, can you tell where each L is?

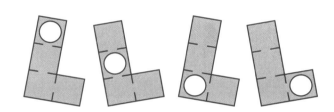

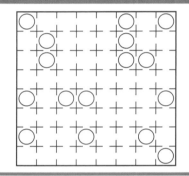

## 304 FUNNY BUNNY

These nine pieces can be put together to make up the rabbit shown in the middle. However, three of them are slightly wrong. Can you see which three they are?

## 305 ACE IN PLACE

The cards Eight to King of each suit, together with the Ace of Hearts, have been placed in a 5 x 5 square. Figures and letters showing the values – 8, 9, 10, J, Q, K and suits C, H, D, S, have been placed at the end of each line across and down. With the Ace in place and the fact that the two cards shown at the top left belong in the shaded squares, can you work out the unique place for each card?

| | | 8 T T | 8 9 Q | 8 K K | T Q K | J Q K J | 9 J J | 9 8 Q K | 8 Q K ~~A~~ J |
|---|---|---|---|---|---|---|---|---|---|
| T S | K S | C D H | C H S | C D S | D C H H | C H S | C S S | D D S H | D D H ~~H~~ |
| 8 J | 9 T K | C H H | C S | | | | | | |
| 8 Q | 9 T Q | C D D | D S | | | | | | |
| 8 K | 8 Q ~~A~~ | C H S | ~~H~~ H S | | | | | A H |
| T J | J K | C H H | D H S | | | (shaded) | | | |
| 9 Q | 9 T K | C H H | D D S | | | | (shaded) | | |

## 306 MAZE MYSTERY

Travel from the entrance to the exit of the maze, filling the path completely to create a picture.

## 307 LOGI-5

Each line, across and down, is to have each of the letters A, B, C, D and E, appearing once each. Also, every shape – shown by the thick lines – must also have each of the letters in it. Can you fill in the grid?

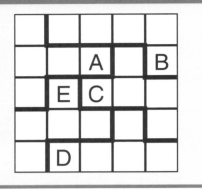

## 309 ALPHACIPHER

The numbers 1 to 26 have been allocated randomly to the letters of the alphabet. The letter values of the words have been added together to give the word values. For example, in GOLF, G might equal 15, O 12, L 20 and F 7, or any other combination of four numbers totalling 54. The theme this time is the phonetic alphabet. What is the value of ZULU?

| ALPHA | 68 | NOVEMBER | 64 |
| BRAVO | 59 | OSCAR | 56 |
| CHARLIE | 63 | PAPA | 48 |
| DELTA | 57 | QUEBEC | 68 |
| ECHO | 45 | ROMEO | 36 |
| FOXTROT | 68 | SIERRA | 54 |
| GOLF | 54 | TANGO | 53 |
| HOTEL | 52 | UNCLE | 50 |
| INDIA | 56 | VICTOR | 47 |
| JULIET | 75 | WHISKEY | 99 |
| KILO | 47 | X-RAY | 46 |
| LIMA | 30 | YANKEE | 65 |
| MIKE | 34 | | |

## 310 WHERE THE L?

Sixteen L-shapes like the ones below have been inserted into a square shape. Each L has one hole, and there are four of each type in the square. No two pieces of the same type are adjacent, even at a corner. They fit together so well that the spaces between pieces do not show. From the locations of the holes, can you tell where each L is?

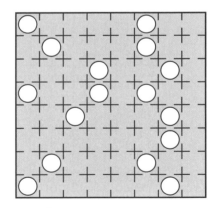

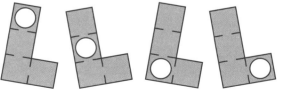

## 308 ARTIST'S MAZE

Can you work your way through this maze, starting from the flower at the top and finishing at the bottom of the chair?

## 311 EASY AS ABC

Each row and column originally contained one A, one B, one C, one D and two blank squares. Each letter and number refers to the first or second of the four letters encountered when travelling in the direction of the arrow. Can you complete the original grid?

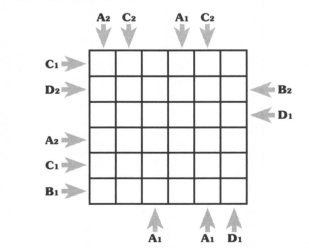

# 312 DOUBLE PUZZLE

Roll up folks, for our special sale offer of two puzzles for the price of one!

Puzzle One: Each colour has been given a value from 1 to 7. Given the totals at the end of each line, can you work out the value of each colour?

Puzzle Two: The picture is a layout of a set of colour dominoes – just like ordinary dominoes but with colours instead of spots. Can you draw in the lines to show each separate domino?

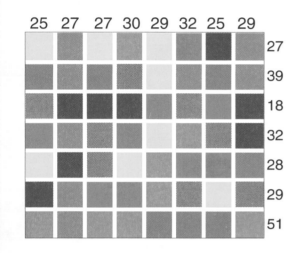

# 313 CUBISM

Which two cubes can be constructed from the template?

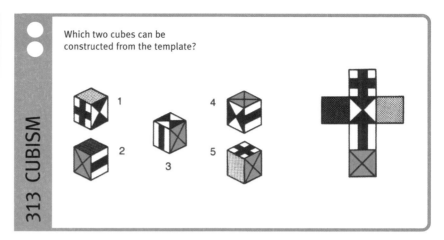

# 314 HAPPY HOUNDS

Can you see which one of the five pieces at the bottom will fit into the arrowed gap in the jigsaw? It's trickier than it looks!

# 315 STRAPPED

The six straps leading from the central hexagon each contain three different instances of the numbers 1 to 18. From the clues given below, can you place each number in the correct position on the correct strap?

**Clues**

1 The six innermost numbers total 64.

2 The single-digit middle number on strap A minus the number outside it produces the outermost number on strap F.

3 There are just two even numbers, one of which is the outermost one, on strap E, but only one on strap F.

4 5 is the innermost number on strap D; the 7 is not on the strap directly opposite.

5 17 and 12 are separated by the 1 on one of the straps.

6 The 10 on one strap, which is immediately next to the 16, is in the same relative position as the 3 on another, but the 6 is further away from the centre than the 15 on an adjacent strap.

7 Strap C, which has only one two-digit number on it, does not contain the 1 or 2, which corresponds in its position with the 13 on another strap.

8 The largest of the three numbers on strap B is not its innermost one; the outermost one is a lower number than the innermost number of the strap opposite, which is ten higher than the corresponding number on strap F.

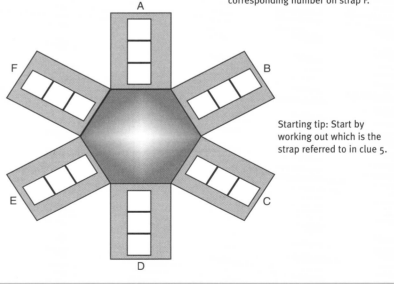

Starting tip: Start by working out which is the strap referred to in clue 5.

## 316 NUMBER BOX ●●

Just fit the numbers into the grid.

| 3 figures | 5 figures |
|---|---|
| 244 | 41322 |
| 432 | 42071 |
| 433 | |
| 456 | 7 figures |
| 459 | 4224545 |
| 521 | 4312344 |
| 522 | 4321345 |
| 565 | 5443099 |
| 623 | 7450975 |
| 625 | 7654456 |
| 662 | |
| 674 | 11 figures |
| 742 | 43136777786 |
| 774 | 43973953013 |
| 853 | 55443135666 |
| 894 | 56562523451 |
| | 68575856944 |
| | 75714244524 |

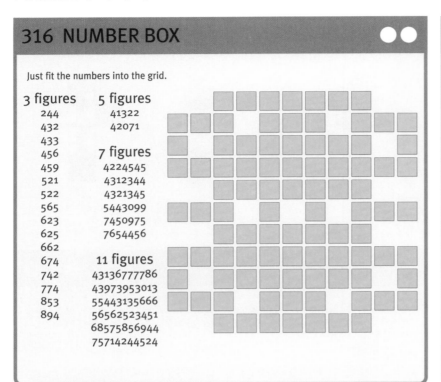

## 318 WEIGHED UP ●●

How many cans are needed to make the third pair of scales balance?

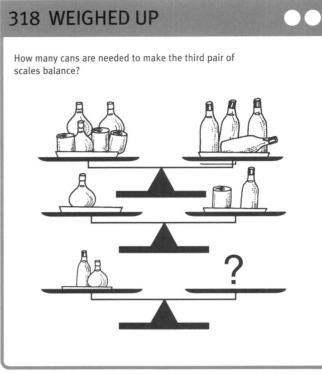

## 317 WANTED! ○

The sheriff is sure that one of the ten men shown is the wanted outlaw in the poster in the top right-hand corner. Can you help identify the suspects?

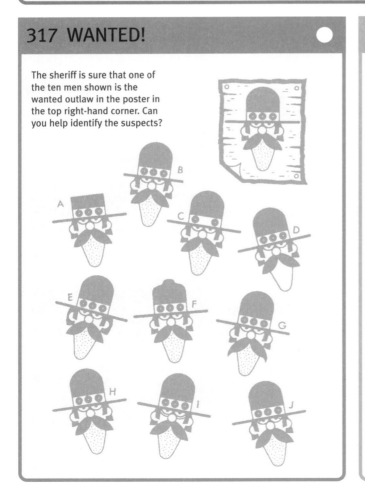

## 319 DOTTY DILEMMA ○

Connect adjacent dots with vertical or horizontal lines so that a single loop is formed with no crossings or branches. Each number indicates how many lines surround it, while empty cells may be surrounded by any number of lines.

```
0     2 0     3     1
  2         2       1
2   3       3 0
    1   3           1
    3     0   1 0   2
2   2 3   1       1
1           1   2
    3 3         0   1
  2       3         1
2   1       2 1     3
```

## 320 LINE UP

Snuffy's Gang found themselves in a police identification parade last week after one of their number committed a spot of smash-and-grab. He was witnessed making a slow getaway, mainly because he was hampered by the weight of the brick, which he had grabbed instead of the jewellery. The guilty party was picked out as standing fourth from the left. From the notes made by a raw recruit to the force, can you name the hapless villain? Snuffy was further left than Clogger and further right than Basher. Alf was not next to Wilf who was not next to Snuffy who was not next to Clogger. If Basher was not on one end then Wilf was not next to Clogger.

## 322 MATCH THAT

This star has five points and is made of ten matches. Remove one match and rearrange the others to make a nine-pointed star.

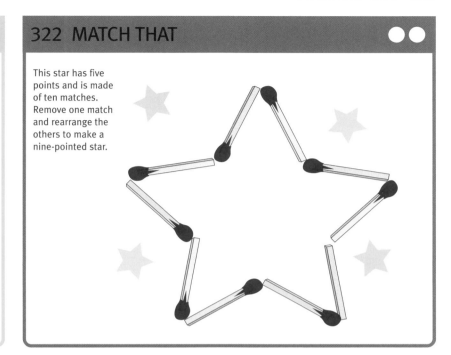

## 321 WHERE THE L?

Sixteen L shapes like the ones below have been fitted into a square shape. Each L has one hole, and there are four of each type in the square. No two pieces of the same type are adjacent, even at a corner. They fit together so well that the spaces between pieces do not show. From the locations of the holes, can you tell where each L is?

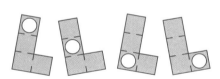

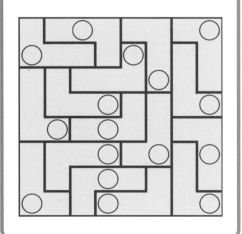

## 323 TEAM PLAY

As the winter bowls season continues at Tinsbury, we report on two matches in the Mixed Fours competition. The final scores were 24–21 and 17–12. From the odds and ends, can you roll your mental jack along the green and draw an accurate line as to the members of each team of four and who won against whom?

1 Each team consisted of two ladies and two gents.
2 Pete was not in John's losing team, which scored more shots than Pauline's but less than Doris'.
3 Dennis, who was not playing with or against Philip, was in the side which scored least shots of any team.
4 Reg's team won their game but not against the team which included both Janet and Pamela.
5 Joan's team won their game against Deirdre's. Neither was skipped by Rita, who won her game.

### REG

| PAMELA | PAULINE |
|--------|---------|
| PETE | PHILIP |
| JANET | JIM |
| JOAN | JOHN |
| DAVE | DEIRDRE |
| DENNIS | DORIS |

### RON

| PAMELA | PAULINE |
|--------|---------|
| PETE | PHILIP |
| JANET | JIM |
| JOAN | JOHN |
| DAVE | DEIRDRE |
| DENNIS | DORIS |

### RITA

| PAMELA | PAULINE |
|--------|---------|
| PETE | PHILIP |
| JANET | JIM |
| JOAN | JOHN |
| DAVE | DEIRDRE |
| DENNIS | DORIS |

### ROSE

| PAMELA | PAULINE |
|--------|---------|
| PETE | PHILIP |
| JANET | JIM |
| JOAN | JOHN |
| DAVE | DEIRDRE |
| DENNIS | DORIS |

## 324 EASY AS ABC

Each row and column originally contained one A, one B, one C, one D and two blank squares. Each letter and number refers to the first or second of the four letters encountered when travelling in the direction of the arrow. Can you complete the original grid?

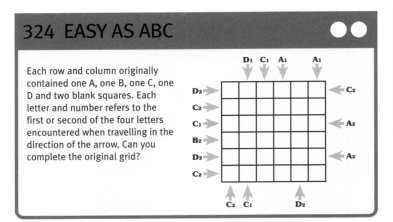

## 325 SUDOKU

Place a number from 1 to 9 in each empty cell so that each row, each column and each 3 x 3 block contains all the numbers from 1 to 9.

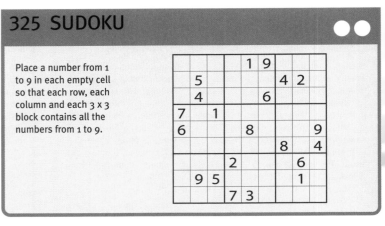

## 326 LOGI-PICK

Following the first diagram, there is a logical rule that determines how the next block is to be filled in. Given these three blocks, can you colour in the fourth?

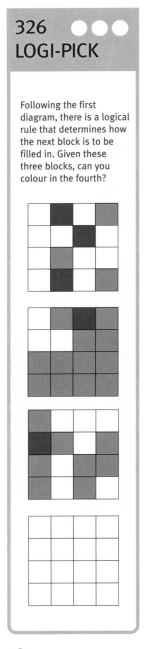

## 327 CARDSHARP

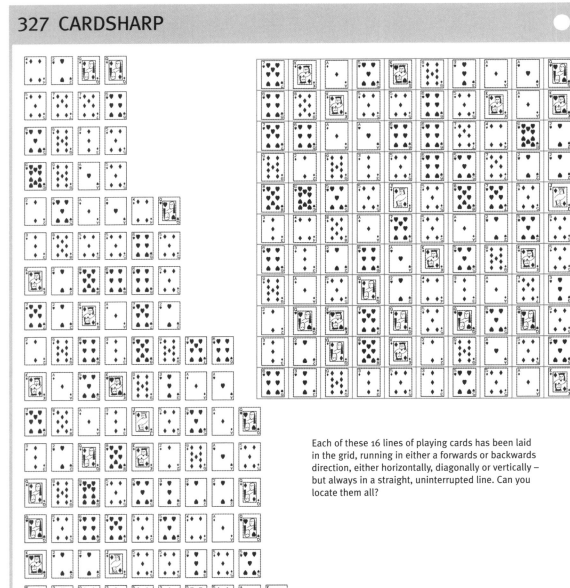

Each of these 16 lines of playing cards has been laid in the grid, running in either a forwards or backwards direction, either horizontally, diagonally or vertically – but always in a straight, uninterrupted line. Can you locate them all?

# 328 OLD HAUNTS

Each of these five ghosts, one of whom is supposedly Mr Windham and another is Blanche Legh, is reputed to haunt a notable property. Can you put a name to each apparition, say where it just may be seen and what special feature distinguishes it from all the other unnerving manifestations to be found at houses open to the public?

1  It is a man who strolls around Claydon House looking for his hand – sent back there without the rest of him after being cut off at the battle of Edgehill.
2  Anne Boleyn is neither ghost A nor the lady who infests Lyme Park. The papers were hidden in the wall at Ham House which is not haunted by ghost E.
3  Take care when driving to Blickling Hall as the ghost sits in a coach with her head in her lap – the horses are headless too. What state the coach driver is in, we shudder to think.
4  Ghost B is the one still searching for his favourite library books – perhaps because the fines due must now outweigh the nation's National Debt.
5  Ghost E is not that of Elizabeth Dysart or the ghost of Felbrigg.
6  Neither Sir Edmund Verney nor the lady in white

who follows her husband's funeral procession is ghost B or C.

| GHOST | OF | AT | FEATURE |
|-------|-----|-----|---------|
| A |  |  |  |
| B |  |  |  |
| C |  |  |  |
| D |  |  |  |
| E |  |  |  |

# 330 SET SQUARE

All the digits from 1 to 9 are used in this grid, but only once. Can you work out their positions in the grid and make the sums work? We've given two numbers to start you off.

| | + | | ÷ | 2 | = 8 |
|---|---|---|---|---|---|
| − | ■ | x | ■ | + | |
| | x | | − | | = 4 |
| ÷ | ■ | ÷ | ■ | ÷ | |
| | + | 6 | − | | = 2 |
| = 4 | | = 6 | | = 2 | |

# 329 ISLAND HOPPING

Each circle containing a number represents an island. The object is to connect each island with vertical or horizontal bridges so that:
*  The number of bridges is the same as the number inside the island
*  There can be up to two bridges between two islands
*  Bridges cannot cross islands or other bridges
*  There is a continuous path connecting all the islands

# 331 COG-ITATE

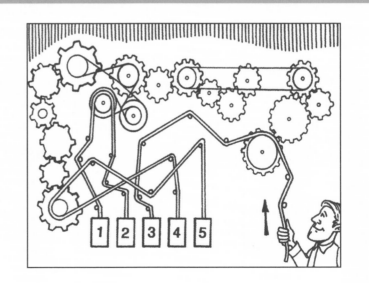

Can you see which two weights will rise and which three will fall when the man releases the tension as shown?

## 332 SPOT THE DIFFERENCE

Can you spot the ten differences between these two pictures?

## 333 DOTTY DILEMMA

Connect adjacent dots with vertical or horizontal lines so that a single loop is formed with no crossings or branches. Each number indicates how many lines surround it, while empty cells may be surrounded by any number of lines.

## 334 DOUBLE PUZZLE

Roll up folks, for our special sale offer – two puzzles for the price of one!

Puzzle One: Each colour has been given a value from 1 to 7. Given the totals at the end of each line, can you work out the value of each colour?

Puzzle Two: The picture is a layout of a set of colour dominoes – just like ordinary dominoes but with colours instead of spots. Can you draw in the lines to show each separate domino?

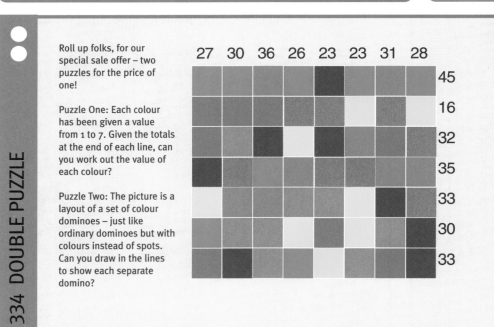

## 335 EASY AS ABC

Each row and column originally contained one A, one B, one C, one D and two blank squares. Each letter and number refers to the first or second of the four letters encountered when travelling in the direction of the arrow. Can you complete the original grid?

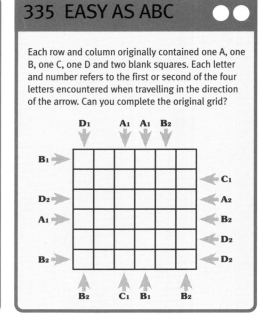

## 336 SHELL NEVER MAKE IT!

Can you help Tamara the Tortoise find her way to the finish?

## 337 IT FIGURES

Place a number from 1 to 9 in each empty cell so that the sum of each vertical or horizontal block equals the number at the top or on the left of that block. Numbers may only be used once in each block.

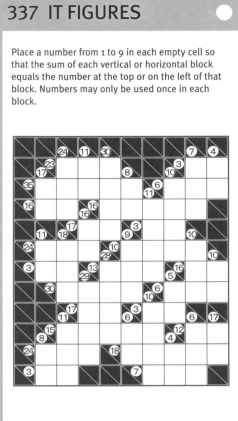

## 338 CUBISM

Which cube is the finished product of the main illustration?

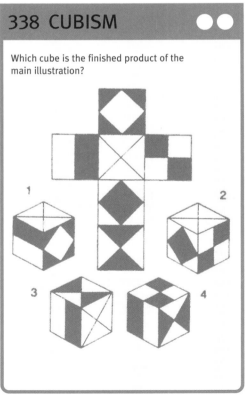

## 339 MAZE MYSTERY

Travel from the entrance to the exit of the maze, filling the path completely to create a picture.

Can you tell which one of the four pieces completes the picture of Butch the bulldog?

## 340 MISSING PIECE

## 341 SPANISH HIGHS

As Columbus and his not-so-merry crew head for the edge of the unknown, attention at the Spanish Court has turned to lighter matters. Each of these four noble suitors is enamoured of an upper-crust lady and has the marriage contract in hand. Can you put the right names on each portion of parchment? Manuel is courting Maria who is not Sutaz or Meeya. Neither Pancho or Sancho is Fign-Diaz who is marrying neither Juanita nor Nidjota. Isabella da Bolla is being pursued by neither Manuel nor Pancho nor Mucho. Herole is after Meeya who is not Rosa who is not marrying Ghiaz. None of these three weddings is the one involving Juan.

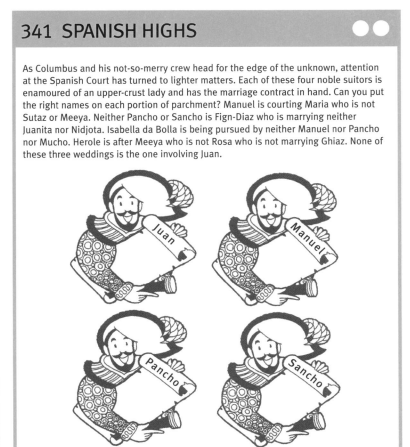

## 342 EASY AS ABC

Each row and column originally contained one A, one B, one C, one D and two blank squares. Each letter and number refers to the first or second of the four letters encountered when travelling in the direction of the arrow. Can you complete the original grid?

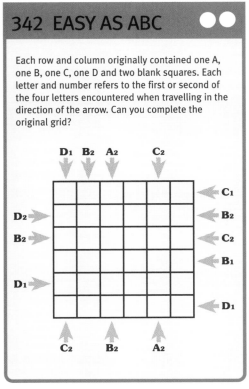

## 343 LOGI-PATH

Use your deductive reasoning to form a pathway from the box marked START to the box marked FINISH moving in either direction horizontally or vertically (but not diagonally). The number at the beginning of every row or column indicates exactly how many boxes in that row or column your pathway must pass through. The small diagram is given as an example of how it works.

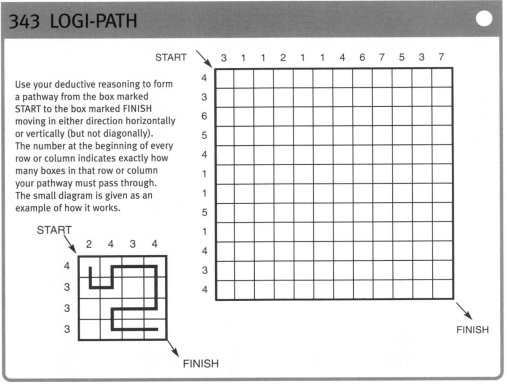

## 344 BATTLESHIPS

Do you remember the old game of battleships? These puzzles are based on that idea. Your task is to find the vessels in the diagram. Some parts of boats or sea squares have already been filled in, and a number next to a row or column refers to the number of occupied squares in that row or column. The boats may be positioned horizontally or vertically, but no two boats or parts of boats are in adjacent squares – horizontally, vertically or diagonally.

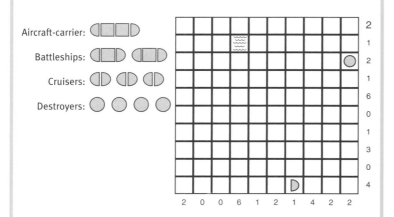

Aircraft-carrier:

Battleships:

Cruisers:

Destroyers:

## 345 WELL SPOTTED

The number in each circle tells you how many of it and its touching neighbours are to be filled in.

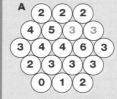
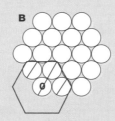
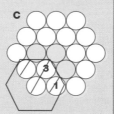

In our example, A, the zero gives a start – put lines through it and its neighbours (B). Three circles can now be filled (C) – lightly, though so the numbers can still be read...

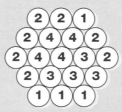

## 346 ODD ONE OUT

Can you see which rabbit is the odd one out?

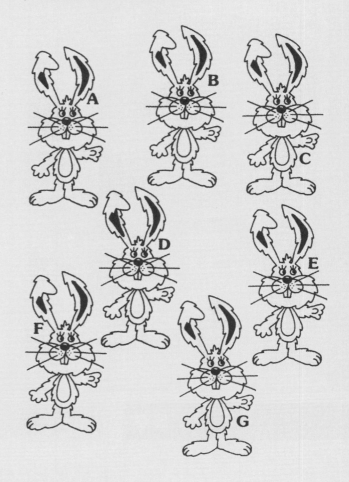

## 347 FILLING IN

Each of the nine empty boxes contains a different digit from 1 to 9. Each calculation is to be treated sequentially rather than according to the 'multiplication first' system. Can you fill in the empty boxes?

|   | + |   | ÷ |   | = | 2 |
| + |   | − |   | ÷ |   |   |
|   | − |   | × |   | = | 8 |
| − |   | × |   | + |   |   |
|   | ÷ |   | − |   | = | 2 |
| = |   | = |   | = |   |   |
| 4 |   | 9 |   | 4 |   |   |

# 348 WHAT'S THEIR LINE?

Four celebrity panellists, aided and abetted by that helpful host, Robin Robertson, have guessed the jobs done by four guests. Can you sign in, please, with each guest's full job title and the name of the celebrity who revealed all?

1 Ken's occupation was guessed by Gerta and he is neither the Hocker nor the Crimper's. No one was a Crimper's Hocker.
2 Miles did not realise Ann was a Slant. Wanda guessed the Posset, which was not Connie's occupation.
3 One occupation was Fledger's Cringe.
4 A lady panellist guessed Taddler's.

Clue 1 has been entered for you.

## GERTA

| ~~ANN~~ | ~~CONNIE~~ |
|---|---|
| ~~ENA~~ | (KEN) |
| ~~CRIMPER'S~~ | FLEDGER'S |
| GRUTTLER'S | TADDLER'S |
| CRINGE | ~~HOCKER~~ |
| POSSET | SLANT |

## MILES

| ANN | CONNIE |
|---|---|
| ENA | ~~KEN~~ |
| CRIMPER'S | FLEDGER'S |
| GRUTTLER'S | TADDLER'S |
| CRINGE | HOCKER |
| POSSET | SLANT |

## NOAH

| ANN | CONNIE |
|---|---|
| ENA | ~~KEN~~ |
| CRIMPER'S | FLEDGER'S |
| GRUTTLER'S | TADDLER'S |
| CRINGE | HOCKER |
| POSSET | SLANT |

## WANDA

| ANN | CONNIE |
|---|---|
| ENA | ~~KEN~~ |
| CRIMPER'S | FLEDGER'S |
| GRUTTLER'S | TADDLER'S |
| CRINGE | HOCKER |
| POSSET | SLANT |

# 349 ISLAND HOPPING

Each circle containing a number represents an island. The object is to connect each island with vertical or horizontal bridges so that:
* The number of bridges is the same as the number inside the island
* There can be up to two bridges between two islands
* Bridges cannot cross islands or other bridges
* There is a continuous path connecting all the islands

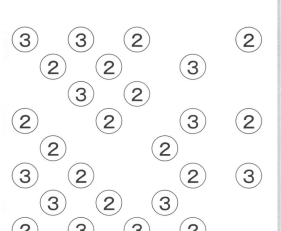

# 350 RADIO DAYS

Untangle the lines to discover which of the old radios is connected to which plug.

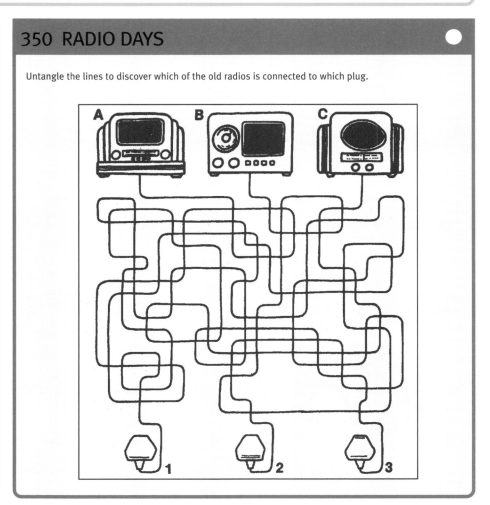

105

## 351 SILHOUETTE

Shade all the shapes which contain a dot to reveal a hidden picture.

## 353 TWO OF A KIND

Can you decide which three objects do not make a pair?

## 352 FRUIT AND VEG

The display on Gert's stall is changed around daily, partly to make yesterday's produce look fresh. Whatever the arrangement, fruit and vegetables always alternate along the rows and down the lines and left and right are as you gaze on wondering if you have the nerve to ask if the bananas are over-ripe. The radishes are two rows higher than the cherries which are two lines further right than the turnips which are directly above the dates which are two places directly left of the figs which are diagonally adjacent to the apples which are in the same line down as the grapes which are in the same line across as the potatoes which are two lines to the right of the lychees which are in the opposite corner to the bananas which are in the same line down as the kumquats which are immediately to the right of the marrows which are lower and further right than the yams but higher than the peas which are further left than the illustrated onions which, of course, are lower than the watercress. Can you put everything in its correct place?

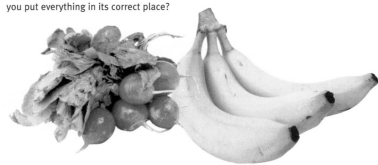

## 354 ISLAND HOPPING

Each circle containing a number represents an island. The object is to connect each island with vertical or horizontal bridges so that:
* The number of bridges is the same as the number inside the island.
* There can be up to two bridges between two islands.
* Bridges cannot cross islands or other bridges.
* There is a continuous path connecting all the islands.

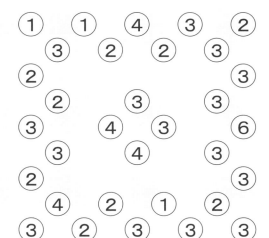

## 355 WELL SPOTTED

The number in each circle tells you how many of it and its touching neighbours are to be filled in.

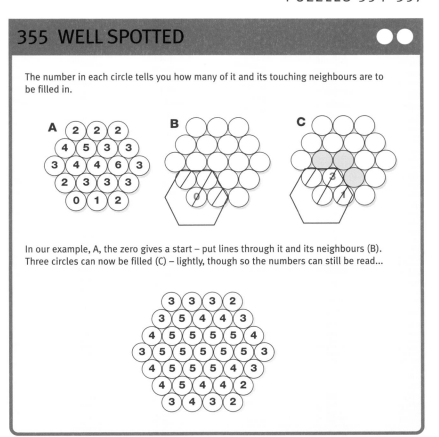

In our example, A, the zero gives a start – put lines through it and its neighbours (B). Three circles can now be filled (C) – lightly, though so the numbers can still be read...

## 356 TAKE FIVE

Complete the following block of 25 circles so that each of the five road signs appears in all horizontal and vertical lines. To get you started we have filled in nine circles.

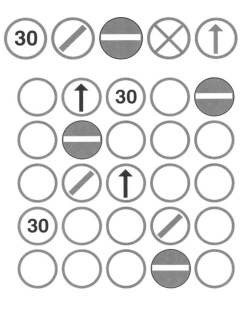

## 357 SQUARE PAIRS

This picture of Old Father Time contains five pairs of identical squares. Can you find them?

## 358 NUMBER KROSS

See how quickly you can fit all these numbers into the grid. We've filled one figure in to start you off.

| 3 figures | 5 figures | 6 figures |
|-----------|-----------|-----------|
| 227 | 11658 | 140448 |
| 301 | 12932 | 140747 |
| 312 | 20818 | 200174 |
| 402 | 21015 | 321904 |
| 513 | 30030 | 366336 |
| 607 | 31526 | 391074 |
| 823 | 31703 | 419838 |
| 905 | 40307 | 426198 |
| | 50334 | 463515 |
| 4 figures | 53614 | 626206 |
| 1601 | 61392 | 710521 |
| 2247 | 63579 | 741029 |
| 3431 | 73713 | 824513 |
| 4152 | 81605 | 885198 |
| 5423 | 87352 | 903529 |
| 6000 | 99703 | 928174 |
| 8998 | | |
| ~~9634~~ | | |

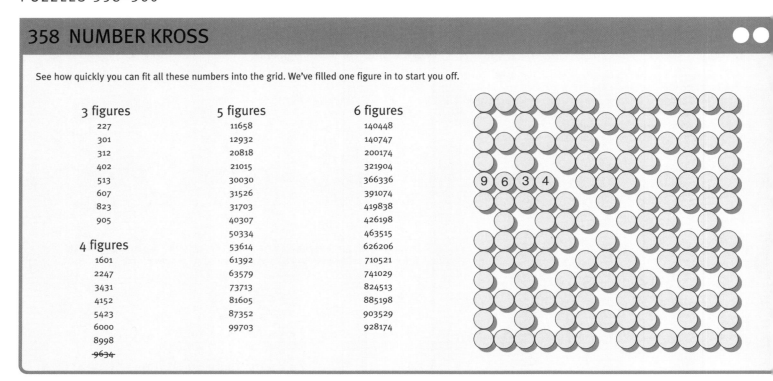

## 359 A LITTLE DEVIL

See how quickly you can spot which letter appears here three times.

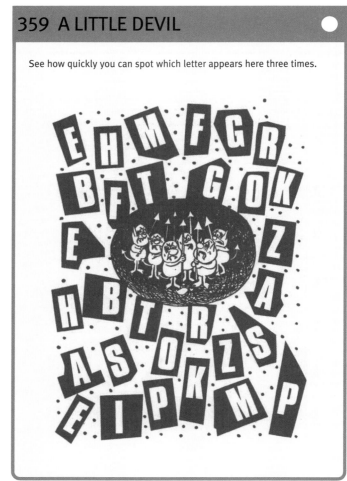

## 360 CUBE ROUTE

The symbols on each face have a meaning – Up, Down, Right or Left. But each sign has a different meaning on each of the three faces. Thus, whatever is, say, up on the top face cannot be up on the left face or the right face. There is a meaning for each symbol which will lead to a unique path joining Start (S) to End (E) and which passes through all three faces. Can you let your brain do the logical walking and make the journey?

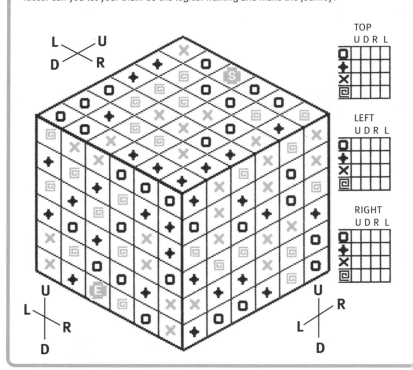

TOP
U D R L

LEFT
U D R L

RIGHT
U D R L

# 361 MENTAL BLOCKS ●●

Which two of the numbered pieces will fit together to make cube 'A'?

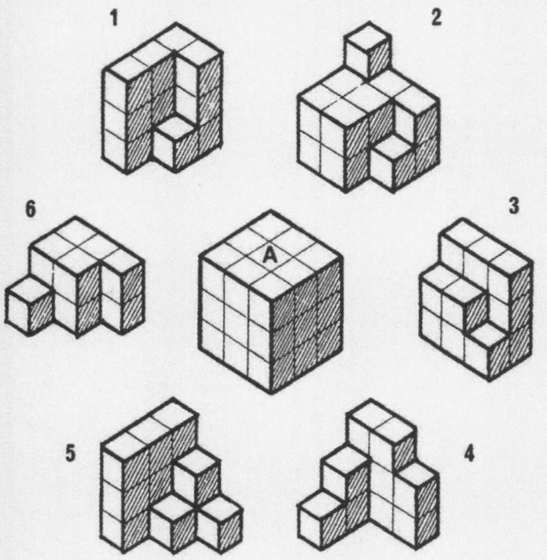

# 363 CIRCLE OF DIGITS ●●●

The figure below consists of three concentric circles divided into eight sectors; the three single-figure numbers in each sector add up to 15. The circles will be referred to as outer, middle and inner and one number in the inner has been inserted to give you a start. From the clues given, can you insert all the other numbers?

## Clues

1 The only 0 appears in the outer circle, where there is no 1 or 3; there is no 9 in the middle and no number is repeated in any sector or circle.

2 All the numbers in sectors A and B are odd; B outer is one more than C inner and one less than H middle, which is one more than H inner; B inner is one less than G outer.

3 The 6 in the outer circle is diagonally opposite the 6 in the inner.

4 C inner is double D inner, while D outer is double D middle; F outer is double F middle, which is double G middle and the same as C outer; E outer is the same as A middle.

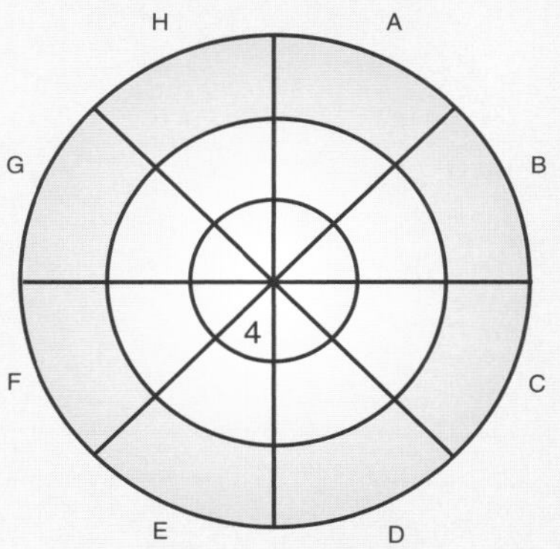

Starting tip: Work out the number in C inner.

# 362 VIDEO RENTAL ●●

Will nothing stop the video boom? These four shops have just opened, to add to the dozen already cluttering Lampwick's side streets. Can you record a summary as to the customer at each shop and the film being rented?

1 D Cryer is at Rent 'N' Rave but is not hiring Gosh! Or Whew!

2 Just Flicks are not hiring out to A Blinkon whose choice is Wow!

3 B Dee-High is not the one choosing Gosh!

4 C Nitt is not at More Movies who are not renting out Wow!

**JUST FLICKS**

| A BLINKON | B DEE-HIGH |
|---|---|
| C NITT | D ~~CRYER~~ |
| GOSH! | HEY! |
| WHEW! | WOW! |

**MORE MOVIES**

| A BLINKON | B DEE-HIGH |
|---|---|
| C NITT | D ~~CRYER~~ |
| GOSH! | HEY! |
| WHEW! | WOW! |

**NITE RATES**

| A BLINKON | B DEE-HIGH |
|---|---|
| C NITT | D ~~CRYER~~ |
| GOSH! | HEY! |
| WHEW! | WOW! |

**RENT 'N' RAVE**

| A ~~BLINKON~~ | B ~~DEE-HIGH~~ |
|---|---|
| C ~~NITT~~ | D (CRYER) |
| ~~GOSH!~~ | HEY! |
| ~~WHEW!~~ | WOW! |

# 364 EASY AS ABC ●

Each row and column originally contained one A, one B, one C, one D and two blank squares. Each letter and number refer to the first or second of the four letters encountered when travelling in the direction of the arrow. Can you complete the original grid?

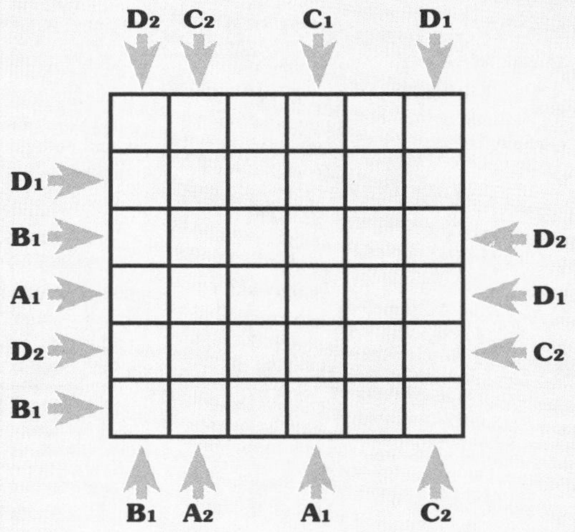

## 365 STAMP DUTY

Which one of the numbered prints has been made by the stamp?

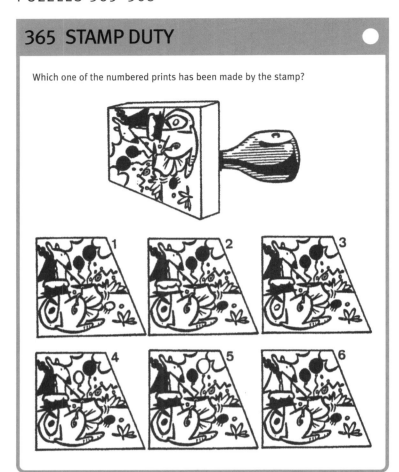

## 367 DOTTY DILEMMA

Connect adjacent dots with vertical or horizontal lines so that a single loop is formed with no crossings or branches. Each number indicates how many lines surround it, while empty cells may be surrounded by any number of lines.

| | 1 | 3 | | | 1 | 2 | 1 | 2 | 2 | |
|---|---|---|---|---|---|---|---|---|---|---|
| 1 | | | 3 | | | | | | | |
| 2 | | | 1 | | | 1 | 3 | 1 | | |
| | 1 | 3 | | | 3 | | | 2 | | |
| 2 | | | 3 | | 1 | | 3 | | | |
| 2 | | | 1 | 2 | | | 2 | | 3 | |
| 0 | | | | | 3 | | | | 2 | |
| 2 | | | 0 | 3 | 1 | | | | 0 | |
| 2 | | | 3 | | | | | | 1 | |
| 3 | | | | | | 2 | | | 0 | |
| 1 | | | | 2 | 1 | 2 | | | 1 | |
| 2 | | | 2 | | | | | | 1 | |
| 2 | | 3 | | | 2 | 3 | | | 1 | |
| | 0 | | 3 | | 2 | | | | 1 | |
| 2 | | | 2 | | | | 1 | 1 | | |
| 0 | 2 | 3 | | | 1 | | | | 1 | |
| | | | | | | 1 | | | 1 | |
| 2 | 1 | 2 | 2 | 2 | | | 1 | 2 | | |

## 366 MAZE-WAYS

Each obstacle along the path carries a penalty as shown in the key in the middle. Can you travel from A to B while incurring a total of 40 penalty points?

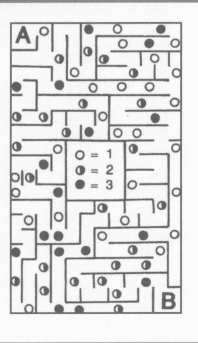

## 368 MOUNT CUBIC

There are six possible directions which will take you from the centre of one face across an edge to the next face on the mountain. Each direction has been given a number from 1 to 6. Can you work out which direction has which number and so find your way from base to peak?

# 369  A BRIDGE TOO FAR

Eight men and eight women are playing bridge at four tables, as shown. At the game in hand, dummy is in a different position at each table, and the contract at each is in a different suit and for a different number of tricks – this number also differs in each case from the table number.  With the following clues, can you position each person, and also say who is dummy and name the contract being played at each table?

Roger (South) is dummy on his table, which is numbered one lower than Connie's and one higher than Harry's, both of whom are in a different position from Roger and from each other, neither being dummy. Fred and Gordon are partners on the remaining table, neither being dummy. Alan (West) is on a table where the contract is 4 Spades. Tessa (dummy) is one table anti-clockwise from Eddie, at whose table the contract is for one trick more than on table 1.

Dummy on table 4 is the person whose name comes first alphabetically on that table. Jane and Dot are in the same position at different tables whose numbers are two apart; this is also true of Kate and Lola, the first-named in each case being at the lower-numbered table. From his seat Peter, who is not on table 2, can see table 2, but not table 4; his contract is in Diamonds, while Michael's table is going for Hearts, but one fewer.

Susie (dummy) has Jane on her left and Harry on her right; her partner is Peter, and the contract is for one more trick than the table number. Connie has Dot on her left, who is not in the same position as Fred. Tessa, whose table is playing a red-suit contract, is in the same relative position as Babs.

|   | Table 1 | Table 2 | Table 3 | Table 4 |
|---|---|---|---|---|
| N |   |   |   |   |
| E |   |   |   |   |
| S |   |   |   |   |
| W |   |   |   |   |
| Contract |   |   |   |   |

(Compass diagram with tables numbered 1, 2, 3, 4 arranged around a N-E-S-W compass)

# 370  TEE TIME

Three old timers play a weekly game of golf on the Golden Lawns 18-hole, par 72, course. Each score at every hole falls into one of five categories. Each golfer gets a different result (excluding zero) in each category. Also, no category has the same result for another player, i.e., if a player has two eagles, he has a different number in the other four and no other player has two eagles. With the score details below and the information given can you fill in their card?

|   | Eagle −2 | Birdie −1 | Par 0 | Bogey +1 | Double Bogey +2 | FINAL SCORE |
|---|---|---|---|---|---|---|
| Parnell Darma |   |   |   |   |   |   |
| Nick Jackliss |   |   |   |   |   |   |
| Barry Clayer |   |   |   |   |   |   |

Nick got twice as many eagles as birdies and together they added up to Barry's pars which were one more than his double bogeys. The number of Parnell's eagles and Barry's bogeys was the same and the total of the two was the same as that of Nick's bogeys added to his lesser number of double bogeys. The total of Parnell's pars and bogeys was one less than Nick's pars and Barry got one less eagles than bogeys whilst Parnell got one more birdie than double bogeys which was the same as Nick's eagles and also Barry's birdies.

## 371 LOGI-5

Can you place the letters A, B, C, D, E, one to each square so that every line across and down contains each letter once and every shape made from five squares also has each letter once?

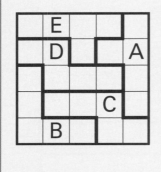

## 372 CELL STRUCTURE

The object is to create white areas surrounded by black walls, so that:

* Each white area contains only one number.
* The number of cells in a white area is equal to the number in it.
* The white areas are separated from each other with a black wall.
* Cells containing numbers must not be filled in.
* The black cells must be linked into a continuous wall.
* Black cells cannot form a square of 2 x 2 or larger.

## 373 FILLING IN

Each of the nine empty boxes contains a different digit from 1 to 9. Each calculation is to be treated sequentially rather than according to the 'multiplication first' system. Can you fill in the empty boxes?

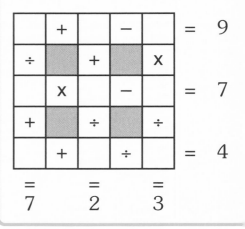

## 374 DOMINO DEAL

A standard set (0 – 0) to (6 – 6) is laid out below. Each domino is placed so the that the larger number will be on the bottom:

i.e.     3        not      6
           6               3

Those top numbers show the four numbers which form the top half of each domino in that column. The bottom numbers, below the grid, give the four bottom numbers for that column. The seven numbers on the left show the numbers which belong in that row. Can you cross-reference the facts and deduce where each domino had been placed? 1*5 is given as a start.

### 'TOP' NUMBERS

| 01 | 12 | 01 | 04 | 01 | 02 | 00 |
|----|----|----|----|----|----|----|
| 15 | 44 | 22 | 56 | 33 | 33 | 1̶2̶ |

|  | | | | | | | |
|-----|---|---|---|---|---|---|---|
| 0 0 0 0 1 4 5 | | | | | | | |
| 0 1 2 5 5 5 6 | | | | | | | |
| | | | | | | | |
| 0 0 2 3 3 4 5 | | | | | | | |
| 2 3 4 4 4 4 6 | | | | | | | |
| | | | | | | | |
| 0 1̶ 1 1 2 3 4 | | | | | | | 1 |
| 1 2 3 5̶ 6 6 6 | | | | | | | 5 |
| | | | | | | | |
| 1 1 2 2 2 3 6 | | | | | | | |
| 3 3 4 5 5 6 6 | | | | | | | |

| 14 | 34 | 22 | 34 | 35 | 04 | 13 |
|----|----|----|----|----|----|----|
| 56 | 56 | 25 | 56 | 66 | 66 | 4̶5̶ |

### 'BOTTOM' NUMBERS

## 375 LOGI-5

Can you place the letters A, B, C, D, E, one to each square so that every line across and down contains each letter once and every shape made from five squares also has each letter once?

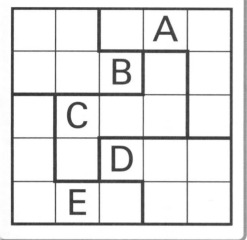

## 377 THE SPECIAL FIVE

Although PA Lette, the Netherlipp artist, has sold or given away most of his paintings, he still keeps five, for various sentimental reasons, on one of his walls. From the clues below, can you indicate in the diagram the title and date of the picture at each position?

1. The picture painted in 1976 hangs directly next to and right of one of a building.

2. There is a larger gap in dates between the paintings at positions A and B than between those at positions D and E. The painting at position A is earlier than the one at B; and the painting at E is earlier than the one at D.

3. The picture entitled Lower Woods is directly next to and left of the one painted in 1988.

4. The date of the picture of St Aidan's Church is immediately between that of the picture at position C and that of Fiddler's Brook, which is more than one place to the right of the picture of St Aidan's Church.

5. The Old Mill was painted during the decade preceding that when PA Lette painted Crane Bay.

Titles: Crane Bay, Fiddler's Brook, Lower Woods, St Aidan's Church, The Old Mill

Dates: 1964, 1976, 1981, 1988, 1992

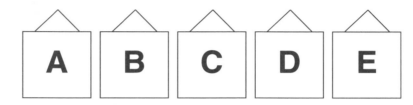

## 376 PACKED LUNCHES

Four office colleagues, bored with trying to think up new variations for their packed lunches, devised a sharing scheme. In the afternoon, each was randomly allocated a sandwich filling, crisp flavour and piece of fruit that he/she would bring in next day. From the clues given, can you work out what each had last Monday?

1 Freddie ate salt and vinegar crisps, and the person, not Felix, who ate a chicken salad sandwich together with cheese and onion crisps did not also have a peach.

2 The cheese and tomato sandwich was eaten by the person who also ate an apple.

3 Felicity who ate the egg mayonnaise sandwich is not the person who had both the ready-salted crisps and the orange.

4 For your vital information, the remaining items on the menu were: ham and mustard sandwiches, prawn cocktail crisps and a banana – any of which may, or may not have been consumed by Fiona.

| NAME | SANDWICH | CRISPS | FRUIT |
|------|----------|--------|-------|
|      |          |        |       |
|      |          |        |       |
|      |          |        |       |
|      |          |        |       |

## 378 DOGGY DUOS

Can you put these dogs into four identical pairs?

## 379 JOIN THE POTS

Can you put together the broken pots to make up five complete ones?

## 381 ISLAND HOPPING

Each circle containing a number represents an island. The object is to connect each island with vertical or horizontal bridges so that:
* The number of bridges is the same as the number inside the island
* There can be up to two bridges between two islands
* Bridges cannot cross islands or other bridges
* There is a continuous path connecting all the islands

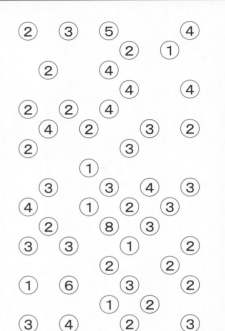

## 380 THE CHAMPIONS CUP

These soccer teams all got through to the quarter-final stage of this major cup competition, much to the delight of their numerous fans who had followed the progress of each team. From the clues given, can you work out the draw for all the stages up to the final and the eventual winners? Chelsea who played and beat Norwich, won one more game than Watford. Southampton lost to the team that played Everton in the semi-finals. Arsenal won one more game than Liverpool, Everton, who won one more game than Arsenal, never met either Chelsea or Spurs.

| Quarter-finals | Semi-finals | Final | Winner |
|---|---|---|---|

# 382 ACE IN PLACE

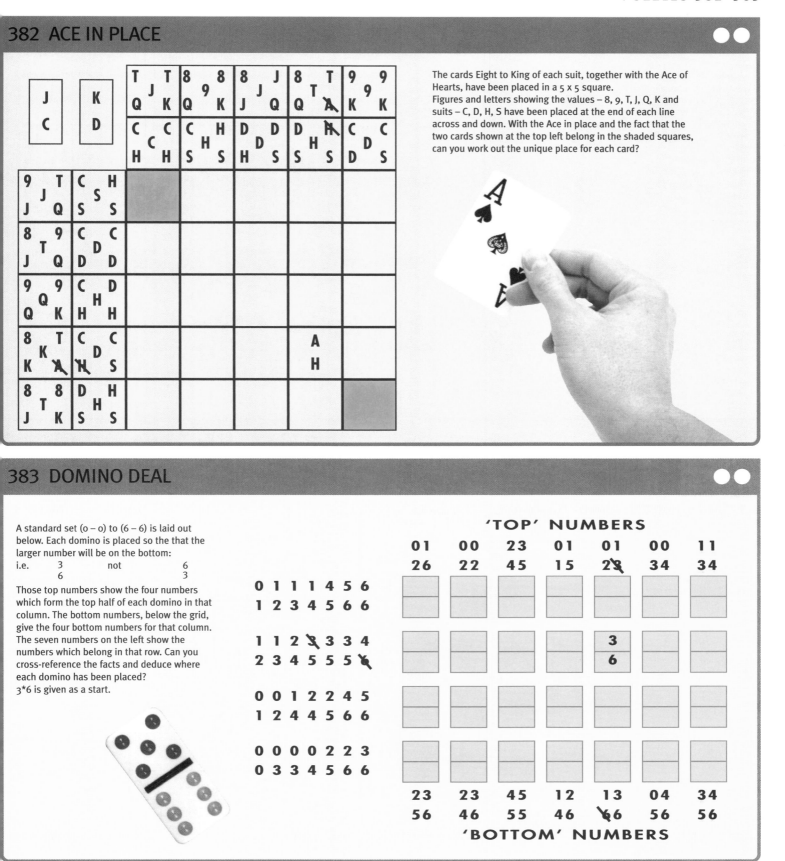

The cards Eight to King of each suit, together with the Ace of Hearts, have been placed in a 5 x 5 square.

Figures and letters showing the values – 8, 9, T, J, Q, K and suits – C, D, H, S have been placed at the end of each line across and down. With the Ace in place and the fact that the two cards shown at the top left belong in the shaded squares, can you work out the unique place for each card?

# 383 DOMINO DEAL

A standard set (0 – 0) to (6 – 6) is laid out below. Each domino is placed so the that the larger number will be on the bottom:

i.e.   3    not    6
      6           3

Those top numbers show the four numbers which form the top half of each domino in that column. The bottom numbers, below the grid, give the four bottom numbers for that column. The seven numbers on the left show the numbers which belong in that row. Can you cross-reference the facts and deduce where each domino has been placed?

3*6 is given as a start.

### 'TOP' NUMBERS

| 01 | 00 | 23 | 01 | 01 | 00 | 11 |
|----|----|----|----|----|----|----|
| 26 | 22 | 45 | 15 | 2~~7~~ | 34 | 34 |

| 0 1 1 1 4 5 6 |
|---|
| 1 2 3 4 5 6 6 |

| 1 1 2 ~~7~~ 3 3 4 |
|---|
| 2 3 4 5 5 5 ~~6~~ |

Grid cell with: 3 / 6 (in fifth column, second row)

| 0 0 1 2 2 4 5 |
|---|
| 1 2 4 4 5 6 6 |

| 0 0 0 0 2 2 3 |
|---|
| 0 3 3 4 5 6 6 |

| 23 | 23 | 45 | 12 | 13 | 04 | 34 |
|----|----|----|----|----|----|----|
| 56 | 46 | 55 | 46 | ~~66~~ | 56 | 56 |

### 'BOTTOM' NUMBERS

115

## 384 DOTTY DILEMMA ●●

Connect adjacent dots with vertical or horizontal lines so that a single loop is formed with no crossings or branches. Each number indicates how many lines surround it, while empty cells may be surrounded by any number of lines.

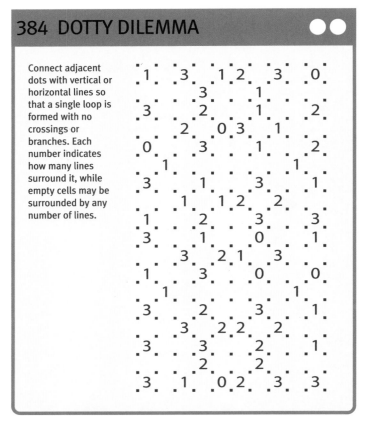

## 385 COG-ITATE ●●

Can you work out which weights will rise, and which will fall when the man pulls the rope?

## 386 OFF YOUR ROCKER ●

In a negative, everything which is really white appears black and everything which is really black appears white. Can you see which one of the four lettered rocking-horses is shown as a negative in the top left-hand corner?

## 387 CUBE IT ●●

Inside the circle are three views of the same cube. Which of the lettered shapes can be folded up to make the cube?

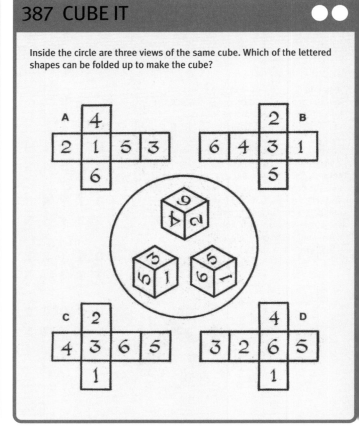

# 388 HOT AIR

If you looked up into the sky last month, you may have seen five hot air balloons, each advertising a different product. Just in case you didn't, the clues here will enable you to say who was flying each patterned balloon, discover the product being advertised by each, and state the material from which the basket underneath each was made.

1  D. Hytes flew the balloon advertising chocolate, but it was not tartan nor was its basket made from burlap.
2  G. Nears flew the brickwork patterned balloon, but not to advertise tea.
3  The balloon with the straw basket was flown by C. Vyewes but its pattern was neither spots nor tartan.
4  The striped balloon was used to advertise coffee but its basket was not made from either straw, wood or burlap.
5  Neither the balloon with the brickwork design, nor the one flown by E. Bargum had a plastic basket, which was on the balloon advertising cars.
6  F. Tathort, gas and fibreglass complete the line-up.

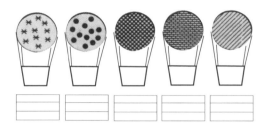

# 389 SUDOKU

Place a number from 1 to 9 in each empty cell so that each row, each column and each 3 x 3 block contains all the numbers from 1 to 9.

|   | 8 |   | 5 |   |   |   | 2 |   |
|---|---|---|---|---|---|---|---|---|
| 1 |   |   |   | 7 |   | 9 |   | 6 |
|   | 3 |   |   |   | 4 |   |   |   |
|   |   | 5 |   |   |   |   |   | 3 |
|   | 7 |   |   |   |   |   | 8 |   |
| 2 |   |   |   |   | 1 |   |   |   |
|   |   |   | 1 |   |   |   | 4 |   |
| 6 |   | 2 |   | 9 |   |   |   | 5 |
|   | 4 |   |   |   | 3 |   | 9 |   |

# 390 BREAKTHROUGH

See how quickly you can break this grid down into the 28 dominoes from which it was formed.

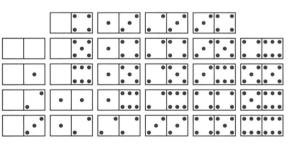

| 0 | 0 | 3 | 6 | 4 | 2 | 3 |
|---|---|---|---|---|---|---|
| 3 | 4 | 4 | 4 | 4 | 5 | 2 |
| 0 | 5 | 5 | 0 | 5 | 5 | 6 |
| 4 | 3 | 3 | 6 | 6 | 6 | 2 |
| 4 | 5 | 3 | 0 | 5 | 1 | 3 |
| 6 | 2 | 2 | 0 | 1 | 1 | 1 |
| 1 | 5 | 2 | 0 | 2 | 4 | 1 |
| 1 | 3 | 6 | 6 | 2 | 1 | 0 |

# 391 FILLING IN

Each of the nine empty boxes contains a different digit from 1 to 9. Each calculation is to be treated sequentially rather than according to the 'multiplication first' system. Can you fill in the empty boxes?

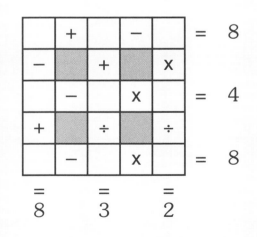

# 392 LOGIQUATIONS

In the following problems the digits 0 to 9 are represented by letters. Within each separate puzzle the same letter always represents the same digit. Can you find the correct values each time so that all sums, both horizontal and vertical, are correct? There is a clue to help start you off.

| ABCD | + | EFGH | = | CBJE |
|------|---|------|---|------|
| −    |   | −    |   | −    |
| JKE  | + | AJCK | = | EHJH |
| BBE  | + | AEE  | = | HJD  |

CLUE: AB + EC = DF

| A | B | C | D | E | F | G | H | J | K |
|---|---|---|---|---|---|---|---|---|---|
|   |   |   |   |   |   |   |   |   |   |

## 393 DOUBLE DANDY

Which two fancily dressed fellows are exactly alike?

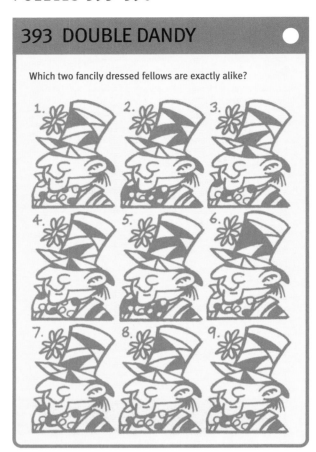

## 395 COURT ORDER

Of the eight Kings and Queens in a pack of cards, four are lined up here. In these clues *TO THE RIGHT/LEFT* means *NEXT DOOR* and not anywhere beyond.

There's a King to the right of a King.
There's a King to the left of a Queen.
There's a Queen to the left of a King.
There's a Queen to the right of a Spade.
There's a Spade next to a Spade.
There's a Club to the left of a Heart.
There's a Club to the right of a Spade.
Can you identify each card?

## 394 SPLIT LIZARDS

Can you put together the split lizards to make up four whole ones?

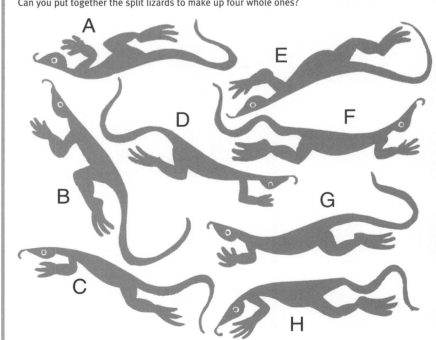

## 396 DOTTY DILEMMA

Connect adjacent dots with vertical or horizontal lines so that a single loop is formed with no crossings or branches. Each number indicates how many lines surround it, while empty cells may be surrounded by any number of lines.

```
.   .   .   .   .   .   .   .   .   .   .
  3                           3
  0       3 0                 0
  3     1         1       1
          3 2
. 1                               0
  0   3   3 1   3         2
  1       1       0       3
            1 2
    2 1               1 3
    2 0               3 1
          2 2
  2     3       3         2
  0   3   2 3     0       2 0
  1                       0
            1 1
    3   3       2   2
    1       3 3       3
    0                 0
```

## 397 ISLAND HOPPING

Each circle containing a number represents an island. The object is to connect each island with vertical or horizontal bridges so that:
* The number of bridges is the same as the number inside the island.
* There can be up to two bridges between two islands.
* Bridges cannot cross islands or other bridges.
* There is a continuous path connecting all the islands.

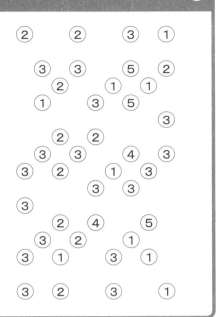

## 398 PIECE OF CAKE

Four of the letter domino segments can be put together to make a complete 'cake', in which adjacent faces match. Which four segments would make the 'cake' shown?

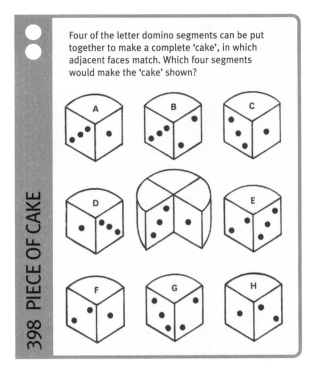

## 399 IN FLIGHT

Six international jet-setters are enjoying a transatlantic flight. From these details can you name the person in each seat and give his/her business?

The three in the window seats are Ms Baddand, the male model and Ella. None of these is the author.

The three in an aisle seat are her Ladyship, Waylite and the magician. None of these is the tourist who is directly in front of a lady.

In consecutively numbered seats, going upwards, are Ron, the croupier and Ghote. None of these is Stewart who is sitting further back than both Mrs Vatripp and Mahatma who are not side by side.

Smayde is next to Hess who is directly behind Adelia who is in an adjacent-numbered seat to the director in seat No.2 and his snores are beginning to bother her.

## 400 BIG BREAK

A snooker break is made up by potting red balls (maximum 15) which are each followed by one of six different colours. The point values of the balls are:

 1  2  3  4  5  6 7

In his next frame, Bob made a break of 71, which ended when he failed to pot a red. In the break he potted one more pink than greens and one more blue than yellows, potting all four colours in the break (none of which was black or brown). How many of each colour ball were potted?

## 401 BRICKWORK

Can you work out how many bricks are missing from this wall?

## 403 SPOT THE DIFFERENCE

Can you spot the ten differences between these two pictures?

## 402 SUDOKU

Place a number from 1 to 9 in each empty cell so that each row, each column and each 3 x 3 block contains all the numbers from 1 to 9.

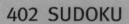

## 404 LOGI-5

Can you place the letters A, B, C, D, E, one to each square so that every line across and down contains each letter once and every shape made from five squares also has each letter once?

# 405 KNOTTY PROBLEM

No wonder this chap's looking puzzled – this piece of string seems to be in a real mess! Can you work out how many knots will appear if the two ends are pulled tightly?

# 406 DOTTY DILEMMA

Connect adjacent dots with vertical or horizontal lines so that a single loop is formed with no crossings or branches. Each number indicates how many lines surround it, while empty cells may be surrounded by any number of lines.

# 407 COG-ITATE

Can you work out which weights will rise, and which will fall when the man releases the rope?

## 408 TOTTERING TOWERS

These piles of bricks aren't the random results of child's play – but clues to the final, at present, blank tower on the right. Like the rest, that tower has one brick in each of the six colours.

The numbers below each heap tell you two things:
(a) How many adjacent pairs of bricks are actually correct in the final tower.
(b) How many adjacent pairs of bricks make a correct pair but the wrong way up.
So:

 would score one on the first number if the final tower had green directly above yellow. It would score one on the second number if the final tower had yellow on top of green. From all of this, can you create the tower before it finally topples?

| PAIRS | | | | | |
|---|---|---|---|---|---|
| Correct | 0 | 1 | 0 | 2 | 5 |
| Reversed | 1 | 1 | 1 | 0 | 0 |

## 409 MOONLIGHTING

From anywhere on the Earth, lovers can gaze up at the night sky and see the Moon. Each day it rises and sets. But if you were having a party on the Moon – what would the Earth be doing? Would it rise and set each day; never rise or never set?

## 410 HAIR STYLES

A saleslady and two others have reached that tedious stage of hairdressing – the hour under the drier. Teresa (who is sitting in the middle) is older than the redhead but younger than the programmer. Mavis is younger than the blonde. Rachel is older than the brunette. The programmer is sitting on the right hand of the secretary's older sister. Can you identify each lady and give her occupation and hair colour?

## 411 PATH-O-LOGICAL

Use your deductive reasoning to form a pathway from the box marked START to the box marked FINISH moving in either direction horizontally or vertically (but not diagonally). The number at the beginning of every row or column indicates exactly how many of the boxes in that row or column your pathway must pass through. A small diagram is provided to serve you as an example.

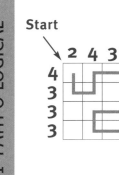

**Start**

| | 2 | 4 | 3 | 4 |
|---|---|---|---|---|
| 4 | | | | |
| 3 | | | | |
| 3 | | | | |
| 3 | | | | |

**Finish**

**Start**

| | 5 | 1 | 1 | 10 | 3 | 3 | 7 | 2 | 1 | 2 |
|---|---|---|---|---|---|---|---|---|---|---|---|
| 5 | | | | | | | | | | |
| 3 | | | | | | | | | | |
| 3 | | | | | | | | | | |
| 3 | | | | | | | | | | |
| 5 | | | | | | | | | | |
| 4 | | | | | | | | | | |
| 1 | | | | | | | | | | |
| 1 | | | | | | | | | | |
| 4 | | | | | | | | | | |
| 6 | | | | | | | | | | |

**Finish**

## 412 MIND JOGGER

Can you discover which of the numbered cards will fit on card A to complete the sum?

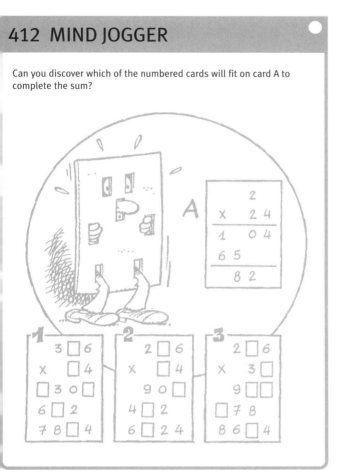

## 413 OFFSIDE

Which two of the numbered pictures have been taken from picture A?

## 414 TEE TIME

Three old-timers play a weekly game of golf on the Golden Lawns 18-hole, par 72, course. Each score at every hole falls into one of five categories. Each golfer gets a different result in each category. Also, no category has the same result for another player, ie, if a player has two eagles, he has a different number in the other four and no other player has two eagles. With the score details below and the information given, can you fill in their card?

Parnell, who did not get the fewest pars, got one more eagle than bogey and the two added up to his number of birdies. This number was the same as Barry's pars which were two fewer than his birdies and two more than his double bogeys. Nick got twice as many pars as birdies and twice as many birdies as double-bogeys of which he had the same number as Barry's eagles. This number was one more than Barry's number of bogeys which was two less than his double bogeys.

| | Eagle −2 | Birdie −1 | Par 0 | Bogey +1 | Double Bogey +2 | FINAL SCORE |
|---|---|---|---|---|---|---|
| Parnell Darma | | | | | | |
| Nick Jackliss | | | | | | |
| Barry Clayer | | | | | | |

## 415 IT FIGURES

Place a number from 1 to 9 in each empty cell so that the sum of each vertical or horizontal block equals the number at the top or on the left of that block. Numbers may only be used once in each block.

## 416 BIRD BRAIN

Which one of these ostriches is holding the diagram with the most triangles on it?

## 417 ISLAND HOPPING

Each circle containing a number represents an island. The object is to connect each island with vertical or horizontal bridges so that:
* The number of bridges is the same as the number inside the island.
* There can be up to two bridges between two islands.
* Bridges cannot cross islands or other bridges.
* There is a continuous path connecting all the islands.

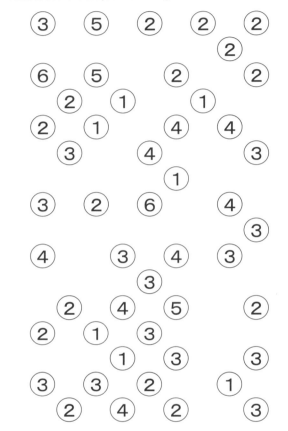

## 418 KARL KRACK'S CIRCUS

Karl Krack, who owns a small travelling circus, believes that variety is the spice of life and for each show he alters the order of his eight acts. Can you work out what the order will be for tonight's performance? The Clever Clowns will come immediately after the Flying Fortresses and two acts before the Crazy Carvellos and Jim the Juggler is three acts before Fred the Fire-eater and two acts after Madame Poll's Parrots. Senor Pedro's Poodles are more than two later in the programme than the Agilles Acrobats.

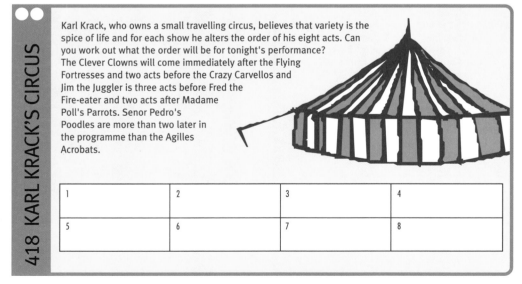

| 1 | 2 | 3 | 4 |
|---|---|---|---|
| 5 | 6 | 7 | 8 |

## 419 STICKY TIME

Move *two* matches only so that you end up with the cherry *outside* the glass.

# 420 RACER FACES

Talk about being two-faced! Can you match up these speedsters' halves correctly?

# 421 PIE-EYED

Before this clown receives the cream pie in the face, can you show him how to divide it into *eight* parts with only *three cuts*?

No, pieces can't be piled up on top of each other – any movement and the cream will escape!

# 422 DOMINO SEARCH

A standard set of dominoes has been laid out, using numbers instead of dots for clarity. Using a sharp pencil and a keen brain, can you draw in the lines to show where each domino has been placed? You may find the check grid useful – crossing off each domino as you find it.

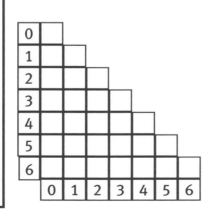

| 2 | 6 | 1 | 4 | 4 | 3 | 0 | 3 |
|---|---|---|---|---|---|---|---|
| 2 | 3 | 5 | 5 | 6 | 6 | 4 | 2 |
| 0 | 1 | 0 | 2 | 1 | 1 | 1 | 4 |
| 5 | 3 | 0 | 0 | 5 | 3 | 0 | 5 |
| 0 | 6 | 1 | 2 | 1 | 6 | 4 | 1 |
| 4 | 3 | 3 | 4 | 0 | 5 | 5 | 6 |
| 2 | 4 | 6 | 3 | 2 | 2 | 6 | 5 |

# 423 MENTAL BLOCKS

Which two of the numbered pieces will fit together to make cube A?

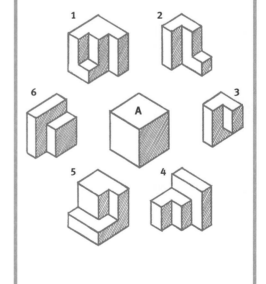

## 424 MAZE MYSTERY

Travel from the entrance to the exit of the maze, filling the path completely to create a picture.

## 425 INTERESTING

How can you legally arrange matters so that your body is buried on the day before you die?

R.I.P.
1715–1830

## 427 SUDOKU

Place a number from 1 to 9 in each empty cell so that each row, each column and each 3 x 3 block contains all the numbers from 1 to 9.

|   | 5 |   |   |   | 1 | 9 |   |   |
|---|---|---|---|---|---|---|---|---|
|   | 4 |   |   | 2 |   |   | 7 |   |
| 1 |   |   | 8 |   |   |   |   | 3 |
|   | 9 | 2 |   |   |   |   |   | 6 |
|   | 1 |   |   | 5 |   |   | 8 |   |
| 4 |   |   |   |   | 9 | 5 |   |   |
| 5 |   |   |   | 6 |   |   |   | 7 |
|   | 9 |   |   | 3 |   |   | 1 |   |
|   |   | 1 | 7 |   |   | 6 |   |   |

## 428 ANTIPATHETIC

A reluctant ant, not wanting to be sent out on yet another food gathering journey, decided to take the longest route back to the nest. Such is its tiny brain, though, that it will only go along the edges of the patio tiles and will not go over any part of its path more than once. What was the longest way home?

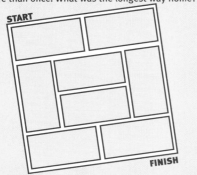

## 426 CHEESE STRAWS

Which one of these lettered paths will lead the mouse to the clock?

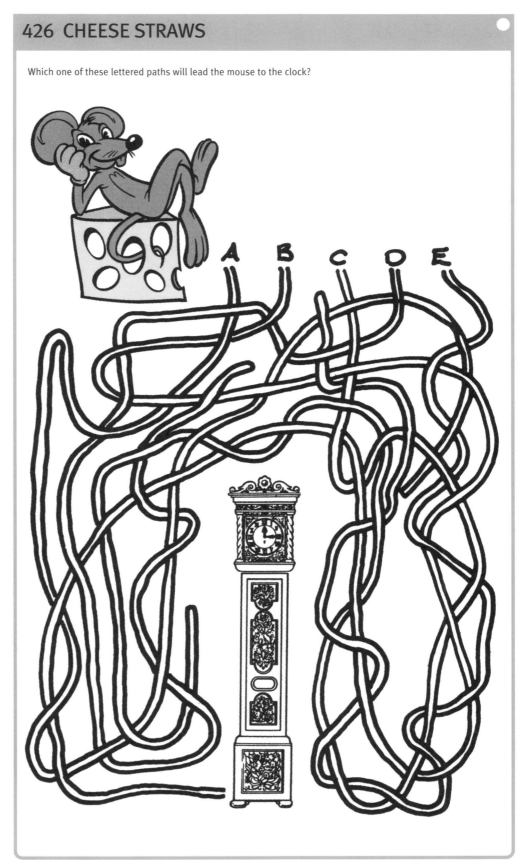

## 429 PARTY TIME

Party time and the table is all set up with eight coloured cakes in position waiting for the children to sit down and tuck in. From the information below can you work out where each child will be sitting?

At Sharon and Paul's party, boys and girls are seated alternately and no child is sitting next to another with the same number of letters in his/her name. The child on one side of the yellow cake has one more letter in his/her name than the child on the other side. Fiona is on one side of the brown cake (chocolate flavour!), which is not where Bob is sitting. Amy is sitting next to Martin but neither has a pink cake. Chloe does not have an orange cake and Jack is not next to the child with the green cake.

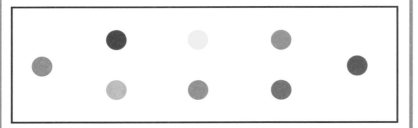

## 431 TOTTERING TOWERS

These piles of bricks aren't the random results of child's play – but clues to the final, at present, blank tower on the right. Like the rest, that tower has one brick in each of the six colours.

The numbers below each heap tell you two things:
(a) How many adjacent pairs of bricks are actually correct in the final tower.
(b) How many adjacent pairs of bricks make a correct pair but the wrong way up.
So:

 would score one on the first number if the final tower had green directly above yellow. It would score one on the second number if the final tower had yellow on top of green. From all of this, can you create the tower before it finally topples?

| PAIRS | | | | | |
|---|---|---|---|---|---|
| Correct | 2 | 1 | 0 | 0 | 5 |
| Reversed | 0 | 0 | 2 | 0 | 0 |

## 430 NUMBER KROSS

See how quickly you can fit all these numbers into the grid. We've filled one figure in to start you off.

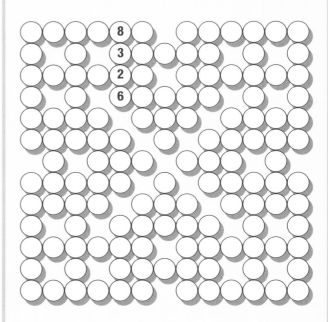

| 3 figures | 5 figures | 6 figures |
|---|---|---|
| 217 | 10439 | 107989 |
| 226 | 14756 | 134871 |
| 304 | 24514 | 172351 |
| 421 | 27190 | 212806 |
| 572 | 30947 | 213071 |
| 815 | 46023 | 316293 |
| 874 | 55326 | 341268 |
| 907 | 57147 | 453527 |
| | 60175 | 551108 |
| **4 figures** | 61513 | 572215 |
| 1740 | 67329 | 581941 |
| 1783 | 73346 | 661630 |
| 6137 | 84168 | 676869 |
| 7576 | 89224 | 713954 |
| 7657 | 90718 | 819201 |
| 8326 | 97179 | 971329 |
| 9083 | | |
| 9447 | | |

# 432 ISLAND HOPPING

Each circle containing a number represents an island. The object is to connect each island with vertical or horizontal bridges so that:
* The number of bridges is the same as the number inside the island.
* There can be up to two bridges between two islands.
* Bridges cannot cross islands or other bridges.
* There is a continuous path connecting all the islands.

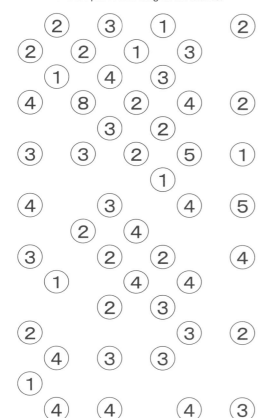

# 433 DRUM ROLL

In a negative, everything which is really black appears white and everything which is really white appears black. Can you tell which one of the seven kettledrums is shown as a negative in the top left-hand corner?

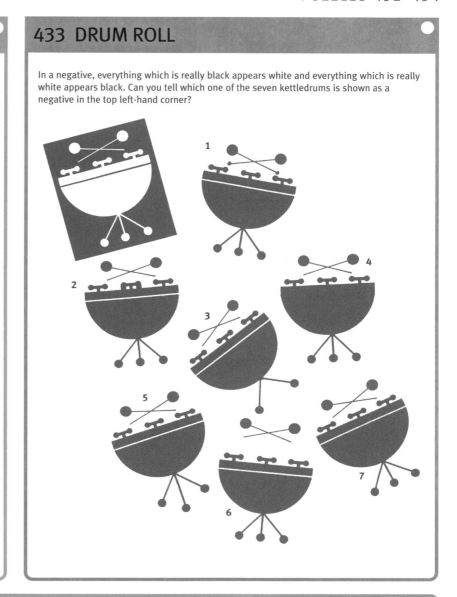

# 434 BREAKTHROUGH

See how quickly you can break this grid down into the 28 dominoes from which it is formed.

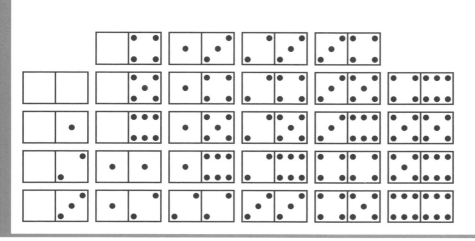

| 2 | 0 | 2 | 1 | 1 | 0 | 1 |
|---|---|---|---|---|---|---|
| 6 | 6 | 3 | 3 | 2 | 2 | 0 |
| 4 | 3 | 5 | 4 | 2 | 6 | 6 |
| 0 | 0 | 0 | 4 | 4 | 6 | 3 |
| 1 | 6 | 5 | 4 | 5 | 5 | 1 |
| 6 | 0 | 3 | 5 | 2 | 5 | 4 |
| 0 | 4 | 3 | 5 | 5 | 1 | 2 |
| 3 | 4 | 1 | 3 | 2 | 1 | 6 |

## 435 DOTTY DILEMMA

Connect adjacent dots with vertical or horizontal lines so that a single loop is formed with no crossings or branches. Each number indicates how many lines surround it, while empty cells may be surrounded by any number of lines.

```
  .   .   .   3   .   .   .   3   .   .
  .2 .3 .0 .1 .   .   .0 .   .   .
  .   .   .   .   .   .3 .2 .0 .   .
  .   .0 .2 .1 .1 .   .   .   .   .
  .   .   .1 .   .2 .   .   .   .   .
  .   .   .3 .   .1 .   .3 .0 .   .
  .   .2 .2 .1 .2 .   .   .2 .   .
  .   .   .   .   .   .   .   .2 .   .
  .1 .2 .   .2 .1 .   .   .3 .   .
  .   .0 .   .3 .2 .   .   .3 .1 .
  .   .3 .   .   .   .   .   .   .
  .   .2 .   .3 .2 .0 .1 .   .   .
  .2 .1 .   .0 .   .   .1 .   .   .
  .   .   .   .2 .   .   .1 .   .
  .   .   .0 .1 .2 .2 .   .   .
  .1 .3 .3 .   .   .   .   .   .
  .   .2 .   .   .1 .3 .3 .3 .
  .   .1 .   .   .1 .   .   .
```

## 436 SUDOKU

Place a number from 1 to 9 in each empty cell so that each row, each column and each 3 x 3 block contains all the numbers from 1 to 9.

| 7 |   |   | 3 | 4 |   |   |   | 5 |
|---|---|---|---|---|---|---|---|---|
|   |   | 2 |   |   | 5 |   |   |   |
|   |   | 1 |   |   |   | 6 |   |   |
| 2 |   |   | 1 |   |   |   | 7 |   |
| 3 |   |   |   |   |   |   |   | 8 |
|   |   | 4 |   |   | 2 |   |   | 9 |
|   |   | 5 |   |   |   |   | 1 |   |
|   |   |   | 6 |   |   | 9 |   |   |
| 4 |   |   |   | 7 | 8 |   |   | 2 |

## 437 EASY AS ABC

Each row and column originally contained one A, one B, one C, one D and two blank squares. Each letter and number refers to the first or second of the four letters encountered when travelling in the direction of the arrow. Can you complete the original grid?

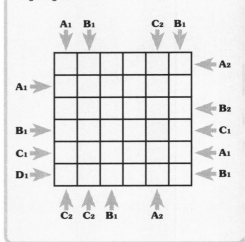

## 439 ODD ONE OUT

All of these aliens are odd, but which one is the odd one out?

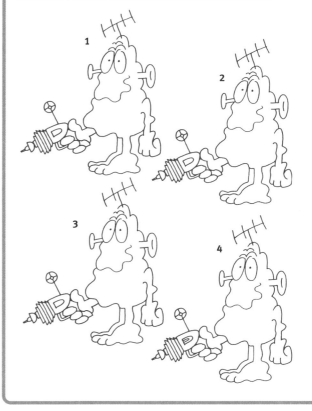

## 438 LOGI-PATH

Use your deductive reasoning to form a pathway from the box marked START to the box marked FINISH moving in either direction horizontally or vertically (but not diagonally). The number at the beginning of every row or column indicates exactly how many boxes in that row or column your pathway must pass through. The small diagram is given as an example of how it works.

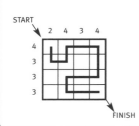

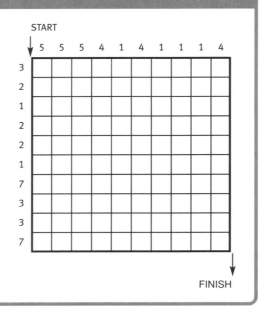

# 440 MOUSE HUNT

This greedy mouse has been raiding the jar of candy. Can you put the fourteen numbered pictures of the jar in the correct order, to show the candy gradually disappearing? Picture 9 is the first, because the jar in that picture contains the most candy.

# 441 LOGIMAZE

The grid is a symbol maze through which you must find a route by moving from one symbol to another according to the progression of the code sequence indicated in figure A. You can start anywhere on the edge of the grid but you must start on a Santa, proceed to the opposite side of the grid (repeating the sequence as often as necessary) and end on a stocking. You can move up, down, left or right, but not diagonally.

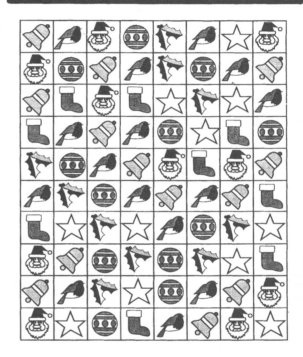

## 442 BREAKTHROUGH

See how quickly you can break this grid down into the 28 dominoes from which it was formed.

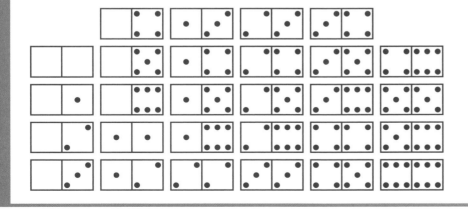

| 2 | 6 | 0 | 6 | 0 | 5 | 3 |
|---|---|---|---|---|---|---|
| 3 | 3 | 3 | 5 | 5 | 6 | 5 |
| 6 | 2 | 0 | 4 | 1 | 6 | 6 |
| 3 | 2 | 1 | 4 | 4 | 3 | 4 |
| 5 | 2 | 4 | 1 | 1 | 1 | 6 |
| 2 | 3 | 0 | 2 | 3 | 2 | 4 |
| 5 | 4 | 1 | 0 | 0 | 1 | 6 |
| 5 | 0 | 1 | 0 | 4 | 5 | 2 |

## 443 NUMBER KROSS

See how quickly you can fit all these numbers into the grid. We've filled one figure in to start you off.

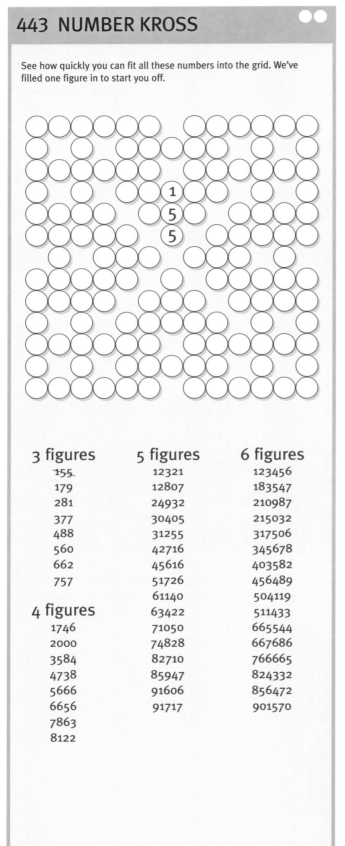

| 3 figures | 5 figures | 6 figures |
|---|---|---|
| ~~155~~ | 12321 | 123456 |
| 179 | 12807 | 183547 |
| 281 | 24932 | 210987 |
| 377 | 30405 | 215032 |
| 488 | 31255 | 317506 |
| 560 | 42716 | 345678 |
| 662 | 45616 | 403582 |
| 757 | 51726 | 456489 |
| | 61140 | 504119 |
| **4 figures** | 63422 | 511433 |
| 1746 | 71050 | 665544 |
| 2000 | 74828 | 667686 |
| 3584 | 82710 | 766665 |
| 4738 | 85947 | 824332 |
| 5666 | 91606 | 856472 |
| 6656 | 91717 | 901570 |
| 7863 | | |
| 8122 | | |

## 444 SPOT THE DIFFERENCE

Can you spot the ten differences between these two pictures?

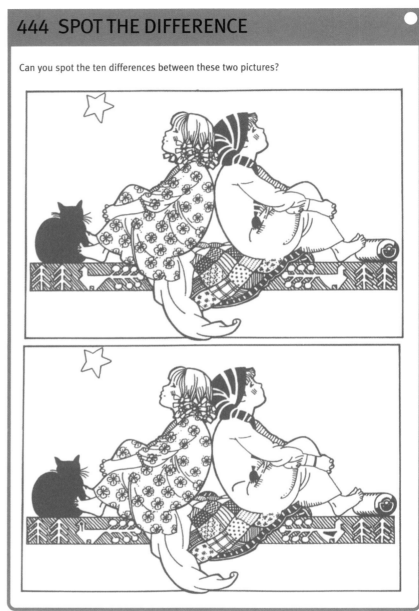

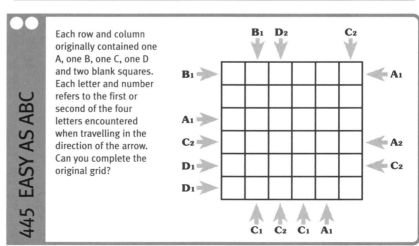

## 445 EASY AS ABC

Each row and column originally contained one A, one B, one C, one D and two blank squares. Each letter and number refers to the first or second of the four letters encountered when travelling in the direction of the arrow. Can you complete the original grid?

# 446 SUDOKU

Place a number from 1 to 9 in each empty cell so that each row, each column and each 3 x 3 block contains all the numbers from 1 to 9.

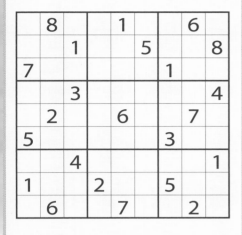

# 447 IT FIGURES

Place a number from 1 to 9 in each empty cell so that the sum of each vertical or horizontal block equals the number at the top or on the left of that block. Numbers may only be used once in each block.

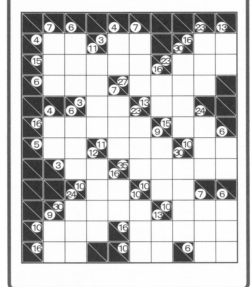

# 448 DOTTY DILEMMA

Connect adjacent dots with vertical or horizontal lines so that a single loop is formed with no crossings or branches. Each number indicates how many lines surround it, while empty cells may be surrounded by any number of lines.

```
  2 2 1 1 3 1 1 3
                    3
   3 2 0 2 0 2 1 2
 1
   3 3 2 1 2 2 2 3
                      1
   3 1 1 0 2 3 2 2
 2
   3 1 2 3
             2 1 3 3
                        0
   3 2 0 2 2 3 1 1
 2
   2 3 1 0 3 1 1 3
                      1
   2 2 2 2 2 2 2 2
 1
   3 1 3 1 2 2 1 2
```

# 449 TOTTERING TOWERS

These piles of bricks aren't the random results of child's play – but clues to the final, at present, blank tower on the right. Like the rest, that tower has one brick with each of the six letters.

The numbers below each heap tell you two things:
(a) How many adjacent pairs of bricks are actually correct in the final tower.
(b) How many adjacent pairs of bricks make a correct pair but the wrong way up.

So:

would score one on the first number if the final tower had an A directly above a C. It would score one on the second number if the final tower had C on top of A. From all of this, can you create the tower before it finally topples?

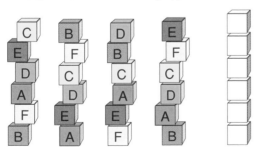

| PAIRS | | | | | |
|---|---|---|---|---|---|
| Correct | 1 | 0 | 0 | 0 | 5 |
| Reversed | 0 | 0 | 2 | 0 | 0 |

# 450 CELL STRUCTURE

The object is to create white areas surrounded by black walls, so that:
* Each white area contains only one number.
* The number of cells in a white area is equal to the number in it.
* The white areas are separated from each other with a black wall.
* Cells containing numbers must not be filled in.
* The black cells must be linked into a continuous wall.
* Black cells cannot form a square of 2 x 2 or larger.

|  |  |  |  |  |  |  |  | 4 |
|---|---|---|---|---|---|---|---|---|
|  |  | 3 |  | 2 |  |  |  |  |
| 2 |  |  |  |  |  | 2 |  | 3 |
|  |  |  |  | 4 |  |  |  |  |
|  |  |  |  |  |  |  |  |  |
|  |  |  |  |  |  |  |  |  |
|  |  | 4 |  | 2 |  |  |  | 3 |
|  |  |  |  |  |  | 3 |  |  |
|  |  |  |  |  |  |  | 2 |  | 3 |
| 3 |  | 3 |  |  |  |  |  |  |

## 451 ISLAND HOPPING

Each circle containing a number represents an island. The object is to connect each island with vertical or horizontal bridges so that:
* The number of bridges is the same as the number inside the island.
* There can be up to two bridges between two islands.
* Bridges cannot cross islands or other bridges.
* There is a continuous path connecting all the islands.

(2) (3) (2) (4) (1)

(2)   (2)   (7) (3)

    (2) (1)   (1)

(3)   (2) (3)   (2)

      (3) (2) (1)

(3)   (2) (8)   (3)

          (4) (5)

(4) (4)

  (1) (2) (6)   (2)

    (4) (2) (3)

(1)   (1) (4)   (1)

  (2)   (2) (1)

(2) (2)   (2)   (3)

(1) (2) (4) (4) (3)

## 452 PLUMB BLUFF!

Which of the numbered boilers belongs in the plumbing system shown?

## 453 SUDOKU

Place a number from 1 to 9 in each empty cell so that each row, each column and each 3 x 3 block contains all the numbers from 1 to 9.

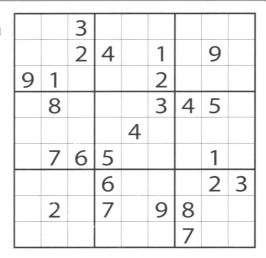

## 454 WATER SPORTS

The architect and four of his friends swim in the same pool. Mark and the dentist both swim laps in the morning. Karl and Mr Harkness sometimes dive together in the afternoons. Mr Jones recently considered the idea of making up a swimming team, using the five of them. He observed that:

• In the 100 metre freestyle – both Mr Harkness and Mr Gainor are slower than Mark.
• Both Mr Harkness and Otto are faster than the economist.
• In the backstroke only Neil is willing to swim more than 50 metres, and Karl will not compete at all.
• In the 50 metres backstroke Mr Ives is faster than Mark. Mark, Otto, and Luke are all slower than the barber. Mark is faster than the critic.
• In the breastroke the critic, the dentist, and the economist are all slower than Mr Franklin. Luke is faster than Mr Ives.
• As to springboard diving: Mr Franklin, Mark and Karl are the three best divers.

Can you identify all five men, giving names and occupations?

## 455 BEAR MAZE

Can you find your way through this maze, starting from the top and finishing at the bottom?

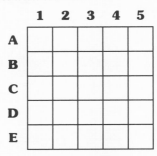

## 456 DOTTY DILEMMA

Connect adjacent dots with vertical or horizontal lines so that a single loop is formed with no crossings or branches. Each number indicates how many lines surround it, while empty cells may be surrounded by any number of lines.

```
. . . 2 . 2 . 3 . 0 . . .
. 2 . 3 . 3 . 1 . . . 3 .
. 0 . 1 . 2 . . 3 . . . .
. . . 3 . . 2 . . . 2 1 .
. 2 . . 0 . . 3 . . . . .
. . . . 1 . 3 . 3 2 2 .
. 1 0 3 2 . 2 . . . . .
. . . . . . . 2 . 3 1 1 .
. . 3 1 2 3 . . . . . .
. . . . . . 3 3 1 3 .
. 2 1 0 . 2 . . . . . .
. . . . . . 3 . 2 0 1 2 .
. 1 0 3 . 2 . 2 . . . .
. . . . 1 . . . 2 . . 2 .
. 2 1 . . 1 . . 2 . . . .
. . . . 1 . . 0 . 3 . 2 .
. 3 . . . 3 . 1 . 3 . 3 .
. . 3 . 3 . 2 . 1 . . .
```

## 457 SQUARE LETTERS

The letters of the alphabet, excluding Z, are entered randomly into a 5 x 5 square so that no two consecutive letters are in the same row or column, or in a diagonal in any direction.

The letters NQG can be read downwards as can TMO. Square E5 is a vowel. D is immediately left of V and immediately above I, which is not in column 2. Row D begins and ends with a vowel, the first alphabetically preceding the latter. Q and T are at opposite ends of a row, and K and S are at the top and bottom respectively of a column. U is diagonally immediately below W. E and R can both be seen on the same long diagonal. C is diagonally adjacent to H; Y is to the immediate right of F, and X is in a corner square.
Can you locate each letter?

|   | 1 | 2 | 3 | 4 | 5 |
|---|---|---|---|---|---|
| A |   |   |   |   |   |
| B |   |   |   |   |   |
| C |   |   |   |   |   |
| D |   |   |   |   |   |
| E |   |   |   |   |   |

135

## 458 LOGI-PATH

Use your deductive reasoning to form a pathway from the box marked START to the box marked FINISH moving in either direction horizontally or vertically (but not diagonally). The number at the beginning of every row or column indicates exactly how many boxes in that row or column your pathway must pass through. The small diagram is given as an example of how it works.

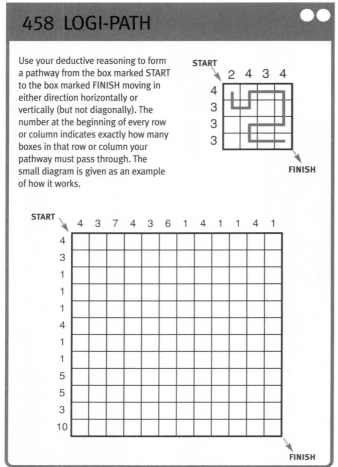

## 459 STRUCTURE MAZE

Can you find your way through this maze?

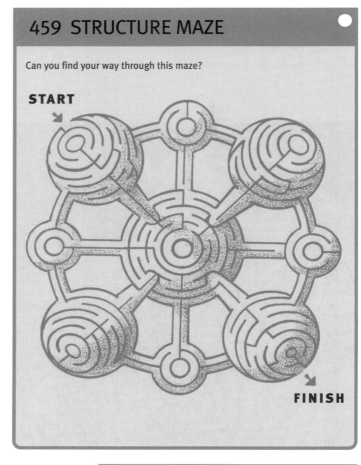

## 460 UPSTAIRS, DOWNSTAIRS

A group of eight people are playing Murder in the Dark and each has hidden in a separate room. Your job is to find them. You are looking at the house from the side and the front and back are as shown. Adjacent rooms share a wall on the same floor. To help you on your way one person has already been found.

1. Fred is not adjacent to Enid.
2. Hebe is directly above Bess.
3. Alan is not directly above Gina.
4. Dave is not adjacent to Enid.
5. Fred is in a back room.
6. Enid is directly below Cary.
7. Dave is on the same side as Gina.

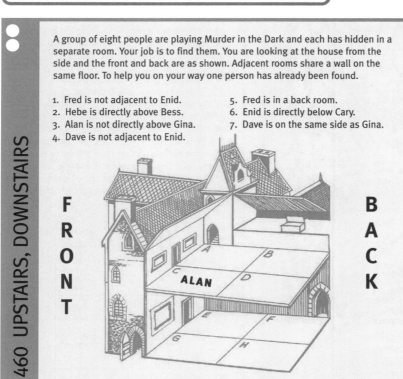

## 461 CODEMASTER

Can you crack the code and say which of these six pictures has been hidden in each empty box?
The two numbers to the right of each row of pictures tells you first, how many pictures are in the right place and second, how many of the pictures are right but in the wrong place. The answer may have the same picture more than once. Just follow the rules of that classic game Master Mind and you'll soon get the picture.

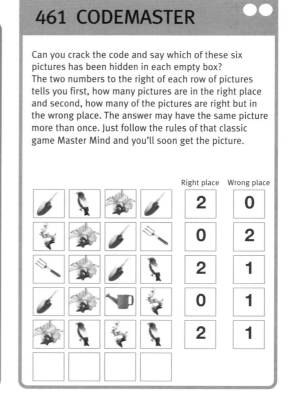

# 462 NUMBER KROSS

See how quickly you can fit all these numbers into the grid. We've filled one figure in to start you off.

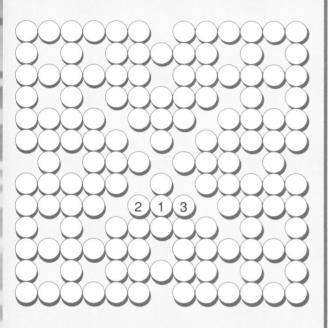

| 3 figures | 5 figures | 6 figures |
|---|---|---|
| ~~213~~ | 10679 | 100200 |
| 412 | 19658 | 121314 |
| 547 | 20184 | 212223 |
| 623 | 29017 | 243444 |
| 721 | 33401 | 312111 |
| 736 | 35709 | 344071 |
| 837 | 40233 | 453324 |
| 941 | 43581 | 463322 |
|  | 49832 | 515253 |
| **4 figures** | 57689 | 543210 |
| 3552 | 69177 | 624896 |
| 4174 | 71705 | 635343 |
| 5342 | 78905 | 703891 |
| 6219 | 81507 | 776976 |
| 7280 | 87174 | 884271 |
| 7475 | 91370 | 921404 |
| 8749 |  |  |
| 9293 |  |  |

# 463 COMPLETE THE SQUARE

Complete the square, using the set of tiles given, so that the same numbers can be read left to right and downwards starting at any point on the diagonal top left to bottom right.

7 5   3 6   4 3   0 3 3

4 8 4   4 0 4   0 3 5

4 2 4

1 3 1 3

7 8 0 2

| 8 | 6 | 2 |
| 5 | 8 | 5 |
| 6 | 4 | 9 |
| 2 | 4 | 0 |

1   1   4
3   3   9
    2   2

## 464 A MATTER OF BERTH

Farmer Nure's small campsite has four plots which at the moment are occupied by 18 tourists from four families. Each immobile home is labelled West, North, East and South which is the caravan nearest to you as you peer through the nettles.

1  Between them, two caravans have two less campers than the total housed in the two motorvans. No van has more than six berths.
2  There are more Larkitts than Spencers and neither family is the one occupying the East plot.
3  There are more Groves than there are in the family from Frumley.
4  The Huggins family is in the South caravan and their family size is one smaller than the size of the family from Welmside.
5  There are more from Tyneham than from Cheaphill and neither family has booked into a motorhome.

# 465 MAZE MYSTERY

Travel from the entrance to the exit of the maze, filling the path completely to create a picture.

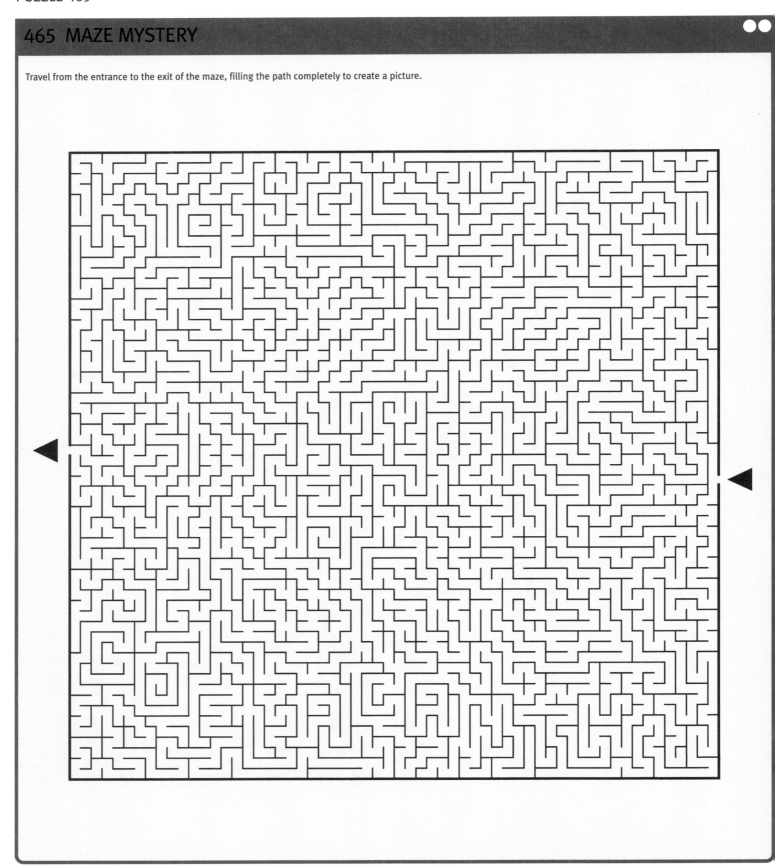

## 466 ACE IN PLACE ●●

The cards Eight to King of each suit, together with the Ace of Hearts, have been placed in a 5 x 5 square. Figures and letters of the values – 8, 9, T, J, Q, K and suits – C, D, H, S have been placed at the end of each line across and down. With the Ace in place and the fact that the two cards shown at the top left belong in the shaded squares, can you work out the unique place for each card?

## 467 DOTTY DILEMMA ●●●

Connect adjacent dots with vertical or horizontal lines so that a single loop is formed with no crossings or branches. Each number indicates how many lines surround it, while empty cells may be surrounded by any number of lines.

## 468 OFF TO UNI

Four school friends are off to different universities to take different courses. Can you complete the enrolment form with each girl's full name, subject and destination?

1 Barbara who is not Moore is studying Physics but not at Princeton.
2 Diana is not Jones who is neither the student going to Harvard nor the one studying Chemistry.
3 The student reading Maths at Yale is not Moore.
4 Clare Taylor is at MIT but is not the student reading Biology who is not Brown nor is either of these Anna.

| FORENAME | SURNAME | SUBJECT | UNIVERSITY |
|---|---|---|---|
|  |  |  |  |
|  |  |  |  |
|  |  |  |  |
|  |  |  |  |

## 469 SUDOKU ●●●

Place a number from 1 to 9 in each empty cell so that each row, each column and each 3 x 3 block contains all the numbers from 1 to 9.

|   |   |   | 5 |   |   |   |   | 3 |
|---|---|---|---|---|---|---|---|---|
|   | 1 |   |   |   | 9 |   |   |   |
|   |   | 2 |   | 6 |   |   |   |   |
| 8 |   |   |   | 7 |   | 5 |   |   |
|   | 6 |   |   |   |   |   | 1 |   |
|   | 9 |   | 3 |   |   |   |   | 4 |
|   |   | 1 |   |   | 8 |   |   |   |
|   | 7 |   |   |   |   | 2 |   |   |
| 4 |   |   |   | 9 |   |   |   |   |

## 470 KARL KRACK'S CIRCUS

Karl Krack, who owns a small travelling circus, believes that variety is the spice of life and for each show he alters the order of his eight acts. Can you work out what the order will be for tonight's performance?

The Flying Fortresses are three acts after Fred the Fire-eater who is not the opening act. The Clever Clowns are two acts before Jim the Juggler who is not the closing act. The Agilles Acrobats are on immediately after the Crazy Carvellos but are before Senor Pedro's Poodles which are two acts before Madame Poll's Parrots.

| 1 | 2 | 3 | 4 |
|---|---|---|---|
| 5 | 6 | 7 | 8 |

## 472 MISMATCHES

The numbers 1–10 are to be entered in the top row of boxes, so that none is in its correct numerical position, counting from left to right, and no two consecutive numbers are adjacent to each other. The letters A–J are to be entered in the bottom row, so that none is in its correct alphabetical position, left to right, none is below its correct number (A=1 B=2 etc.), and no two consecutive letters, and no vowels, are adjacent. The number 1 is not with letter I; the letter below 9 is one place earlier in the alphabet than that below 8. The second number from the left is three higher than the number of the letter below it; the eighth number from the left is two lower than the number of its letter. The left-hand number is two lower than the right-hand number; the left-hand letter is three later in the alphabet than the right-hand letter. The fourth and seventh from the left are vowels – the numbers above them total 10. 10 is somewhere left of A; 8 is somewhere left of D; 2 is somewhere right of E, and 4 is somewhere right of C. The third letter from the left is three earlier in the alphabet than the sixth. There is one box between 4 (left) and D, and one between A (left) and 7. Can you match numbers and letters?

| | | | | | | | | | |
|---|---|---|---|---|---|---|---|---|---|
| | | | | | | | | | |
| | | | | | | | | | |

## 474 LOGIPICK

Following the first diagram, there is a logical rule that determines how the next block is to be filled in. Given these three blocks, can you colour in the fourth?

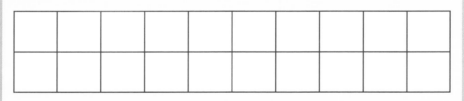

## 471 SUDOKU

Place a number from 1 to 9 in each empty cell so that each row, each column and each 3 x 3 block contains all the numbers from 1 to 9.

| | | | | 5 | 8 | 4 | | |
|---|---|---|---|---|---|---|---|---|
| | 2 | 3 | | | | | | |
| 6 | 7 | | | 1 | | | 3 | |
| 4 | | | 2 | | | | | |
| 1 | | | | | | | | 9 |
| | | | 3 | | | | | 7 |
| | 3 | | | 4 | | | 2 | 6 |
| | | | | | 3 | 7 | | |
| | 5 | 8 | 9 | | | | | |

## 473 DOTTY DILEMMA

Connect adjacent dots with vertical or horizontal lines so that a single loop is formed with no crossings or branches. Each number indicates how many lines surround it, while empty cells may be surrounded by any number of lines.

# 475 FOOTBALL CRAZY

Can you tell which two different balls appear three times in this picture?

# 476 LOGI-5

Each line, across and down, is to have each of the five colours appearing once each. Each colour must also appear just once in each shape, shown by thick lines. Can you colour in this crazy quilt, or mark each square with its correct letter B, G, R, V or Y?

|   | V |   | Y |   |
|---|---|---|---|---|
|   |   |   |   |   |
|   |   |   | B |   |
|   |   |   |   | G |
|   | R |   |   |   |

# 477 CODE MASTER

Just follow the rules of that classic puzzle, Master Mind, to crack the number code. The first number tells you how many of the digits are exactly correct – the right digit in the right place (✓✓). The second number tells you how many digits are the correct number but are not in the right place (✓). By comparing the information given by each line, can you work out which number goes in which place?

|   |   |   |   | ✓✓ | ✓ |
|---|---|---|---|----|----|

| 2 | 5 | 9 | 4 | 0 | 1 |
| 4 | 3 | 6 | 9 | 0 | 1 |
| 0 | 5 | 9 | 8 | 1 | 2 |
| 7 | 2 | 1 | 0 | 1 | 1 |
| 5 | 9 | 7 | 1 | 0 | 2 |

## 478 TOTTERING TOWERS

These piles of bricks aren't the random results of child's play – but clues to the final, at present, blank tower on the right. Like the rest, that tower has one brick with each of the six letters.

The numbers below each heap tell you two things:
(a) How many adjacent pairs of bricks are actually correct in the final tower.
(b) How many adjacent pairs of bricks make a correct pair but the wrong way up.

So: would score one on the first number if the final tower had an A directly above a C. It would score one on the second number if the final tower had C on top of A. From all of this, can you create the tower before it finally topples?

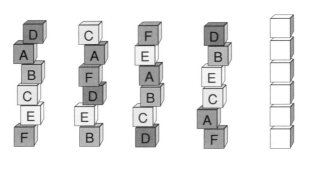

PAIRS

| | | | | | |
|---|---|---|---|---|---|
| Correct | 0 | 0 | 0 | 1 | 5 |
| Reversed | 0 | 3 | 1 | 1 | 0 |

## 479 BITS AND PIECES

Which one of the numbered pieces can be used to repair the cat's tankard?

## 480 BATTLESHIPS

Do you remember the old game of battleships? These puzzles are based on that idea. Your task is to find the vessels in the diagram. Some parts of boats or sea squares have already been filled in, and a number next to a row or column refers to the number of occupied squares in that row or column. The boats may be positioned horizontally or vertically, but no two boats or parts of boats are in adjacent squares – horizontally, vertically or diagonally.

Aircraft carrier:

Battleships:

Cruisers:

Destroyers:

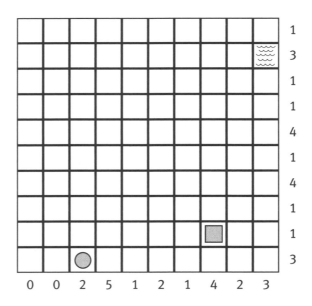

## 481 SUDOKU

Place a number from 1 to 9 in each empty cell so that each row, each column and each 3 x 3 block contains all the numbers from 1 to 9.

| | | | 9 | | | 8 | | |
|---|---|---|---|---|---|---|---|---|
| 6 | 1 | | | 7 | | | 9 | |
| | | 2 | | | | 5 | | |
| | | | 1 | | 2 | | | 7 |
| | 5 | | | | | | 4 | |
| 8 | | | 3 | | 4 | | | |
| | | 9 | | | | 3 | | |
| | 7 | | | 6 | | | 2 | 8 |
| | 4 | | | | 5 | | | |

# 482 NUMBER KROSS

See how quickly you can fit all these numbers into the grid. We've filled one figure in to start you off.

8 3 2

| 3 figures | 5 figures | 6 figures |
|-----------|-----------|-----------|
| 161 | 10703 | 116285 |
| 256 | 11802 | 162564 |
| 378 | 23326 | 216432 |
| 430 | 29110 | 263646 |
| 562 | 30879 | 357874 |
| 656 | 37207 | 384858 |
| 777 | 41296 | 412241 |
| ~~832~~ | 42407 | 478439 |
| | 59275 | 538458 |
| | 60417 | 583218 |
| | 69292 | 645444 |
| 4 figures | 70596 | 715227 |
| 1133 | 79828 | 759657 |
| 1762 | 80903 | 843358 |
| 2656 | 89134 | 958555 |
| 3675 | 97126 | 967864 |
| 4864 | | |
| 5254 | | |
| 6047 | | |
| 8398 | | |

# 483 BUBBLE TROUBLE

How many bubbles has this breathless girl blown?

# 484 TRACERY MAZE

Can you find your way through this maze?

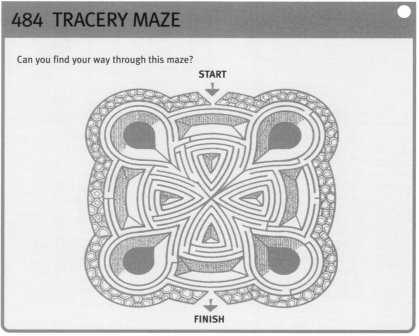

## 485 NUMBER KROSS

See how quickly you can fit all these numbers into the grid. We've filled one figure in to start you off.

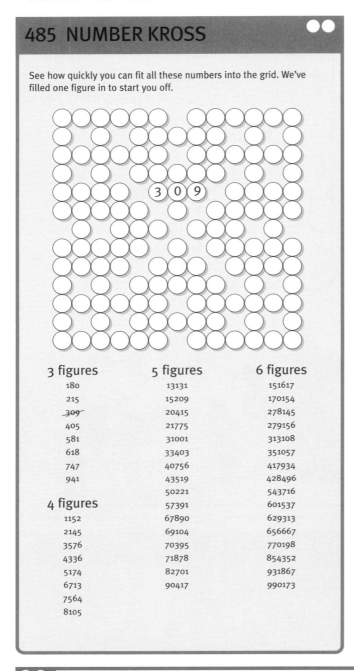

| 3 figures | 5 figures | 6 figures |
|-----------|-----------|-----------|
| 180 | 13131 | 151617 |
| 215 | 15209 | 170154 |
| ~~309~~ | 20415 | 278145 |
| 405 | 21775 | 279156 |
| 581 | 31001 | 313108 |
| 618 | 33403 | 351057 |
| 747 | 40756 | 417934 |
| 941 | 43519 | 428496 |
|  | 50221 | 543716 |
| **4 figures** | 57391 | 601537 |
| 1152 | 67890 | 629313 |
| 2145 | 69104 | 656667 |
| 3576 | 70395 | 770198 |
| 4336 | 71878 | 854352 |
| 5174 | 82701 | 931867 |
| 6713 | 90417 | 990173 |
| 7564 |  |  |
| 8105 |  |  |

## 486 PIXELATED PICS

The numbers in the squares tell you how many of it and its neighbours are to be filled in. A square can have up to eight neighbours.

```
1 2 3
8 X 4
7 6 5
```

Using logic alone and the filled cell, can you fill in the pixels and create a celebratory still-life?

| 0 | 2 | 1 | 2 | 1 | 0 | 1 | 2 |
|---|---|---|---|---|---|---|---|
|   | 2 |   | 4 | 1 | 3 | 1 | 1 | 3 |
| 0 |   | 6 |   | 3 | 1 | 3 | 2 | 3 | 1 |
|   | 3 |   | 5 | 1 | 1 | 3 | 3 | 1 |
| 2 |   | 4 |   | 3 | 0 | 1 | 4 | 1 | 0 |
|   | 3 |   | 3 | 3 | 0 | 3 | 3 | 0 |
| 3 |   | 3 |   | 3 | 0 | 0 | 3 | 0 | 0 |
|   | 3 |   | 3 | 3 | 0 | 3 | 3 | 0 |
| 3 |   | 2 |   | 3 | 1 | 1 | 5 | 1 | 0 |
|   | 3 |   | 1 | 3 | 1 | 6 | 6 | 1 |
| 3 |   | 0 |   | 3 | 5 | 6 | 9 | 6 | 2 |
|   | 4 |   | 2 | 4 | 4 | 6 | 6 | 4 |
| 3 |   | 4 |   | 5 | 6 | 4 | 3 | 3 | 2 |
|   | 6 |   | 6 | 3 | 2 | 1 | 0 | 1 |
| 3 |   | 4 |   | 5 | 4 | 3 | 1 | 2 | 2 |
|   | 4 |   | 2 | 3 | 1 | 3 | 2 | 4 |
| 3 |   | 0 |   | 3 | 3 | 1 | 3 | 5 | 2 |
|   | 3 |   | 0 | 3 | 0 | 2 | 6 | 3 |
| 3 |   | 3 |   | 4 | 2 | 2 | 5 | 3 | 0 |
|   | 3 |   | 3 | 2 | 1 | 4 | 3 | 0 |

## 487 EASY AS ABC

Each row and column originally contained one A, one B, one C, one D and two blank squares. Each letter and number refers to the first or second of the four letters encountered when travelling in the direction of the arrow. Can you complete the original grid?

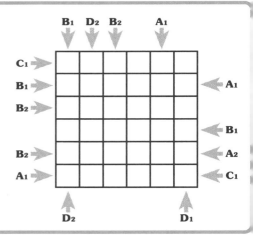

## 488 CODE MASTER

Just follow the rules of that classic puzzle, Master Mind, to crack the number code. The first number tells you how many of the digits are exactly correct – the right digit in the right place (✓✓). The second number tells you how many digits are the correct number but are not in the right place (✓). By comparing the information given by each line, can you work out which number goes in which place?

| | | | | | ✓✓ | ✓ |
|---|---|---|---|---|---|---|
| 2 | 4 | 3 | 1 | 5 | 0 | 2 |
| 8 | 2 | 1 | 3 | 4 | 2 | 0 |
| 1 | 9 | 6 | 2 | 7 | 1 | 3 |
| 6 | 4 | 1 | 7 | 9 | 0 | 4 |
| 7 | 5 | 9 | 6 | 8 | 1 | 2 |

## 489 SUDOKU

Place a number from 1 to 9 in each empty cell so that each row, each column and each 3 x 3 block contains all the numbers from 1 to 9.

| | | | | 2 | 3 | 4 | 9 | |
|---|---|---|---|---|---|---|---|---|
| | 1 | | | | 6 | 8 | | |
| | 2 | | | | | | | |
| | 5 | 8 | | | | | | |
| | 9 | 4 | | | 7 | | 6 | 3 |
| | | | | | | | 2 | 5 |
| | | | | | | | | 1 |
| | | | | 9 | 4 | | | 7 |
| | | 6 | 3 | 2 | 5 | | | |

# 490 DOTTY DILEMMA

Connect adjacent dots with vertical or horizontal lines so that a single loop is formed with no crossings or branches. Each number indicates how many lines surround it, while empty cells may be surrounded by any number of lines.

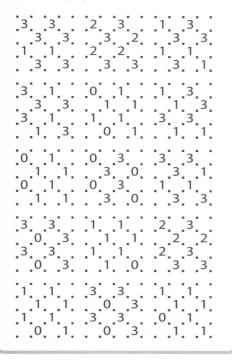

# 492 IT FIGURES

Place a number from 1 to 9 in each empty cell so that the sum of each vertical or horizontal block equals the number at the top or on the left of that block. Numbers may only be used once in each block.

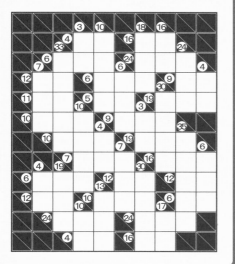

# 491 TOTTERING TOWERS

These piles of bricks aren't the random results of child's play – but clues to the final, at present, blank tower on the right. Like the rest, that tower has one brick in each of the six colours.
The numbers below each heap tell you two things:
(a) How many adjacent pairs of bricks are actually correct in the final tower.
(b) How many adjacent pairs of bricks make a correct pair but the wrong way up.

So: would score one on the first number if the final tower had green directly above yellow. It would score one on the second number if the final tower had yellow on top of green. From all of this, can you create the tower before it finally topples?

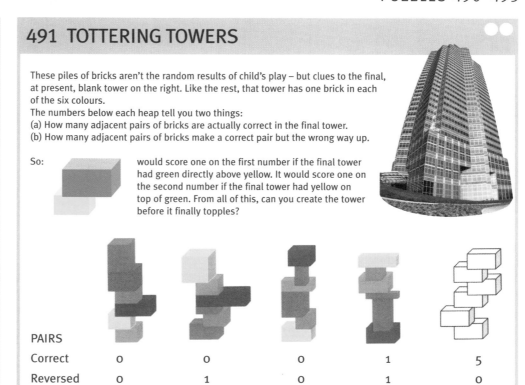

| PAIRS | | | | | |
|---|---|---|---|---|---|
| Correct | 0 | 0 | 0 | 1 | 5 |
| Reversed | 0 | 1 | 0 | 1 | 0 |

# 493 SHIP MATES

Can you pair up each of these pictures with its identical twin?

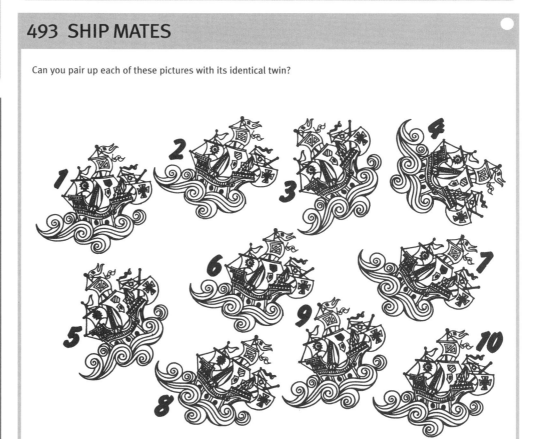

145

## 494 PAPER CHASE

Which one of the four paths must this rabbit run along in order to pick up the greatest number of pieces of paper?

## 495 CELL STRUCTURE

The object is to create white areas surrounded by black walls, so that:
* Each white area contains only one number.
* The number of cells in a white area is equal to the number in it.
* The white areas are separated from each other with a black wall.
* Cells containing numbers must not be filled in.
* The black cells must be linked into a continuous wall.
* Black cells cannot form a square of 2 x 2 or larger.

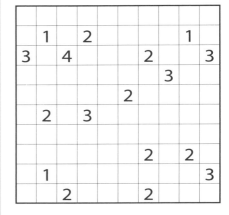

## 496 DIS-ENGAGED

Not for the first time, the Engagements column of the South Fork Gazette has upset the parents of several brides-to-be. After the computer threw a fit, attempts by Herbert, the school-leaver screen-minder, just added to the confusion. The result was that, when the printed version hit the news-stands, no name in each announcement actually belonged with any of the other three. Can you name the now not-so-happy couples?

### ENGAGEMENTS

The engagement is announced between:

Ann Chovies & Ed Lynes.
Ann Noble & Frank Copes.
Bella Daball & Frank Stamps.
Cher Chovies & Horace Stamps.
Cher Noble & Gary Baldy.
Bella Brakes & Ed Baldy.
Dawn Brakes & Horace Copes.
Cher Brakes & Frank Lynes.

## 497 CAROUSEL

The Carousel is a popular ride with the toddlers at Orles Fair. There are eight different animals on it and, so that the children don't get bored with it, Sid Slick, the owner, changes the positions of the animals each day. With the position of the horse given and the knowledge that the animals face and move in a clockwise direction, see if you can use the clues to work out the positions of each animal and child on today's ride.

1 No child is either next to or opposite another with the same initial.
2 Biddie is opposite the camel and two places in front of Robin.
3 Brian is opposite the zebra and two places behind the unicorn.
4 The emu is opposite Simon and immediately behind Tess's animal, which is opposite the peacock.
5 Tom is opposite the horse, but is not next to either the peacock or Simon.
6 There is also a dragon on the Carousel, Sheila is one of the riders and both birds have girls sitting on them.
7 The elephant is two places in front of Rose.

## 500 SUM COLUMNS

Move as few numbers as possible so that both columns have the same total!

| | |
|---|---|
| 0 | 5 |
| 8 | 7 |
| 4 | 9 |
| 2 | 1 |
| 3 | 6 |
| 17 | 28 |

## 498 CUBE ROUTE

The symbols on each face have a meaning – Up, Down, Right or Left. Each sign has only one meaning which is the same for every face. There is a direction for each symbol which will lead to a unique path joining Start (S) to End (E) and which passes through all three faces. Can you let your brain do the logical walking and make the journey?

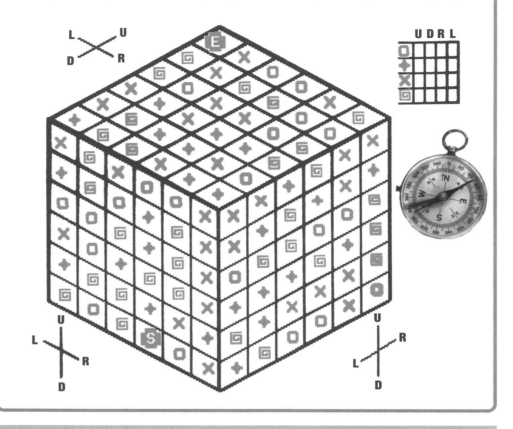

## 499 NINE-CARD TRICK

Cards numbered from 2 to 10, which is not in the right-hand column, are set out as shown in the diagram with one card face up.

The numbers on any three cards in a line, vertically, horizontally or diagonally, add up to the same total. No card shares an edge with one of its own colour or a corner with one of its own suit and also there are more Diamonds than Hearts. Can you correctly identify the other eight cards?

## 501 SUDOKU

| | | 5 | 6 | | 7 | 4 | | |
|---|---|---|---|---|---|---|---|---|
| | 9 | | 1 | | 2 | | 5 | |
| 1 | | | 5 | 8 | 4 | | | 2 |
| 6 | 5 | 8 | | | | 1 | 9 | 7 |
| | | 3 | | | | 5 | | |
| 9 | 4 | 1 | | | | 6 | 2 | 3 |
| 5 | | | 3 | 7 | 1 | | | 4 |
| | 7 | | 8 | | 9 | | 1 | |
| | | 6 | 2 | | 5 | 8 | | |

## 502 SUDOKU

| | 3 | | | 9 | | | 6 | |
|---|---|---|---|---|---|---|---|---|
| 6 | | 1 | 8 | | 5 | 4 | | 7 |
| | 8 | | 3 | | 1 | | 2 | |
| | 6 | 7 | 5 | | 8 | 2 | 1 | |
| 5 | | | | | | | | 4 |
| | 4 | 3 | 2 | | 9 | 6 | 7 | |
| | 2 | | 9 | | 3 | | 5 | |
| 3 | | 9 | 1 | | 6 | 8 | | 2 |
| | 7 | | | 5 | | | 9 | |

## 503 SUDOKU

| | 8 | | 1 | | 7 | | 4 | |
|---|---|---|---|---|---|---|---|---|
| 6 | | 7 | | | | 3 | | 5 |
| | 2 | | 8 | 5 | 6 | | 1 | |
| 2 | | 8 | | 6 | | 5 | | 3 |
| | | 6 | 5 | | 3 | 8 | | |
| 1 | | 3 | | 9 | | 4 | | 6 |
| | 6 | | 7 | 1 | 2 | | 3 | |
| 7 | | 2 | | | | 1 | | 4 |
| | 3 | | 6 | | 9 | | 5 | |

## 504 SUDOKU

| | | | 1 | | 7 | | | |
|---|---|---|---|---|---|---|---|---|
| 4 | | 5 | | | | 1 | | 3 |
| 9 | | 1 | 3 | 2 | 5 | 4 | | 8 |
| 2 | 4 | | | | | | 8 | 6 |
| 8 | | | 6 | | 4 | | | 7 |
| 7 | 1 | | | | | | 9 | 4 |
| 5 | | 4 | 7 | 8 | 3 | 9 | | 1 |
| 6 | | 7 | | | | 8 | | 2 |
| | | | 4 | | 2 | | | |

## 505 SUDOKU

| | 4 | | 9 | | 8 | | 5 | |
|---|---|---|---|---|---|---|---|---|
| 8 | 5 | | | | | | 4 | 3 |
| | | 2 | 5 | | 4 | 7 | | |
| | 9 | 6 | 7 | | 3 | 5 | 2 | |
| | | | | 5 | | | | |
| | 7 | 4 | 6 | | 9 | 8 | 3 | |
| | | 9 | 3 | | 5 | 4 | | |
| 2 | 3 | | | | | | 7 | 9 |
| | 8 | | 1 | | 2 | | 6 | |

## 506 SUDOKU

| 8 | | 7 | 9 | | 3 | 5 | | 6 |
|---|---|---|---|---|---|---|---|---|
| | | | 6 | | 7 | | | |
| | 2 | 5 | | | | 3 | 7 | |
| 2 | | 3 | | 1 | | 6 | | 7 |
| | | | | | | | | |
| 1 | | 9 | | 7 | | 4 | | 2 |
| | 8 | 4 | | | | 1 | 9 | |
| | | | 3 | | 4 | | | |
| 7 | | 6 | 5 | | 1 | 2 | | 3 |

## 507 SUDOKU

| | 1 | | 5 | | 3 | | 8 | |
|---|---|---|---|---|---|---|---|---|
| 2 | | 9 | 7 | | 1 | 6 | | 3 |
| | 8 | | 6 | | 9 | | 7 | |
| 8 | 6 | 3 | | | | 7 | 9 | 5 |
| | | | | | | | | |
| 1 | 4 | 5 | | | | 3 | 6 | 2 |
| | 3 | | 2 | | 4 | | 5 | |
| 5 | | 6 | 1 | | 7 | 8 | | 4 |
| | 7 | | 8 | | 5 | | 2 | |

## 508 SUDOKU

| | | 9 | | | | | | |
|---|---|---|---|---|---|---|---|---|
| 4 | | | 1 | | | | | 7 |
| 2 | 5 | | 4 | 7 | | | 9 | 8 |
| | 9 | 2 | | | 4 | 6 | 8 | |
| 8 | 1 | | | 2 | | | 7 | 4 |
| | 4 | 7 | 8 | | | 9 | 1 | |
| 3 | 8 | | | 6 | 1 | | 2 | 9 |
| 9 | | | | 7 | | | | 5 |
| | | | | | 4 | | | |

## 509 SUDOKU

|   |   |   | 6 |   | 5 |   |   |   |
|---|---|---|---|---|---|---|---|---|
|   | 3 |   |   | 7 |   |   | 8 |   |
| 6 |   | 9 | 8 |   | 4 | 5 |   | 2 |
| 3 |   |   | 1 | 4 | 7 |   |   | 9 |
|   |   | 7 |   |   |   | 2 |   |   |
| 8 |   |   | 9 | 2 | 3 |   |   | 1 |
| 1 |   | 3 | 4 |   | 2 | 7 |   | 8 |
|   | 9 |   |   | 5 |   |   | 6 |   |
|   |   |   | 7 |   | 9 |   |   |   |

## 510 SUDOKU

| 1 |   | 4 |   |   |   | 8 |   |   |
|---|---|---|---|---|---|---|---|---|
| 3 |   | 2 | 9 |   |   | 6 | 5 |   |
|   |   | 6 | 3 |   |   |   |   |   |
|   |   |   | 7 | 3 |   |   |   |   |
| 6 |   | 8 | 4 |   | 2 |   |   |   |
|   | 3 |   |   | 1 | 6 | 5 | 4 |   |
| 4 | 7 |   |   | 9 |   | 6 | 2 | 8 |
|   |   | 3 | 6 |   |   |   |   |   |
|   |   | 9 |   | 2 |   |   | 3 | 4 |

## 511 SUDOKU

|   |   | 6 |   | 4 |   |   |   |   |
|---|---|---|---|---|---|---|---|---|
|   |   | 1 | 9 |   | 3 |   | 8 |   |
|   |   | 3 |   | 8 | 6 | 1 |   | 9 |
| 6 | 2 |   |   | 9 | 5 |   | 1 |   |
| 3 |   |   |   |   |   |   |   | 5 |
| 9 | 1 |   |   | 3 | 7 |   | 8 |   |
|   |   | 2 |   | 6 | 9 | 4 |   | 1 |
|   |   | 4 | 7 |   |   | 9 |   | 6 |
|   |   | 9 |   |   | 1 |   |   |   |

## 512 SUDOKU

|   |   |   |   |   |   |   |   |   |
|---|---|---|---|---|---|---|---|---|
| 5 |   | 7 |   |   |   | 3 |   | 9 |
| 1 | 3 | 4 |   |   |   | 6 | 7 | 5 |
|   |   | 5 | 7 |   | 1 | 4 |   |   |
| 9 |   |   |   |   |   |   |   | 8 |
|   | 7 | 3 |   | 2 |   | 5 | 9 |   |
|   |   | 8 | 9 |   | 2 | 1 |   |   |
|   | 4 |   | 1 |   | 5 |   | 3 |   |
|   |   | 1 | 3 | 7 | 8 | 9 |   |   |

## 513 SUDOKU

|   |   | 4 | 5 |   |   |   | 2 |   |
|---|---|---|---|---|---|---|---|---|
|   |   |   | 4 |   | 7 |   |   | 9 |
| 8 |   |   | 1 | 7 |   | 3 |   |   |
| 2 |   |   | 3 |   |   | 8 | 4 |   |
|   | 4 | 7 |   |   | 6 |   |   |   |
|   |   | 8 |   | 2 |   | 1 | 5 |   |
|   | 5 |   | 8 |   | 1 | 2 | 7 | 3 |
| 6 |   | 2 | 7 |   | 3 | 4 |   |   |
|   | 1 |   |   |   | 9 |   |   |   |

## 514 SUDOKU

|   |   |   | 2 |   | 7 |   |   |   |
|---|---|---|---|---|---|---|---|---|
|   | 1 | 7 | 5 |   | 6 | 4 | 8 |   |
| 9 |   |   |   | 1 |   |   |   | 5 |
|   | 2 |   | 3 |   | 4 |   | 5 |   |
|   |   | 4 |   | 7 |   | 3 |   |   |
|   | 8 |   | 9 |   | 5 |   | 6 |   |
| 3 |   |   |   | 5 |   |   |   | 8 |
|   | 9 | 5 | 4 |   | 1 | 6 | 2 |   |
|   |   | 7 |   | 2 |   |   |   |   |

## 515 SUDOKU

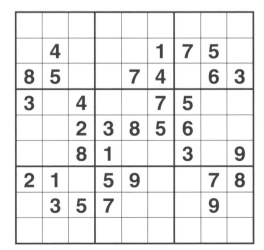

|   | 4 |   |   |   | 1 | 7 | 5 |   |
|---|---|---|---|---|---|---|---|---|
| 8 | 5 |   |   | 7 | 4 |   | 6 | 3 |
| 3 |   | 4 |   |   | 7 | 5 |   |   |
|   |   | 2 | 3 | 8 | 5 | 6 |   |   |
|   |   | 8 | 1 |   |   | 3 |   | 9 |
| 2 | 1 |   | 5 | 9 |   |   | 7 | 8 |
|   | 3 | 5 | 7 |   |   |   | 9 |   |
|   |   |   |   |   |   |   |   |   |
|   |   |   |   |   |   |   |   |   |

## 516 SUDOKU

|   | 2 |   | 1 | 6 | 4 |   | 9 |   |
|---|---|---|---|---|---|---|---|---|
|   | 6 |   | 2 | 9 | 5 |   | 7 |   |
| 9 | 1 |   |   | 8 |   |   | 4 | 7 |
| 6 |   | 4 |   |   |   | 3 |   | 8 |
|   |   |   | 4 | 2 | 7 |   |   |   |
|   |   | 1 |   |   |   | 7 |   |   |
|   | 3 |   | 9 |   | 1 |   | 8 |   |
|   | 9 | 6 |   | 7 |   | 2 | 5 |   |
|   |   |   |   |   |   |   |   |   |

## 517 SUDOKU

|   |   | 5 |   |   |   | 6 |   |   |
|---|---|---|---|---|---|---|---|---|
| 4 |   |   |   | 3 | 1 | 7 |   |   |
| 9 | 6 | 1 |   | 7 |   |   | 4 |   |
| 1 | 9 | 7 |   |   | 6 |   | 8 |   |
|   |   |   | 3 |   | 5 |   |   |   |
|   | 4 |   | 8 |   |   | 1 | 6 | 2 |
|   | 7 |   |   | 6 |   | 5 | 3 | 8 |
|   |   | 8 | 9 | 2 |   |   |   | 7 |
|   |   | 4 |   |   |   | 2 |   |   |

## 518 SUDOKU

|   | 3 | 4 | 1 |   |   |   |   |   |
|---|---|---|---|---|---|---|---|---|
|   |   |   | 2 | 3 |   |   | 7 |   |
| 1 | 5 |   |   |   | 4 | 8 |   |   |
|   |   | 6 | 4 |   |   | 7 |   |   |
|   | 8 |   |   |   |   |   | 1 |   |
| 2 |   | 1 | 6 |   | 8 |   | 4 | 3 |
|   | 1 |   | 3 |   | 7 |   |   | 4 |
|   | 7 |   |   | 4 |   | 1 |   | 5 |
| 9 |   |   | 8 |   |   | 3 |   |   |

## 519 SUDOKU

|   | 2 |   |   | 4 | 5 |   | 7 |   |
|---|---|---|---|---|---|---|---|---|
| 1 |   | 5 |   | 3 |   |   |   |   |
|   |   |   | 6 |   |   | 4 |   |   |
|   | 1 | 4 |   |   |   |   | 6 | 8 |
| 8 | 6 | 2 |   |   |   | 7 | 4 | 5 |
| 5 | 7 |   |   |   |   | 3 | 1 |   |
|   |   | 7 |   |   | 4 |   |   |   |
|   |   |   |   | 9 |   | 6 |   | 7 |
|   | 9 |   | 1 | 6 |   |   | 3 |   |

## 520 SUDOKU

|   |   |   |   |   |   |   |   |   |
|---|---|---|---|---|---|---|---|---|
|   |   |   | 4 | 7 |   | 3 |   |   |
| 9 | 4 |   | 1 |   |   |   | 7 | 2 |
|   | 7 | 6 |   |   | 1 |   | 4 | 5 |
|   | 5 | 9 | 3 |   | 4 | 8 | 6 |   |
| 4 | 2 |   | 7 |   |   | 9 | 1 |   |
| 7 | 9 |   |   |   | 6 |   | 2 | 1 |
|   | 4 |   |   | 9 | 3 |   |   |   |
|   |   |   |   |   |   |   |   |   |

## 521 SUDOKU

|   |   | 3 |   |   | 9 | 2 | 6 |   |
|---|---|---|---|---|---|---|---|---|
| 6 |   | 8 |   | 2 |   |   |   |   |
|   |   |   | 8 |   | 7 |   | 3 | 4 |
| 4 | 3 |   | 1 | 9 |   |   |   | 6 |
|   |   | 6 |   |   |   |   |   | 7 |
| 1 | 5 |   | 4 | 7 |   |   |   | 9 |
|   |   |   | 9 |   | 3 |   | 1 | 2 |
| 5 |   | 1 |   | 8 |   |   |   |   |
|   |   | 9 |   |   | 1 | 8 | 7 |   |

## 522 SUDOKU

|   |   | 1 | 4 |   |   | 6 |   |   |
|---|---|---|---|---|---|---|---|---|
|   | 4 |   | 5 | 7 |   |   |   |   |
|   | 7 |   |   |   | 2 |   |   | 5 |
|   | 2 |   |   | 1 | 9 |   |   | 4 |
| 5 | 3 |   | 8 |   | 7 |   | 6 | 1 |
| 1 |   |   | 3 | 4 |   |   | 8 |   |
| 6 |   |   | 7 |   |   |   | 5 |   |
|   |   |   |   | 9 | 3 |   | 2 |   |
|   | 3 |   |   |   | 6 | 4 |   |   |

## 523 SUDOKU

|   |   | 3 |   | 1 |   |   | 7 |   |
|---|---|---|---|---|---|---|---|---|
|   |   |   |   |   | 4 |   | 6 | 8 |
|   | 2 |   | 8 |   | 3 |   |   |   |
| 9 | 6 |   | 2 | 3 |   | 5 | 1 |   |
| 8 | 3 |   |   |   | 1 |   |   | 6 |
|   |   |   |   | 6 | 8 |   |   |   |
| 6 |   | 4 |   |   |   |   |   | 1 |
| 3 |   |   |   | 6 | 2 | 4 |   |   |
|   | 1 | 2 |   | 8 | 9 |   |   |   |

## 524 SUDOKU

|   |   |   |   |   |   |   |   |   |
|---|---|---|---|---|---|---|---|---|
|   |   | 9 | 1 | 5 |   | 8 |   | 6 |
| 8 |   |   | 6 |   | 3 | 5 | 4 |   |
|   | 5 | 3 |   | 6 |   | 1 |   | 9 |
|   | 2 |   | 8 |   |   |   | 7 |   |
| 7 | 6 |   | 3 |   |   | 4 |   | 8 |
|   | 3 |   | 4 |   | 1 | 2 | 6 |   |
|   |   | 5 | 2 | 7 | 3 |   |   | 1 |
|   |   |   |   |   |   |   |   |   |

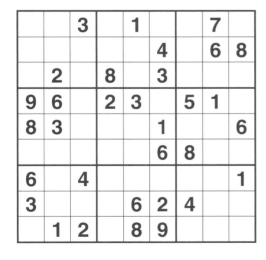

153

## 525 SUDOKU

| | | 7 | | | | 1 | 2 | |
|---|---|---|---|---|---|---|---|---|
| 5 | | | | 9 | 1 | | | 7 |
| | 6 | 2 | 4 | | 3 | | | 5 |
| | | | 3 | 6 | | 2 | 7 | |
| | | | | | 2 | | 8 | |
| | 2 | | 5 | | 9 | 3 | | |
| | | 8 | | | | 9 | | 3 |
| 2 | 7 | | 6 | | | 4 | | |
| 6 | 1 | | | | | | 5 | |

## 526 SUDOKU

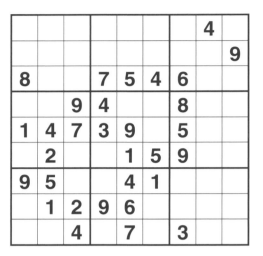

| | | | | | | | 4 | |
|---|---|---|---|---|---|---|---|---|
| | | | | | | | | 9 |
| 8 | | | 7 | 5 | 4 | 6 | | |
| | | 9 | 4 | | | 8 | | |
| 1 | 4 | 7 | 3 | 9 | | 5 | | |
| | 2 | | | 1 | 5 | 9 | | |
| 9 | 5 | | | 4 | 1 | | | |
| | 1 | 2 | 9 | 6 | | | | |
| | 4 | | | 7 | | 3 | | |

## 527 SUDOKU

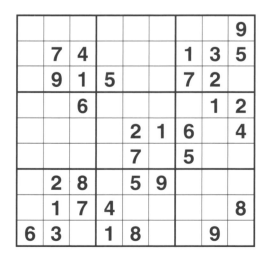

| | | | | | | | | 9 |
|---|---|---|---|---|---|---|---|---|
| | 7 | 4 | | | | 1 | 3 | 5 |
| | 9 | 1 | 5 | | | 7 | 2 | |
| | | 6 | | | | | 1 | 2 |
| | | | 2 | 1 | 6 | | | 4 |
| | | | | 7 | | 5 | | |
| | 2 | 8 | | 5 | 9 | | | |
| | 1 | 7 | 4 | | | | | 8 |
| 6 | 3 | | 1 | 8 | | | 9 | |

## 528 SUDOKU

| | | | | | | | | 7 |
|---|---|---|---|---|---|---|---|---|
| | | 5 | 7 | | 3 | 2 | | 6 |
| | 1 | 2 | 4 | | 6 | | | 5 |
| | 7 | 9 | | | | | 2 | |
| | | | | | 1 | 7 | 6 | 3 |
| | 4 | 3 | | 6 | | | | |
| | 5 | | | 3 | | | | 2 |
| | | | 1 | 5 | | | | 4 |
| 3 | 6 | 4 | | 7 | | 5 | 1 | |

## 529 SUDOKU

|   |   | 4 |   |   |   |   |   | 5 |
|---|---|---|---|---|---|---|---|---|
|   | 7 |   |   | 9 |   | 2 |   |   |
|   |   | 8 |   | 1 | 7 |   |   | 9 |
|   |   | 3 |   |   | 2 | 5 | 4 |   |
| 2 |   | 6 | 5 |   | 3 | 8 |   | 7 |
|   | 9 | 5 | 6 |   |   | 3 |   |   |
| 5 |   |   | 8 | 3 |   | 2 |   |   |
|   | 4 |   | 9 |   |   |   | 8 |   |
| 8 |   |   |   |   | 1 |   |   |   |

## 530 SUDOKU

|   |   | 8 |   | 5 |   | 1 |   |   |
|---|---|---|---|---|---|---|---|---|
|   |   | 3 | 4 | 7 |   |   |   |   |
| 5 |   |   | 8 |   | 1 |   |   | 7 |
|   | 5 | 3 | 9 |   | 8 | 7 | 6 |   |
| 4 | 8 |   |   |   |   |   | 1 | 2 |
|   | 1 | 6 | 4 |   | 2 | 5 | 3 |   |
| 8 |   |   | 7 |   | 3 |   |   | 5 |
|   |   |   | 5 | 2 | 6 |   |   |   |
|   |   | 5 |   | 8 |   | 3 |   |   |

## 531 SUDOKU

| 7 |   |   |   |   |   |   |   | 9 |
|---|---|---|---|---|---|---|---|---|
|   | 1 | 4 |   | 6 |   | 3 | 8 |   |
|   |   |   | 3 |   | 5 |   |   |   |
|   | 8 |   |   |   |   |   | 5 |   |
| 9 | 3 |   | 8 |   | 2 |   | 1 | 6 |
|   |   |   |   | 3 |   |   |   |   |
|   |   | 9 | 5 |   | 7 | 1 |   |   |
|   | 7 | 5 |   |   |   | 8 | 3 |   |
|   |   | 8 |   | 1 |   | 7 |   |   |

## 532 SUDOKU

|   | 1 |   |   | 3 | 6 |   |   |   |
|---|---|---|---|---|---|---|---|---|
| 9 |   |   |   |   |   |   |   |   |
|   |   |   | 4 |   | 1 | 2 |   | 3 |
|   |   | 3 | 9 |   |   |   | 1 | 6 |
| 1 |   |   |   |   |   |   |   | 2 |
| 6 |   | 2 |   |   | 3 |   | 9 | 8 |
|   |   | 8 |   |   |   |   | 2 | 9 |
|   |   |   | 7 |   | 9 | 1 |   |   |
|   |   | 1 | 6 | 2 | 4 | 7 |   |   |

# ANSWERS

## 1

A – Maria – heraldic dragon – 1825;
B – William V – shield – 1745;
C – Karl II – crossed swords – 1865;
D – Josef III – wreath of laurels – 1785.

## 2

| | | | | | | |
|---|---|---|---|---|---|---|
| 5 | 0 | 1 | 2 | 0 | 3 | 2 |
| 5 | 2 | 4 | 6 | 4 | 6 | 2 |
| | | | | | | |
| 5 | 2 | 2 | 3 | 0 | 2 | 6 |
| 6 | 3 | 5 | 4 | 6 | 4 | 6 |
| | | | | | | |
| 3 | 1 | 0 | 0 | 1 | 3 | 0 |
| 5 | 3 | 1 | 0 | 2 | 3 | 3 |
| | | | | | | |
| 1 | 4 | 4 | 1 | 4 | 1 | 0 |
| 5 | 5 | 6 | 6 | 4 | 1 | 5 |

## 3

| From | Al | Bob | Chris | Don | Ed |
|---|---|---|---|---|---|
| Al Harkness | | 2 | 4 | 1 | 3 |
| Bob Jarrett | 3 | | 2 | 4 | 1 |
| Chris Farley | 1 | 3 | | 2 | 4 |
| Don Insley | 4 | 1 | 3 | | 2 |
| Ed Gainor | 2 | 4 | 1 | 3 | |

## 4

## 5

Pictures 3 and 5

## 6

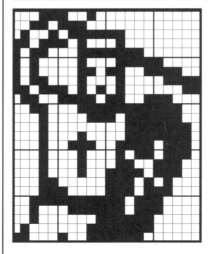

## 7

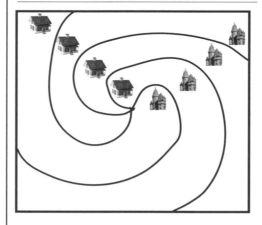

## 8

## 9

**1** BE DE BG BE  **2** DF AF BF(Down)  **3** BG CG DF BF CF
**4** AG DF(Down) AG  **5** BG BF AF BF  **6** CG DG AE CE
DG  **7** AE DE BE AF DE  **8** CE CG  **9** BE DF
**10** CG  DG  CF

## 10

Waistcoat g

## 11

13 red, 3 yellow, 3 brown, 3 blue, 4 pink

## 12

a – The spots become the same colour as the central colour of the wing of the previous butterfly.

## 13

| | | | | | | |
|---|---|---|---|---|---|---|
| 3 | 0 | 1 | 0 | 1 | 4 | 6 |
| 4 | 1 | 5 | 6 | 3 | 4 | 6 |
| | | | | | | |
| 5 | 3 | 2 | 2 | 3 | 1 | 2 |
| 5 | 5 | 2 | 3 | 6 | 2 | 5 |
| | | | | | | |
| 5 | 0 | 1 | 2 | 2 | 0 | 3 |
| 6 | 5 | 6 | 6 | 4 | 2 | 3 |
| | | | | | | |
| 1 | 1 | 0 | 4 | 0 | 4 | 0 |
| 4 | 1 | 3 | 6 | 0 | 5 | 4 |

## 14

## 15

## 16

| C |   |   | A | B |
|---|---|---|---|---|
|   | B | C |   | A |
| A |   | B |   | C |
|   | C | A | B |   |
| B | A |   | C |   |

## 17

RED = $0.72
BLUE = $0.68
YELLOW = $2.00
GREEN = $0.88

## 18

The cactus in the top-right corner was left.

The purchases were:

| Madge | Kim | Laura | Jackie | Cactus |
|---|---|---|---|---|
| Laura | Laura given | Kim | Madge | Jackie |
| Jackie | Laura | Jackie given | Kim | Madge |
| Kim | Jackie | Madge | Kim given | Laura |
| Madge given | Madge | Jackie | Laura | Kim |

## 19

| PERSON | JOB | FEATURE |
|---|---|---|
| ALF | BLACKSMITH | MONOCLE |
| FRED | LAWYER | PANAMA |
| GEORGE | MAIL MAN | BEARD |
| TOM | DOCTOR | CRAVAT |

## 20

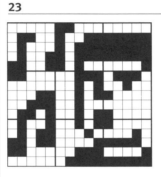

## 21

89. If you work out the ways for forming 5 cents, 10 cents, 15 cents, 20 cents, 25 cents ... you get this famous sequence:

1, 2, 3, 5, 8 ... the Fibonacci Series, where each number is the sum of the previous two. Continuing the sequence is a lot quicker than counting all the ways for 50 cents.

## 22

| 6 | 3 | 2 | 5 | 0 | 4 | 3 |
|---|---|---|---|---|---|---|
| 6 | 5 | 2 | 5 | 4 | 5 | 3 |

| 5 | 1 | 4 | 1 | 3 | 2 | 2 |
|---|---|---|---|---|---|---|
| 6 | 6 | 4 | 5 | 4 | 6 | 3 |

| 0 | 0 | 0 | 3 | 0 | 2 | 2 |
|---|---|---|---|---|---|---|
| 5 | 3 | 6 | 6 | 2 | 5 | 4 |

| 1 | 1 | 0 | 4 | 0 | 1 | 1 |
|---|---|---|---|---|---|---|
| 1 | 3 | 1 | 6 | 0 | 4 | 2 |

## 23

## 24

## 25

| 1 | 1 | 1 | 1 | 4 | 3 | 2 |
|---|---|---|---|---|---|---|
| 3 | 6 | 2 | 5 | 4 | 4 | 4 |

| 0 | 3 | 3 | 0 | 5 | 5 | 1 |
|---|---|---|---|---|---|---|
| 5 | 3 | 5 | 4 | 5 | 6 | 1 |

| 0 | 2 | 0 | 2 | 0 | 1 | 3 |
|---|---|---|---|---|---|---|
| 1 | 5 | 0 | 3 | 3 | 4 | 6 |

| 4 | 0 | 2 | 2 | 6 | 0 | 4 |
|---|---|---|---|---|---|---|
| 6 | 2 | 2 | 6 | 6 | 6 | 5 |

## 26

| Mr Grey | Mr Pink | Mr Green |
|---|---|---|
| Opel White | VW Grey | Skoda Red |

| Mr Blue | Mr White |
|---|---|
| Lancia Green | Jaguar Blue |

## 27

| A FELIX | B ISAAC | C KEITH | D CLIVE |
|---|---|---|---|
| E LYDIA | F HENRY | G AGNES | H DAVID |
| I GRACE | J JOYCE | K BERYL | L EMILY |

## 28

```
5 2 1 0 4    3   2   3 2 1 9 4
3   3 8    1 2 6 6 3   9   0
6   0   1   0   2   0   3   1
0   0   8 7 6   0   6   0   3
6 2 2 7 1     9 3 5     2 9 9 9 4
      7       2       7 2
6 5 0 1 8       5 0 2 4 2     1
7     2 0 3 9 3   1   5 8 8
1 1 0 3 7 5       9       4 6 3
  9       4 5 2 7 0 6   9
9 1 2 0 3     4 1 9     8 3 1 1 8
3     1   6 9 0     0       9
9 3 6 6 1     3   0   9 0 4 6 0
0       5 0 7   2 3 3       3
6 0 8 8 5     1 3 0   5 0 5 5 1
```

## 29

The begonia in the middle of the back row was left. The plants were purchased or given as follows:

| NORMA | LEN | BEGONIA LEFT | KEVIN | MARY |
|---|---|---|---|---|
| MARY | LEN GIVEN | NORMA | LEN | KEVIN |
| LEN | KEVIN | MARY GIVEN | KEVIN | NORMA |
| NORMA GIVEN | NORMA | KEVIN | MARY | LEN |
| KEVIN | MARY | LEN | NORMA | MARY GIVEN |

## 30

| 10 | 21 | 23 | 7 | 4 |
|---|---|---|---|---|
| 25 | 1 | 18 | 13 | 16 |
| 5 | 14 | 20 | 9 | 2 |
| 8 | 11 | 6 | 22 | 19 |
| 15 | 24 | 3 | 17 | 12 |

## 31

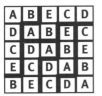

| A | B | E | C | D |
|---|---|---|---|---|
| D | A | B | E | C |
| C | D | A | B | E |
| E | C | D | A | B |
| B | E | C | D | A |

## 32

Oxford

## 33

| DAY | FROM SHE | & HE | TO SHE | & HE |
|---|---|---|---|---|
| THURSDAY | PAM | TOM | FAY | LES |
| FRIDAY | MAY | JIM | SUE | BOB |
| SATURDAY | JOY | SAM | KAY | DON |
| SUNDAY | LIZ | ALF | DOT | TIM |

## 34

| 7 | 2 | 6 | 4 | 9 | 3 | 8 | 1 | 5 |
|---|---|---|---|---|---|---|---|---|
| 3 | 1 | 5 | 7 | 2 | 8 | 9 | 4 | 6 |
| 4 | 8 | 9 | 6 | 5 | 1 | 2 | 3 | 7 |
| 8 | 5 | 2 | 1 | 4 | 7 | 6 | 9 | 3 |
| 6 | 7 | 3 | 9 | 8 | 5 | 1 | 2 | 4 |
| 9 | 4 | 1 | 3 | 6 | 2 | 7 | 5 | 8 |
| 1 | 9 | 4 | 8 | 3 | 6 | 5 | 7 | 2 |
| 5 | 6 | 7 | 2 | 1 | 4 | 3 | 8 | 9 |
| 2 | 3 | 8 | 5 | 7 | 9 | 4 | 6 | 1 |

## 35

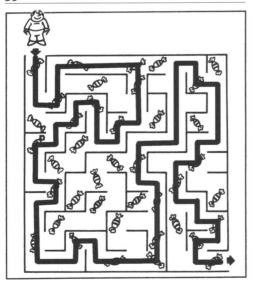

## 36

| Mr Black | Mr White | Mr Green | Mr Grey | Mr Red |
|---|---|---|---|---|
| Lada | Renault | Ford | Nissan | Toyota |
| Grey | Blue | Red | White | Black |

## 37

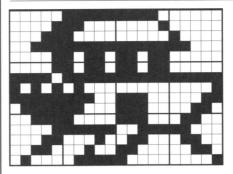

## 38

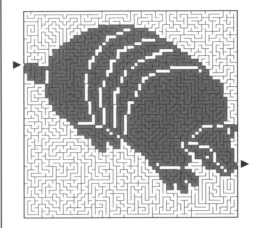

## 39

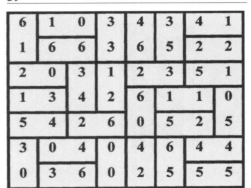

## 40

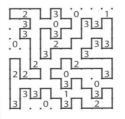

## 41

| Mr Green | Mr Brown | Mr White | Mr Grey | Mr Black |
|---|---|---|---|---|
| BMW | Audi | Volvo | Fiat | Ford |
| Grey | Green | Black | Red | Brown |

## 42

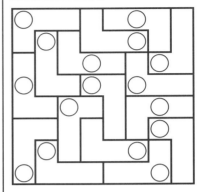

## 43

| 4 | 6 | 4 | 3 |
|---|---|---|---|
| 3 | 3 | 2 | 2 |
| 5 | 5 | 5 | 4 |
| 6 | 4 | 2 | 6 |
| 5 | 6 | 3 | 2 |

## 44

| 1 | 4 | 2 | ■ | 3 | 2 | 1 | 8 | ■ | 7 | 1 |
|---|---|---|---|---|---|---|---|---|---|---|
| 4 | 3 | 1 | ■ | 8 | 5 | 7 | 9 | ■ | 8 | 2 |
|   | 5 | 7 | 8 | 9 | ■ | 2 | 4 | 1 | 6 | 3 |
| 1 | 2 | ■ | 1 | 6 | 2 | 3 | ■ | 6 | 9 | 8 |
| 3 | 1 | 2 | 5 | ■ | 1 | 5 | 2 | 3 | ■ |   |
|   | ■ | 1 | 2 | 3 | ■ | 4 | 2 | 5 | 1 | ■ |
| 1 | 2 | 4 | ■ | 1 | 3 | 2 | 5 | ■ | 9 | 6 |
| 3 | 1 | 5 | 6 | 2 | ■ | 4 | 1 | 6 | 2 | 3 |
| 2 | 4 | ■ | 7 | 4 | 6 | 1 | ■ | 7 | 1 | 2 |
| 5 | 6 | 8 | 9 | ■ | 8 | 5 | 6 | 9 | ■ |   |
|   | ■ | 7 | 8 | 9 | 5 | ■ | 9 | 8 | 4 | 7 |
| 5 | 8 | 9 | ■ | 8 | 9 | 3 | 7 | ■ | 8 | 9 |
| 3 | 2 | 4 | 1 | 6 | ■ | 6 | 8 | 9 | 7 | ■ |
| 2 | 9 | ■ | 4 | 7 | 1 | 2 | ■ | 6 | 9 | 7 |
| 1 | 3 | ■ | 2 | 4 | 3 | 1 | ■ | 8 | 6 | 9 |

## 45

Boot C

## 46

Going clockwise starting with the host, the players are: Syd, Mail man (1). Malcolm, Baker (4). Lionel, Jockey (3). Keith, Doctor (5). Jerry, Bookmaker (2). Gus, Financier (7). Wilf, Salesman (6). The number indicates the player's position in the line.

## 47

No. 4

**48**

**49**

Figure 1 has an extra fold of material on his arm. Figure 2 has an extra detail on his right sandal. Figure 3 has more hair. Figure 4 has a wristband.

**50**

Andrew and Dolly Gould, Kansas City. Brian and Edna Hedges, New York. Colin and Floe Jacobs, New Orleans.

**51**

| 0 | 0 | 1 | 5 | 4 | 5 | 2 | 6 |
|---|---|---|---|---|---|---|---|
| 1 | 0 | 5 | 3 | 6 | 1 | 4 | 2 |
| 3 | 5 | 0 | 4 | 5 | 3 | 4 | 1 |
| 2 | 5 | 6 | 5 | 6 | 1 | 3 | 6 |
| 2 | 3 | 2 | 3 | 2 | 4 | 3 | 6 |
| 0 | 0 | 5 | 0 | 2 | 1 | 0 | 6 |
| 4 | 3 | 6 | 1 | 1 | 4 | 2 | 4 |

**52**

Red, Blue, Lavender, Blue

**53**

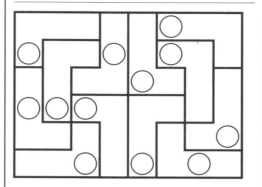

**54**

**55**

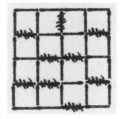

**56**

| CONTACT | EMPLOYEE | METHOD | PLACE |
|---------|----------|--------|-------|
| BOOKMAKER | TANIA | E-MAIL | BURNLEY |
| CAR SALES | WILF | INTERNET | DENMARK |
| MOTHER | SEAN | FAX | ACCRINGTON |
| PARTNER | RHODA | PHONE | CANADA |

**57**

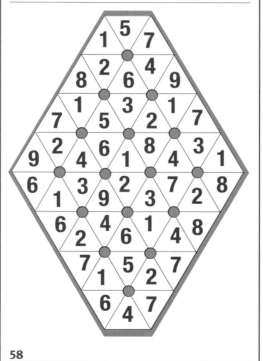

**58**

Print 3

**59**

D. Each square has the top right quarter cut off. This leaves three smaller squares. In the next picture each of those has its top right quarter removed and so on.

**60**

```
2 8 1 4 6    3    3    4 1 7 0 3
4    8    0    4 3 3 1 2    3 6    2
9    2    0    0 2    0 6    2    4
7    0    4 0 7    6    3    2    8
1 4 0 9 9    9 6 4    6 3 4 9    1
         2       6          5 4
8 1 9 5 5    1    8 8 0 8    4 0
2       3 1 9 2 7    5 1    9 0
5 5 2 8 8 1       7       3 7 2
      9       1 4 2 8 0 7    6 4
5 3 9 0 4    3 4 7    8 3 0 1 3
0       0    3    1 0    4    2
7 0 9 5 0    2    3    3 6 6 3 8
2       2 9 9    6 0 9    1
1 2 7 5 6    6 5 6    9 4 2 7 0
```

**61**

One of the green books is missing.

**62**

| 5 | 6 | 3 | 7 | 9 | 2 | 4 | 1 | 8 |
|---|---|---|---|---|---|---|---|---|
| 4 | 9 | 1 | 5 | 6 | 8 | 3 | 2 | 7 |
| 8 | 7 | 2 | 1 | 4 | 3 | 9 | 5 | 6 |
| 9 | 8 | 7 | 6 | 2 | 5 | 1 | 4 | 3 |
| 1 | 5 | 6 | 9 | 3 | 4 | 8 | 7 | 2 |
| 3 | 2 | 4 | 8 | 1 | 7 | 6 | 9 | 5 |
| 7 | 3 | 9 | 2 | 8 | 1 | 5 | 6 | 4 |
| 6 | 4 | 5 | 3 | 7 | 9 | 2 | 8 | 1 |
| 2 | 1 | 8 | 4 | 5 | 6 | 7 | 3 | 9 |

**63**

**64**

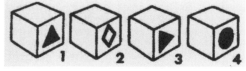

## 65

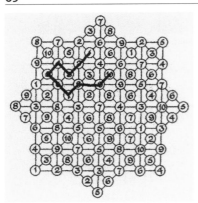

## 66

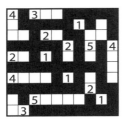

| 8 | 0 | 3 | 2 | 7 | 9 | 8 | 0 | 9 | 7 | 9 |
|---|---|---|---|---|---|---|---|---|---|---|
| 7 | 4 | 7 | 1 | 1 | 2 | 2 | 4 | 9 | 3 | 6 |
| 8 | 3 | 5 | 8 | 2 | 3 | 0 | 9 | 0 | 5 | 0 |
| 4 | 4 | 4 | 9 | 6 | 2 | 4 | 3 | 7 | 8 | 3 |
| 8 | 0 | 0 | 3 | 8 | 1 | 6 | 0 | 8 | 6 | 3 |
| 4 | 1 | 8 | 9 | 2 | 5 | 8 | 5 | 8 | 9 | 2 |
| 1 | 2 | 3 | 5 | 9 | 5 | 7 | 2 | 3 | 1 | 4 |
| 5 | 7 | 5 | 7 | 6 | 7 | 1 | 6 | 1 | 6 | 6 |
| 1 | 7 | 9 | 6 | 5 | 4 | 5 | 2 | 0 | 3 | 1 |
| 0 | 5 | 0 | 7 | 6 | 6 | 9 | 4 | 2 | 1 | 4 |

## 67

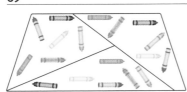

## 68

Chuck's date isn't Beth (clue 3) or Cathy (clue 4), so is Alice. Thus Art is heavier than Chuck (1), who (3) is heavier than Beth's date; so Beth's date isn't Art - he's Bill. By elimination, Art's date is Cathy. Since Art is heavier than Chuck, who is heavier than Bill (above), Art is man F, Chuck is E and Bill is D. Bill's date is Beth and Chuck's is Alice (above); so Beth is taller than Alice (2), who is taller than Cathy – thus Beth is woman C, Alice is A and Cathy is B.

## 69

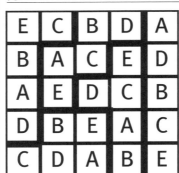

## 70

| 1 | 3 |   |   | 2 | 1 | 4 |   | 9 | 3 |   |
|---|---|---|---|---|---|---|---|---|---|---|
| 2 | 1 | 3 |   | 7 | 4 | 9 | 6 |   | 8 | 2 |
| 4 | 2 | 5 | 3 | 6 | 1 |   | 9 | 8 | 7 | 1 |
|   |   | 2 | 1 | 5 |   | 9 | 8 | 6 |   |   |
| 4 | 2 | 1 |   | 8 | 9 | 7 |   | 9 | 8 | 7 |
| 1 | 4 |   | 7 | 9 | 6 | 8 | 4 |   | 9 | 2 |
| 3 | 1 | 2 | 6 | 4 |   | 6 | 2 | 4 | 3 | 1 |
|   | 1 | 9 |   |   |   | 3 | 1 |   |   |   |
| 6 | 1 | 3 | 4 | 2 |   | 5 | 1 | 2 | 3 | 4 |
| 9 | 7 |   | 8 | 5 | 7 | 9 | 6 |   | 1 | 9 |
| 8 | 3 | 1 |   | 3 | 1 | 6 |   | 9 | 2 | 8 |
|   |   | 2 | 3 | 1 |   | 8 | 9 | 7 |   |   |
| 8 | 9 | 7 | 5 |   | 1 | 7 | 5 | 4 | 3 | 2 |
| 9 | 7 |   | 2 | 1 | 4 | 3 |   | 8 | 1 | 4 |
| 7 | 1 |   | 1 | 3 | 2 |   |   | 7 | 1 |   |

## 71

11 red, 3 brown, 2 blue, 1 pink, 5 black.

## 72

$6 \times 3 + 9 - 6 = 21$

$4 \times 4 + 2 + 3 = 21$

$3 \times 5 + 10 - 4 = 21$

## 73

The lines should be drawn from 6 to 36, 8 to 29 and 19 to 45.

## 74

D and J

## 75

| E | C | B | D | A |
|---|---|---|---|---|
| B | A | C | E | D |
| A | E | D | C | B |
| D | B | E | A | C |
| C | D | A | B | E |

## 76

|   | A |   | C | B |
|---|---|---|---|---|
| C |   | B | A |   |
| A | B | C |   |   |
|   | C |   | B | A |
| B |   | A |   | C |

## 77

Each square tile has neighbours – tiles that share an edge Look at the number of each colour, red or blue, in the tile and its neighbours. Whichever colour occurs most often that is the new colour of the cell. If the number of neighbouring colours is the same, the square is left empty.

## 78

| 6 | 7 | 9 | 0 | 7 | 3 |   | 3 | 2 | 4 | 3 | 1 | 8 |
| 2 |   |   | 2 | 0 | 5 | 8 | 5 |   | 1 |   |   | 5 |
| 5 | 0 | 6 | 3 | 4 | 2 |   | 2 | 8 | 6 | 1 | 4 | 1 |
| 3 |   | 1 |   | 3 |   | 1 | 7 | 8 |   | 3 |   | 4 |
| 3 |   | 8 |   | 0 |   |   | 1 |   | 3 |   | 5 | 8 | 3 |
| 1 | 2 | 5 | 5 | 0 | 7 |   | 8 | 0 | 2 | 2 | 0 | 2 |   | 6 |
|   |   | 9 |   |   | 2 |   | 1 |   |   |   | 3 | 4 | 8 |
|   | 8 |   | 7 |   | 7 |   | 8 | 3 | 2 | 1 | 9 | 2 |
|   | 3 |   | 2 | 3 | 4 | 0 | 0 | 6 |   | 2 |   | 1 |
| 1 | 1 | 0 | 9 | 1 |   |   | 3 |   |   | 6 | 1 | 9 | 3 |
|   | 2 |   |   | 4 |   | 4 | 3 | 9 | 1 | 1 | 4 |   | 9 |
| 5 | 3 | 0 | 4 | 6 |   | 0 |   | 0 |   | 5 | 3 | 2 | 5 |
| 1 |   |   | 5 |   |   | 1 |   | 9 | 1 | 6 | 2 |   | 2 |
| 9 | 3 | 8 | 3 |   | 9 | 0 | 4 |   | 3 |   | 2 | 8 | 1 |
| 0 |   |   | 5 |   |   | 6 |   | 2 | 2 | 3 | 1 |   | 8 |

## 79

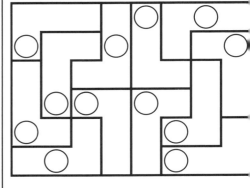

## 80

| 2 | 5 | 9 | 8 | 4 | 6 | 3 | 7 | 1 |
|---|---|---|---|---|---|---|---|---|
| 7 | 4 | 3 | 9 | 5 | 1 | 6 | 8 | 2 |
| 8 | 1 | 6 | 3 | 7 | 2 | 5 | 4 | 9 |
| 5 | 6 | 7 | 2 | 3 | 4 | 9 | 1 | 8 |
| 4 | 8 | 1 | 5 | 9 | 7 | 2 | 6 | 3 |
| 3 | 9 | 2 | 6 | 1 | 8 | 4 | 5 | 7 |
| 1 | 7 | 5 | 4 | 2 | 3 | 8 | 9 | 6 |
| 9 | 2 | 8 | 7 | 6 | 5 | 1 | 3 | 4 |
| 6 | 3 | 4 | 1 | 8 | 9 | 7 | 2 | 5 |

**81**

| | | | | | | | |
|---|---|---|---|---|---|---|---|
| 1 | + | 4 | ÷ | 5 | | =1 |
| + | ■ | x | ■ | x | | |
| 9 | + | 3 | ÷ | 2 | | = 6 |
| – | ■ | – | ■ | – | | |
| 7 | + | 6 | – | 8 | | = 5 |
| = | | = | | = | | |
| 3 | | 6 | | 2 | | |

**82**

John and Zoe Young, Jester and Ballerina.
Mark and Ann Turner, King and Fairy.
Norman and Leila West, Pirate and Nurse.
Steve and Rose Downs, Eskimo and Cowgirl.

**83**

| B | A | | C | D | |
|---|---|---|---|---|---|
| D | A | | B | C | |
| | C | D | A | | B |
| A | D | B | C | | |
| B | | C | D | A | |
| C | | | B | D | A |

**84**

| 7 | 8 | 1 | 2 | 9 | 5 | 6 | 4 | 3 |
|---|---|---|---|---|---|---|---|---|
| 5 | 9 | 4 | 6 | 3 | 1 | 7 | 8 | 2 |
| 6 | 3 | 2 | 8 | 7 | 4 | 9 | 1 | 5 |
| 8 | 4 | 6 | 1 | 2 | 3 | 5 | 9 | 7 |
| 2 | 7 | 9 | 4 | 5 | 6 | 1 | 3 | 8 |
| 3 | 1 | 5 | 7 | 8 | 9 | 2 | 6 | 4 |
| 4 | 5 | 8 | 9 | 1 | 7 | 3 | 2 | 6 |
| 1 | 2 | 3 | 5 | 6 | 8 | 4 | 7 | 9 |
| 9 | 6 | 7 | 3 | 4 | 2 | 8 | 5 | 1 |

**85**

2 Diamonds, 3 Hearts, 6 Clubs,
8 Spades, 9 Hearts

**86**

UP = A, D, E: DOWN = B, C

**87**

| 5 | 0 | 1 | 0 | 6 | | 7 | | 6 | | 7 | 1 | 2 | 0 | 9 |
|---|---|---|---|---|---|---|---|---|---|---|---|---|---|---|
| 0 | | 5 | | 0 | | 1 | 0 | 2 | 1 | 1 | | 7 | | 8 |
| 6 | | 7 | | 4 | 0 | 0 | | 2 | | 0 | | 6 | | 0 |
| 2 | 0 | 1 | 8 | 5 | | 6 | 1 | 0 | | 1 | 5 | 1 | 3 | 1 |
| | | 0 | | | 3 | | | | 1 | | | 4 | | |
| 8 | 9 | 9 | 0 | 5 | | 3 | 2 | 9 | 0 | 9 | | 8 | | 4 |
| 8 | | | 3 | 9 | 2 | 4 | 6 | | 5 | | 3 | 6 | | 4 |
| 3 | 3 | 0 | 5 | 1 | 4 | | | 5 | | | 9 | 8 | 3 | |
| | 8 | | | 8 | 6 | 1 | 2 | 3 | 4 | | 1 | | 7 | |
| 9 | 1 | 2 | 0 | 6 | | 1 | 6 | 8 | | 8 | 3 | 2 | 4 | 7 |
| 1 | | 8 | | 5 | 5 | 0 | | 3 | | 8 | | | 8 | |
| 3 | 5 | 0 | 1 | 6 | | 2 | | 3 | | 3 | 2 | 1 | 9 | 8 |
| 2 | | | 8 | 9 | 2 | | 7 | 0 | 2 | | | 0 | | |
| 4 | 0 | 1 | 1 | 8 | | 9 | 5 | 6 | | 1 | 0 | 8 | 6 | 0 |

**88**

Girls 4 and 6.

**89**

**90**

| 5 | 8 | 0 | 1 | 0 | 3 | 4 | 0 | 1 | 6 | 3 |
|---|---|---|---|---|---|---|---|---|---|---|
| 6 | 7 | 4 | 5 | 2 | 0 | 8 | 5 | 8 | 9 | 0 |
| 6 | 9 | 4 | 6 | 0 | 6 | 2 | 1 | 2 | 4 | 7 |
| 4 | 7 | 4 | 2 | 3 | 1 | 4 | 0 | 8 | 7 | 5 |
| 4 | 8 | 5 | 9 | 6 | 8 | 0 | 3 | 9 | 7 | 2 |
| 4 | 3 | 7 | 4 | 7 | 1 | 9 | 2 | 1 | 3 | 2 |
| 6 | 2 | 5 | 1 | 0 | 6 | 1 | 6 | 1 | 3 | 6 |
| 7 | 8 | 9 | 7 | 0 | 2 | 7 | 8 | 3 | 8 | 3 |
| 0 | 9 | 1 | 2 | 3 | 5 | 5 | 3 | 9 | 8 | 5 |
| 7 | 9 | 4 | 2 | 9 | 6 | 5 | 8 | 1 | 5 | 9 |

**91**

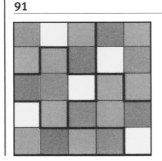

**92**

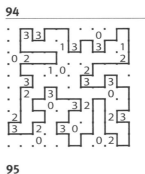

**93**

**94**

**95**

| 0 | 2 | 1 | 2 | 0 | 3 | 1 |
|---|---|---|---|---|---|---|
| 2 | 4 | 1 | 5 | 5 | 5 | 6 |

| 0 | 6 | 1 | 1 | 1 | 2 | 1 |
|---|---|---|---|---|---|---|
| 0 | 6 | 5 | 4 | 3 | 6 | 2 |

| 3 | 0 | 4 | 2 | 0 | 4 | 5 |
|---|---|---|---|---|---|---|
| 4 | 3 | 4 | 2 | 6 | 6 | 6 |

| 0 | 0 | 3 | 4 | 5 | 2 | 3 |
|---|---|---|---|---|---|---|
| 4 | 1 | 6 | 5 | 5 | 3 | 3 |

## 96

```
  7 2 6 4 9 3       5 2 4 6 3 1 9
7   1   0   2         1   1     3
8 3 0 2 2 6 9     5 1 9 9 5     7
3   1   6   4         7   5 3 0 2
9 3 0 3     8 0 3 1 0 3     6   6
1   1   3 9 6         5 2 5 0 0 8
4     7   5   3 3 5 4     2   8
  9 3 8 1 1 8         8     4
  5   1   0   1 4 3 8 1 1 6
4 0 3 6 2 5     0     1     0
1     3     5 8 6     3 2 1 6 5
1 2 8   1     3   2   5 3   3
0   1 2 2 5 8 9     2 8 5   4
7 9 3   1   6 2 3 3     1 8 0 9
4   9 2 8 5 1         7   0
```

## 97

| BOX | BIRD | EGGS |
| --- | --- | --- |
| 1 | BRENDA | 5 |
| 2 | FELICITY | 2 |
| 3 | DEIRDRE | 6 |
| 4 | EDWINA | 4 |
| 5 | ABIGAIL | 1 |
| 6 | CLARISSA | 3 |

## 98

A and E

## 99

```
1 9 2 8 1     4   5     6 7 7 6 8
5   4   3   9 2 2 0 0     1   2
3   4   5   6   7   8   9   0
4   6   9 5 4   3   2   1   0
8 3 7 2 8     7 7 9     6 3 0 9 1
        5         4         3   3
5 2 6 7 3     4 8 1 9 0     0
5     3 5 5 4 3   2     2 4 1
1 1 6 2 3 8       9       2 4 9
7         2 6 8 9 8 2     4
3 0 7 1 4     4 2 3     5 3 5 0 9
6     4   6 1 4   0         0
7 9 8 0 5   9   5   8 2 6 9 7
7         9 7 0   1 1 6       2
2 8 9 0 6     3 0 6     7 4 7 8 3
```

## 100

```
2 6 7 4 9 3 8 5 1
9 5 1 2 8 6 4 3 7
4 8 3 7 5 1 9 6 2
1 7 6 3 2 8 5 4 9
3 9 5 1 4 7 2 8 6
8 4 2 9 6 5 7 1 3
7 1 8 5 3 2 6 9 4
6 2 4 8 1 9 3 7 5
5 3 9 6 7 4 1 2 8
```

## 101

```
2 1 1 3
3 5 2 2
3 3 5 2
1 2 5 5
5 1 1 3
```

## 102

Flying saucer 4.

## 103

Up = A, D and E
Down = B and C

## 104

Hiatus could not have served for twelve years (clue 4). Nor could this have been Blunderbuss or Rictus (clue 1), so the man with that length of service must have been Voluminus. He could not have been from Syria (clue 2) or Germania (clue 4) and the man from Africa had 11 years' service, so Voluminus must have been from Gallia and must therefore have been stationed on the west wall (clue 3). Blunderbuss must therefore have been on the east wall (clue 1). The man on the north wall had served for nine years in the legion (clue 3). He could not have been Hiatus (clue 4), so must have been Rictus and Hiatus must consequently have been on the south wall and, from clue 4, the man from Germania must have been Blunderbuss on the east wall. By elimination, he must have served for ten years. Finally, Rictus, with his nine years' service, cannot have been from Africa (clue 3), so he must have been from Syria, leaving Hiatus on the south wall as the African with eleven years of service.

In summary:
North, Rictus, Syria, nine years.
East, Blunderbuss, Germania, ten years.
South, Hiatus, Africa, eleven years.
West, Voluminus, Gallia, twelve years.

## 105

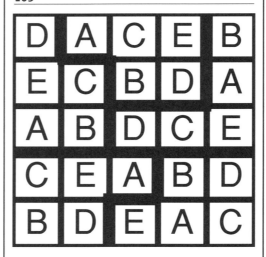

```
D A C E B
E C B D A
A B D C E
C E A B D
B D E A C
```

## 106

```
4 2 0 4 3 9 3 1 3 8
8 3 5 8 5 1 2 4 0 4
9 1 4 6 1 8 2 0 5 7
2 7 3 7 0 3 8 9 3 9
5 0 9 6 8 2 4 2 1 4
9 7 2 1 7 5 3 6 5 8
3 1 4 9 2 8 0 2 3 2
```

## 107

| 7 | + | 1 | − | 5 | = | 3 |
| --- | --- | --- | --- | --- | --- | --- |
| + | | + | | x | | |
| 4 | + | 8 | ÷ | 2 | = | 6 |
| − | | ÷ | | − | | |
| 6 | x | 3 | − | 9 | = | 9 |
| = | | = | | = | | |
| 5 | | 3 | | 1 | | |

## 108

```
8 9 3 1 7 6 5 4 2
1 7 6 4 5 2 8 9 3
4 5 2 8 3 9 7 1 6
6 1 7 5 8 4 3 2 9
2 4 5 3 9 1 6 8 7
9 3 8 2 6 7 1 5 4
7 2 4 6 1 8 9 3 5
5 8 9 7 2 3 4 6 1
3 6 1 9 4 5 2 7 8
```

## 109

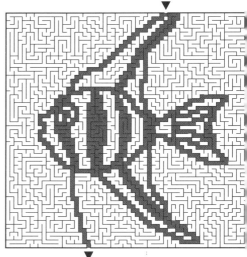

## 110

## 111

| HE | JOB | SHE | JOB | PLOY |
|---|---|---|---|---|
| A HOUND | DIRECTOR | H BEE-P | PERSONNEL | GET DRUNK |
| B PUSHIE | ACCOUNTANT | G PURRS | SECRETARY | PLAY TAPE |
| C NUTTING | CLERK | I NOAH | TYPIST | MEET HUS. |
| D VEEUS | SALESMAN | J BEECY | GEN. MAN | TAKE PIC |
| E STENDER | DRIVER | F ISHENT | DIRECTOR | SHOW FILE |

## 112

## 113

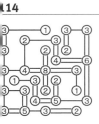

## 114

## 115

```
2 9 3 0 6   4   9   7 2 4 3 1
6   0   7   2 9 3 1 7   8   4
8   1   1   6   7   2   8   7
1   1   5 4 1   7   1   3   2
7 3 5 3 8   8 2 0   3 9 7 9 2
      9       9       9   2
7 5 3 6 8     3 7 3 0 4   0
0     1 1 9 0 3   4   3 6 6
7 6 3 0 8 1     6     5 5 2
  2     4 9 3 9 1 8   1
5 2 7 8 9   4 1 3   7 2 4 2 2
0     3   6 7 3   6     1
4 0 0 1 3   1   0   4 9 9 8 0
6     7 4 5   1 7 2     1
8 6 2 6 1   2 9 6   1 5 7 0 4
```

## 116

: and G

## 117

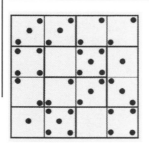

## 118

| E | B | C | A | D |
|---|---|---|---|---|
| A | E | B | D | C |
| D | C | A | E | B |
| C | D | E | B | A |
| B | A | D | C | E |

## 119

| LADY | ORANGES | DATES | TOPS |
|---|---|---|---|
| MRS FEATHERBED | 0 | 1 | 2 |
| MRS FLOWERPOT | 1 | 1 | 1 |
| MRS GREENGAGE | 2 | 1 | 0 |

## 120

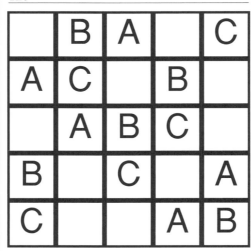

## 121

E, L and O

## 122

| 1 | Jerry | 9 | Jack |
|---|---|---|---|
| 2 | Alice | 10 | Christine |
| 3 | Daisy | 11 | Enid |
| 4 | Mary | 12 | Charley |
| 5 | Tom | 13 | George |
| 6 | Bernard | 14 | Kate |
| 7 | Joan | 15 | Lottie |
| 8 | Freddy | 16 | Peter |

## 123

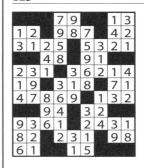

## 124

Hein was with Rudig and Jan was with Wouter. Hence it was Roel who had no alibi.

## 125

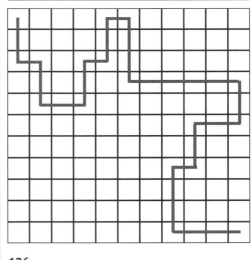

## 126

9, 13, 3, 10, 1, 11, 6, 7, 14, 2, 12, 8, 4, 5

## 127

## 128

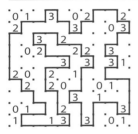

## 129

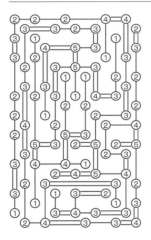

## 130

12 reds, 2 yellows, 3 browns, 4 blues, 3 blacks.

## 131

| B | C | E | A | D |
|---|---|---|---|---|
| D | A | B | E | C |
| E | D | A | C | B |
| C | E | D | B | A |
| A | B | C | D | E |

## 132

```
  3 4 1 7 1 2   5 2 7 3 5 5 9
8   3   7   2     4   7     1
6 1 5 7 2 4 8   2 8 1 3 5   0
2   1   6   4     2   1 6 2 2
5 9 2 1   6 3 7 9 0 1   1 6
6   7   9 4 3     7 2 9 3 6 2
1     1   3   8 2 7 3   9 6
  3 1 4 5 1 7     0   8
  9   6   1   9 9 2 1 3 4 9
4 1 0 3 5 5   5     7     1
6     0     1 5 0   2 7 4 0 3
7 8 2   5     9   9   8 2
1   1 8 7 3 3 2   8 8 8
6 2 9   6   4 5 7 0   3 1 6 0
9   1 3 8 0 4   1 6
```

## 133

## 134

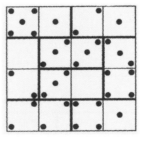

## 135

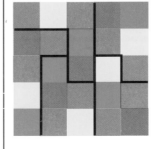

## 136

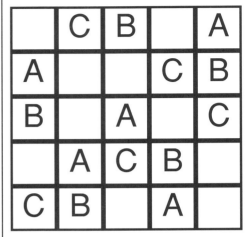

## 137

| BEAR | SLEEPER | CEREAL | BROKE |
|------|---------|--------|-------|
| CARMEN | WYN | CHAFFLAKES | CHAIR |
| FRED | GOLDIE | RICYPOPS | SIDEBOARD |
| MAMA | CHER | MUESLI MUNCH | BOOKCASE |
| PAPA | DAWN | WEETY BRICKS | TABLE |
| TEDDY | CILLA | BRAN BITS | DESK |

## 138

| GIRL | BOY | BOY | BOY |
|------|-----|-----|-----|
| AVA | BRIAN | ERIC | GARY |
| GLADYS | COLIN | DAVID | HENRY |
| MARIAN | ALAN | FRANK | IAN |

## 139

| 1 | 8 | 3 | 4 | 9 | 6 | 5 | 2 | 7 |
|---|---|---|---|---|---|---|---|---|
| 2 | 5 | 4 | 3 | 7 | 8 | 9 | 6 | 1 |
| 9 | 7 | 6 | 5 | 1 | 2 | 4 | 3 | 8 |
| 8 | 1 | 2 | 7 | 3 | 5 | 6 | 4 | 9 |
| 6 | 9 | 5 | 8 | 2 | 4 | 1 | 7 | 3 |
| 4 | 3 | 7 | 1 | 6 | 9 | 8 | 5 | 2 |
| 5 | 2 | 1 | 6 | 8 | 3 | 7 | 9 | 4 |
| 3 | 6 | 8 | 9 | 4 | 7 | 2 | 1 | 5 |
| 7 | 4 | 9 | 2 | 5 | 1 | 3 | 8 | 6 |

## 140

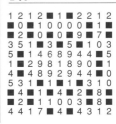

The combination is 2981890.

## 141

| 3 | 1 | 3 | 4 | 1 | 3 | 1 | 4 |
|---|---|---|---|---|---|---|---|
| 1 | 4 | 1 | 4 | 5 | 6 | 0 | 6 |
| 1 | 3 | 5 | 0 | 5 | 2 | 6 | 5 |
| 6 | 5 | 2 | 4 | 2 | 3 | 2 | 4 |
| 0 | 0 | 0 | 2 | 0 | 5 | 6 | 5 |
| 6 | 4 | 0 | 6 | 2 | 5 | 6 | 0 |
| 1 | 4 | 2 | 1 | 2 | 3 | 3 | 3 |

## 142

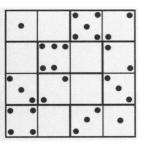

## 143

Up = B and C and E
Down = A and D

## 144

Seven bunches have all three colours

## 145

14 reds, 4 yellows, 3 greens, 2 blues, 5 pinks

## 146

| 0 | 1 | 3 | 2 |
|---|---|---|---|
| 1 | 2 | 3 | 2 |
| 2 | 2 | 0 | 0 |
| 1 | 1 | 1 | 0 |
| 3 | 3 | 0 | 3 |

## 147

Picture 4

## 148

| 4 | 2 | 2 | 3 |
|---|---|---|---|
| 4 | 2 | 5 | 5 |
| 4 | 5 | 3 | 5 |
| 5 | 2 | 3 | 4 |
| 3 | 2 | 3 | 4 |

## 149

| | Eagle | Birdie | Par | Bogey | Double Bogey | FINAL SCORE |
|---|---|---|---|---|---|---|
| PARNELL DARMA | 4 | 1 | 6 | 5 | 2 | 72 |
| NICK JACKLISS | 3 | 5 | 7 | 2 | 1 | 65 |
| BARRY CLAYER | 1 | 8 | 2 | 3 | 4 | 73 |

## 150

| C | | A | B |
|---|---|---|---|
| B | | C | A |
| | A | | C | B |
| | C | B | | A |
| A | B | | C |

## 151

9 + (3 x 2) + 6 = 21
7 − 4 + 9 + 9 = 21
(3 x 5 − 8) x 3 = 21

## 152

| 2 | + | 8 | ÷ | 5 | = | 2 |
|---|---|---|---|---|---|---|
| ÷ | | + | | x | | |
| 1 | + | 7 | − | 3 | = | 5 |
| + | | − | | − | | |
| 4 | x | 9 | ÷ | 6 | = | 6 |
| = | | = | | = | | |
| 6 | | 6 | | 9 | | |

## 153

| 2 | 4 | 3 | 3 | 0 | 3 | 3 | 1 |
|---|---|---|---|---|---|---|---|
| 4 | 1 | 1 | 6 | 1 | 6 | 4 | 3 |
| 5 | 2 | 4 | 5 | 4 | 4 | 1 | 5 |
| 4 | 2 | 0 | 1 | 5 | 3 | 5 | 2 |
| 3 | 6 | 2 | 0 | 4 | 6 | 0 | 1 |
| 3 | 2 | 1 | 0 | 0 | 5 | 5 | 2 |
| 6 | 6 | 2 | 6 | 5 | 0 | 6 | 0 |

## 154

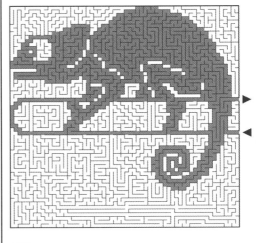

## 155

A 12, B 20, C 4, D 8, E 16, F 18, G 9, H11, J 14, K 21, L 10, M 2, N 23, P 5, Q 17, R 7, S 1, T 15, U 13, V 3, W 6, X 24, Y 19, Z 22

## 156

A is 35, B is 40, C is 25 and D is 20.

## 157

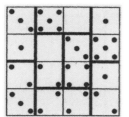

## 158

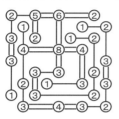

## 159

Alan – 2B, 1Y, 7V.
Dawn – 3R, 1B, 4G, 2Y.
John – 2R, 5B, 3Y.
Mary – 3R, 4G, 2Y, 1V.

## 160

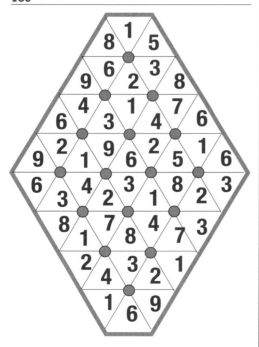

## 161

| 77 | 84 | 61 | 68 | 75 |
|----|----|----|----|----|
| 66 | 73 | 80 | 82 | 64 |
| 85 | 62 | 69 | 71 | 78 |
| 74 | 76 | 83 | 65 | 67 |
| 63 | 70 | 72 | 79 | 81 |

## 162

| 6 | + | 4 | – | 5 | = | 5 |
|---|---|---|---|---|---|---|
| + |   | + |   | – |   |   |
| 9 | – | 8 | + | 1 | = | 2 |
| ÷ |   | – |   | × |   |   |
| 3 | + | 7 | ÷ | 2 | = | 5 |
| = |   | = |   | = |   |   |
| 5 |   | 5 |   | 8 |   |   |

## 163

## 164

| 2 | 1 | 1 | 3 | 5 | 7 | 4 | 7 |
|---|---|---|---|---|---|---|---|
| 1 | 6 | 3 | 4 | 7 | 5 | 2 | 6 |
| 4 | 1 | 2 | 3 | 2 | 6 | 1 | 6 |
| 6 | 3 | 5 | 7 | 2 | 3 | 3 | 7 |
| 1 | 4 | 4 | 1 | 4 | 3 | 6 | 6 |
| 5 | 7 | 4 | 5 | 3 | 6 | 5 | 7 |
| 5 | 1 | 2 | 2 | 4 | 5 | 2 | 7 |

## 165

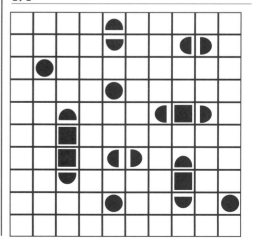

## 166

```
    5 4 3 7 4 8     9 7 8 3 2 8 8
  9   2   4   1     0   4     1
  1 5 0 5 2 1 3     3 2 0 9 4     4
  8   7   4   7     6   1 6 2 6
  6 3 9 5   3 3 5 6 4 2   2   0
  2   9   9 8 0     7 1 0 3 2 7
  2     8   2 8 1 1 8   9   2
      1 2 2 0 7 4     8   6
    0   1   7   4 9 5 6 1 3 4
  7 9 3 6 1 2   3     6     1
  8     0     7 0 2   3 6 1 2 5
  6 9 9   3     2   1   0   9
  2   1 0 0 3 4 1   3 8 8   7
  4 6 0   1   7 6 7 7   4 5 9 0
  3   3 9 9 4 2     2   1
```

## 167

| 8 | 2 | 8 | 1 | 0 | 5 | 2 | 8 | 5 | 0 | 1 |
|---|---|---|---|---|---|---|---|---|---|---|
| 8 | 7 | 3 | 7 | 4 | 4 | 6 | 3 | 3 | 9 | 3 |
| 0 | 4 | 4 | 2 | 7 | 3 | 8 | 9 | 2 | 7 | 0 |
| 3 | 5 | 1 | 6 | 8 | 4 | 0 | 9 | 2 | 3 | 4 |
| 1 | 8 | 3 | 8 | 0 | 6 | 0 | 5 | 8 | 1 | 4 |
| 1 | 6 | 0 | 9 | 1 | 3 | 6 | 5 | 6 | 6 | 7 |
| 9 | 7 | 5 | 6 | 2 | 2 | 0 | 2 | 5 | 0 | 7 |
| 0 | 4 | 5 | 9 | 9 | 6 | 7 | 1 | 5 | 1 | 9 |
| 1 | 7 | 3 | 2 | 7 | 9 | 6 | 5 | 7 | 2 | 9 |
| 4 | 1 | 5 | 9 | 9 | 4 | 8 | 3 | 2 | 8 | 2 |

## 168

1 Crazy Carvellos
2 Fred the Fire-eater
3 Madame Poll's Parrots
4 Clever Clowns
5 Jim the Juggler
6 Senor Pedro's Poodles
7 Flying Fortresses
8 Agiles Acrobats

## 169

| 6 | 7 | 6 | 7 | 6 | 6 | 6 | 3 |
|---|---|---|---|---|---|---|---|
| 2 | 4 | 2 | 7 | 5 | 1 | 5 | 1 |
| 1 | 3 | 3 | 1 | 4 | 2 | 5 | 4 |
| 2 | 6 | 4 | 7 | 5 | 3 | 4 | 7 |
| 2 | 1 | 7 | 1 | 2 | 5 | 1 | 1 |
| 7 | 6 | 2 | 7 | 2 | 3 | 6 | 5 |
| 5 | 5 | 3 | 3 | 4 | 3 | 4 | 4 |

## 170

Ten bunches have all three colours.

## 171

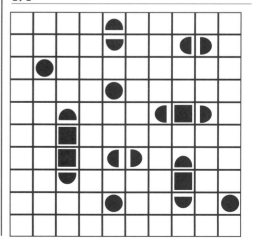

## 172

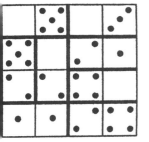

## 173

F, J, C, I, A, H, B, G, E, L, D, K

## 174

| 2 | 7 | 3 | 5 | 8 | 4 | 9 | 1 | 6 |
|---|---|---|---|---|---|---|---|---|
| 6 | 8 | 5 | 1 | 3 | 9 | 2 | 7 | 4 |
| 4 | 1 | 9 | 7 | 6 | 2 | 3 | 8 | 5 |
| 3 | 5 | 4 | 9 | 7 | 6 | 1 | 2 | 8 |
| 9 | 6 | 8 | 2 | 5 | 1 | 4 | 3 | 7 |
| 1 | 2 | 7 | 8 | 4 | 3 | 6 | 5 | 9 |
| 8 | 3 | 2 | 4 | 9 | 7 | 5 | 6 | 1 |
| 7 | 9 | 6 | 3 | 1 | 5 | 8 | 4 | 2 |
| 5 | 4 | 1 | 6 | 2 | 8 | 7 | 9 | 3 |

## 175

```
1 0 5 9 2 1     3 4 4 3 5 3
6       9 0 1 7 3   1       5
6 6 8 8 9 6     7 1 3 7 5   2
9   1   1   2 0 4   0   1   3
2   7   0       7   1   3 0 1
7 8 9 1 2 1   8 3 6 3 4 3   4
    7       0   0         9 1 9
  6   5   1   9 7 7 0 2 7
  0   6 2 0 7 3 2     2   3
5 5 0 7 3       3     3 4 0 1 7
  2   8   4 0 3 0 4 4   2
4 3 1 5 0   1   7     6 0 3 7
1   1     5   8 8 6 6       2
9 1 7 1     7 2 3       0   8 1 8
0       1   8   1 8 5 3     3
```

## 176

| 4 | 7 | 2 | 9 | 9 | 2 | 5 | 6 | 3 | 7 | 2 |
|---|---|---|---|---|---|---|---|---|---|---|
| 4 | 3 | 7 | 0 | 4 | 1 | 2 | 2 | 0 | 4 | 7 |
| 0 | 9 | 8 | 5 | 9 | 9 | 3 | 8 | 3 | 1 | 9 |
| 0 | 5 | 3 | 6 | 4 | 6 | 1 | 4 | 6 | 8 | 8 |
| 6 | 6 | 3 | 0 | 7 | 7 | 5 | 5 | 2 | 6 | 0 |
| 7 | 5 | 1 | 9 | 3 | 4 | 1 | 1 | 4 | 1 | 9 |
| 9 | 0 | 6 | 6 | 1 | 0 | 0 | 1 | 5 | 8 | 3 |
| 8 | 1 | 2 | 5 | 8 | 7 | 2 | 7 | 3 | 1 | 2 |
| 4 | 0 | 8 | 5 | 9 | 4 | 5 | 2 | 7 | 8 | 6 |
| 3 | 4 | 3 | 9 | 5 | 8 | 0 | 7 | 6 | 8 | 2 |

## 177

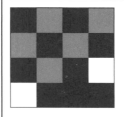

## 178

Seven bunches have all three colours.

## 179

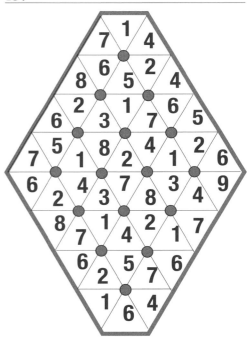

Each square tile has neighbours – tiles that share an edge.
The corners have just two neighbours, those along the edge
have three and the ones in the middle have four.
For each square, check its neighbours' colours (red or black)
– whichever colour occurs least often that is the new colour
of the cell. If the number of neighbouring colours is the
same, the square is left empty.

## 180

1—D, 2—B, 3—A, 4—C

## 181

| 1 | JESSE JONES | WELLS FARGO |
|---|---|---|
| 2 | FRANK FOSTER | JAIL |
| 3 | CHUCK CARSON | SALOON |
| 4 | DAVE DALTON | BANK |
| 5 | ROCKY RAWLINGS | TRADING POST |

## 182

| 3 | 5 | 7 | 1 | 9 | 6 | 8 | 2 | 4 |
|---|---|---|---|---|---|---|---|---|
| 6 | 9 | 8 | 2 | 5 | 4 | 7 | 1 | 3 |
| 1 | 4 | 2 | 8 | 3 | 7 | 5 | 9 | 6 |
| 2 | 3 | 5 | 7 | 8 | 9 | 6 | 4 | 1 |
| 7 | 6 | 4 | 3 | 1 | 2 | 9 | 8 | 5 |
| 9 | 8 | 1 | 4 | 6 | 5 | 2 | 3 | 7 |
| 4 | 7 | 6 | 9 | 2 | 1 | 3 | 5 | 8 |
| 8 | 1 | 9 | 5 | 7 | 3 | 4 | 6 | 2 |
| 5 | 2 | 3 | 6 | 4 | 8 | 1 | 7 | 9 |

## 183

| D | B | A | C |   |   |
|---|---|---|---|---|---|
| A | D |   | B |   | C |
|   |   | C | D | A | B |
|   |   | B | A | C | D |
| C | A | D |   | B |   |
| B | C |   |   | D | A |

## 184

Solution shown in diamond grid.

## 185

| 4 | + | 7 | − | 9 | = | 2 |
|---|---|---|---|---|---|---|
| + |   | + |   | − |   |   |
| 6 | + | 3 | − | 8 | = | 1 |
| − |   | ÷ |   | + |   |   |
| 1 | x | 5 | − | 2 | = | 3 |
| = |   | = |   | = |   |   |
| 9 |   | 2 |   | 3 |   |   |

## 186

| B | D |   | A | C |
|---|---|---|---|---|
| D |   | A | C | B |
|   | C | A | D | B |
| A |   | B | C | D |
| C | D |   | B | A |
| B | A | C |   | D |

## 187

Tangles a, b and d will not form a knot. Tangle c will form a knot.

## 188

Pictures 2 and 3

## 189

28 triangles

## 190

1+7, 2+4, 3+6, 5+8

## 191

13 red, 2 green, 3 blue, 5 pink, 3 black

## 192

| 3 | 6 | 6 | 5 |
|---|---|---|---|
| 4 | 4 | 3 | 4 |
| 0 | 0 | 0 | 5 |
| 6 | 5 | 3 | 3 |
| 0 | 6 | 4 | 5 |

## 193

Johnny is number 3 (clue 3). Number 1 cannot be Darren Poole (clue 2), or Shaun (clue 1), so he must be Garry. So, from clue 4, boy number 2 must have green boots. Those of lad number 4 cannot be red (clue 1), or brown (clue 2), so they must be black. So, from clue 4, Johnny, in position 3, must be Waters. Shaun's surname is not Brook (clue 1), so it must be Burne, leaving Garry's as Brook. So Shaun is not in position 2 (clue 3), and must be lad 4, wearing the black boots. By elimination, this leaves boy 2, in the green boots, as Darren Poole. So, from clue 2, the brown

boots must belong to the lad in position 1, Garry, leaving Johnny Waters wearing the red boots.

In summary:
1, Garry Brook, brown.
2, Darren Poole, green.
3, Johnny Waters, red.
4, Shaun Burne, black.

## 194

```
  7 1 3 6 4 8   1 6 3 8 4 2 5
5   7   3   1     5 3       9
2 1 5 2 2 6 0   7 3 0 1 4   9
4   0   3   1     9   3 2 5 0
9 0 5 4   3 2 6 4 1 9   3   3
3   0   4 8 3     1 0 3 6 0 0
9     4   4 2 9 2 1     9   4
  5 3 8 0 1 8       3   0
  6   3   0   6 6 0 3 2 9 9
4 0 9 2 1 4   4       0     3
0     6       8 0 9   2 7 3 2 8
3 5 8   6     8 1   1 1   1
6   2 3 5 7 9 8   1 6 1   0
4 4 4   1   4 2 3 0     6 3 0 7
7   3 9 9 0 2     8   6
```

## 195

Horse 3

## 196

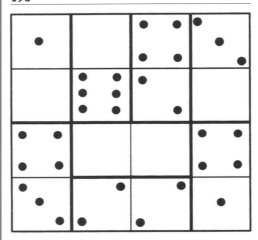

## 197

Albert – 1R, 3B, 6V
Anne – 4B, 3G, 1Y, 2V
Barbara – 4R, 5G, 1Y
George – 3R, 1B, 6Y

## 198

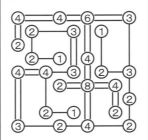

## 199

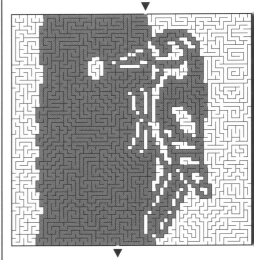

| 1 | 2 | 4 | 5 | 2 | 3 | 2 | 3 |
|---|---|---|---|---|---|---|---|
| 1 | 5 | 6 | 4 | 4 | 2 | 3 | 1 |
| 1 | 4 | 2 | 2 | 1 | 0 | 3 | 4 |
| 2 | 5 | 1 | 6 | 5 | 6 | 3 | 3 |
| 3 | 5 | 4 | 6 | 6 | 2 | 5 | 1 |
| 0 | 5 | 3 | 6 | 4 | 6 | 1 | 0 |
| 0 | 4 | 5 | 0 | 6 | 0 | 0 | 0 |

## 200

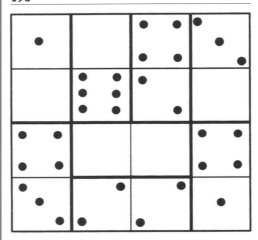

## 201

```
5 8       2 5
3 9 1   2 1 3 5
2 5 4 1 3   2 1 5
1 7     4 1 3   3 1
      6 2     1 3 4 2
      7 9       1 2
7 5 8 9     8 2
9 6     8 9 7     5 3
8 9 7     8 9 5 7 6
    8 9 5 7   1 8 9
      6 3       9 7
```

## 202

1, 3 and 4 will knot, 2 will not.

## 203

Apart from the nine smaller squares, there is a tenth to be seen in 1/2/4/5, an eleventh in 2/3/5/6, a twelfth in 4/5/7/8, a thirteenth in 5/6/8/9 and one large square made up of all nine smaller squares.

## 204

| J | W | G | Z | U | P | E |
|---|---|---|---|---|---|---|
| B | R | N | P | X | H | U |
| D |   | Y | K | S | F | M |
| V | F | D | M | I | Y | S |
| L |   | A | R | E |   | W |
| G |   | K | I | O | T | C |
| Q | B | V | X | Z | J | O |
| N | T | Q | C | A | L | H |

## 205

## 206

Susan's surname is Niven (clue 4) and Knight is the quiz host (clue 2), so Laura the newsreader (clue 3) must be Robins, and Knight's first name must be Donna. By elimination, Susan Niven must be the presenter. She didn't train to be a nurse (clue 4) or a teacher (clue 5), so must have trained as a lawyer. Donna Knight didn't train to be a teacher (clue 1), so must have trained as a nurse, leaving newsreader Laura Robins as the former student teacher.

In summary:
Donna Knight, quiz host, nurse.
Laura Robins, newsreader, teacher.
Susan Niven, presenter, lawyer.

## 207

41. In order, the numbers are 1, 4, 7, 11, 14, 17... numbers that are made from straight lines only. The shop only stocks 1s, 4s and 7s!

## 208

60. It was, as suggested, worth finding out how many squares there are altogether, which is the sum of 1+4+9+16+25+36+49+64—square numbers. Only squares with an odd number of cells along a side can be more of one colour than the other so we need half of every other number in that series ie, 2+8+18+32=60.

## 209

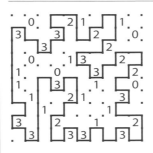

## 210

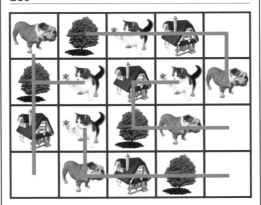

## 211

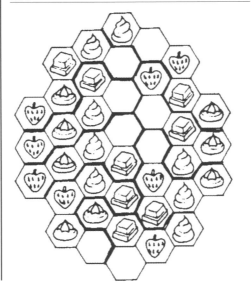

## 212

3 and 8

## 213

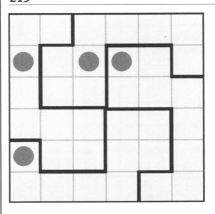

## 214

A Owen and Vince
B Nick and Rob
C Pete and Tom
D Sam and Will

## 215

## 216

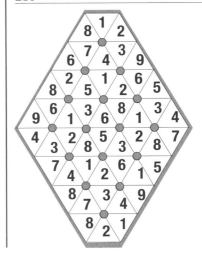

## 217

The clocks add on an hour and ten minutes each time, so the final clock will show the time as half past twelve.

## 218

| 1 | 2 | 4 | 5 | 1 | 1 | 1 | 3 |
|---|---|---|---|---|---|---|---|
| 6 | 2 | 2 | 5 | 6 | 2 | 5 | 3 |
| 2 | 1 | 2 | 5 | 6 | 3 | 6 | 3 |
| 2 | 6 | 4 | 5 | 0 | 4 | 0 | 4 |
| 0 | 3 | 0 | 5 | 6 | 0 | 0 | 0 |
| 5 | 3 | 6 | 5 | 4 | 4 | 6 | 3 |
| 3 | 1 | 4 | 1 | 4 | 0 | 1 | 2 |

## 219

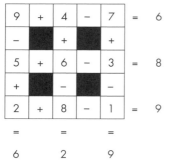

## 220

Rosalind painted in oils (clue 2), so the watercolour painting of the windmill, which was not by Nadine (clue 3), must have been done by Josephine, leaving Nadine as the artist who used pen and ink. So she did not draw the pond (clue 4), and must have depicted the local church, so she is Ms Frame (clue 1). By elimination, Rosalind's oil painting must be of the pond. Her surname is not Canvass (clue 2), so it must be Pallett, leaving Canvass as the surname of Josephine.

In summary:
Josephine Canvass, windmill, watercolour.
Nadine Frame, local church, pen and ink.
Rosalind Pallett, pond, oils.

## 221

11 bunches have all three colours.

## 222

| 1 | 2 | 3 | 5 | 9 | 7 | 4 | 6 | 8 |
|---|---|---|---|---|---|---|---|---|
| 7 | 6 | 8 | 2 | 1 | 4 | 3 | 5 | 9 |
| 5 | 4 | 9 | 8 | 3 | 6 | 2 | 7 | 1 |
| 8 | 7 | 5 | 6 | 4 | 1 | 9 | 2 | 3 |
| 3 | 1 | 6 | 9 | 8 | 2 | 5 | 4 | 7 |
| 4 | 9 | 2 | 3 | 7 | 5 | 1 | 8 | 6 |
| 9 | 3 | 7 | 4 | 5 | 8 | 6 | 1 | 2 |
| 2 | 5 | 1 | 7 | 6 | 3 | 8 | 9 | 4 |
| 6 | 8 | 4 | 1 | 2 | 9 | 7 | 3 | 5 |

## 223

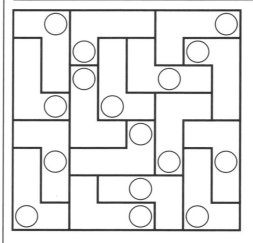

## 224

Dogs A and D.

## 225

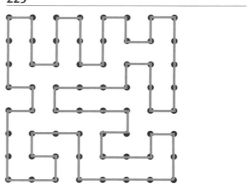

## 226

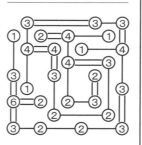

## 227

Box 1

## 228

```
    9 4 3 2 0 1     5 1 7 3 4 8 4
9   6   7   0         3   7     2
2 3 6 1 7 1 2   4 8 2 0 6   1
0   2   3   3       2   7 3 2 6
3 9 7 9   7 3 9 9 9 8   7   0
0   8   4 2 1     1 9 3 7 6 7
7   4   1   1 7 6 2   0   2
  6 1 8 2 4 3         4   4
  3   2   2   2 7 1 9 3 8 3
4 7 6 2 3 6   1   7     1
0   1       7 2 9   3 7 0 2 2
4 0 1   3     6   4   9   9
3   7 6 0 6 3 6   2 1 4   4
3 1 1   1   6 9 1 3   9 0 3 2
1   4 8 8 7 2     3   1
```

## 229

| 1 | x | 4 | ÷ | 2 | = | 2 |
|---|---|---|---|---|---|---|
| + |   | x |   | x | | |
| 9 | ÷ | 3 | + | 7 | = | 10 |
| ÷ |   | ÷ |   | − | | |
| 5 | + | 6 | − | 8 | = | 3 |
| = | | = | | = | | |
| 2 | | 2 | | 6 | | |

## 230

Beth – 1R, 2G, 4Y, 3V
Brian – 4R, 3B, 2G, 1V
Gloria – 3R, 4B, 1G, 2Y
Pete –1B, 3G, 2Y, 4V

## 231

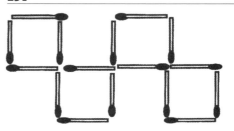

## 232

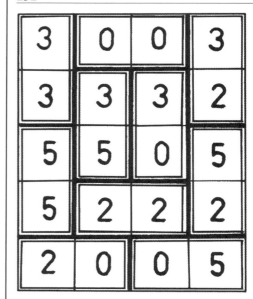

**233**

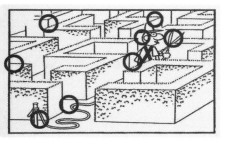

**234**

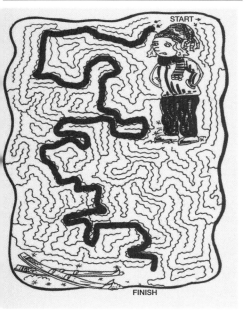

**235**

No. 1

**236**

|   | A | B | D | C |
|---|---|---|---|---|
| C | D |   | A | B |
| B | A |   | D | C |
| A |   | B | C | D |
|   | C | D | B | A |
| D | B | C | A |   |

**237**

| 1 | x | 2 | + | 5 | = | 7 |
|---|---|---|---|---|---|---|
| x |   | + |   | + |   |   |
| 9 | + | 4 | − | 7 | = | 6 |
| − |   | ÷ |   | ÷ |   |   |
| 8 | x | 3 | ÷ | 6 | = | 4 |

= 1    = 2    = 2

**238**

| 6 | 4 | 5 | 3 | 3 | 3 | 4 | 5 |
|---|---|---|---|---|---|---|---|
| 0 | 0 | 6 | 6 | 0 | 3 | 2 | 1 |
| 3 | 0 | 2 | 5 | 2 | 6 | 4 | 2 |
| 6 | 1 | 3 | 2 | 2 | 5 | 5 | 1 |
| 0 | 6 | 0 | 5 | 0 | 4 | 3 | 1 |
| 5 | 4 | 1 | 5 | 0 | 2 | 4 | 4 |
| 4 | 1 | 2 | 1 | 3 | 6 | 1 | 6 |

**239**

35

**240**

29

**241**

Arthur–2 begonias, 3 cyclamen,
1 gardenia and 4 jasmines
Barry–1 African violet,
4 cyclamen, 3 gardenias and 2 jasmines.
Connie–6 African violets,
3 begonias and 1 cyclamen.
Debbie–1 African violet,
3 begonias, 4 gardenias and 2 jasmines

**242**

4–8, 1–10, 5–7, 3–9, 2–6

**243**

| A | B | C | D |
|---|---|---|---|
| ALAN | FRED | LUCY | CLEO |
| E | F | G | H |
| IRMA | EDNA | JOHN | GWEN |
| I | J | K | L |
| BABS | HUGH | KARL | DAVE |

**244**

Rabbit C

**245**

```
7 1 9 3    8 5 1 5 4    5 9 1 2
2       2 1        2       3       7
2       5 8 1 3 3    7 2 9 3 1 0
8 6 5 5        9 2 7           0
    5 0 1 9        2 6 5 9
6 4 3        3 5 0 1 2    2       3
    9 0 9 2        4 1 8 3    8
4 1 2        4 7 0 7 5        8 2
    1 5 0 1 0        1 2 0 9 4 4
    3       3 8 5 5 8 1        2
    4       2           6 1 0 8
3 9 3 6 9        7 0 3 2 2    3
9       7 6 0 7 4    1 7 8 3 0
1       2       6       0 3       5
8 3 3 4    4 4 3 4 7    5 1 3 4
```

**246**

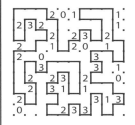

**247**

**248**

| CRACKER | FORENAME | SURNAME | GIFT | DECOR | COLOUR |
|---|---|---|---|---|---|
| 1 | AUDREY | YAPP | KNIFE | REINDEER | SILVER |
| 2 | JOCK | LEWIS | SCARF | CAKES | RUBY |
| 3 | PAUL | WILLIAMS | BIRO | STARS | GOLD |
| 4 | TRICIA | COLE | PIC. | TINSEL | BRONZE |

**249**

Weights 1 and 4 will fall, and
weights 2 and 3 will rise.

**250**

9 bunches have all three colours.

**251**

Print No 4

## 252

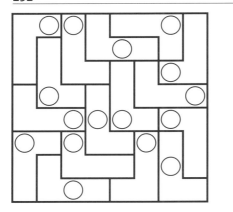

## 253

| 2 | ÷ | 1 | + | 5 | = | 7 |
|---|---|---|---|---|---|---|
| × | | | + | | | + |
| 6 | × | 8 | ÷ | 4 | = | 12 |
| − | | | ÷ | | | ÷ |
| 7 | + | 3 | − | 9 | = | 1 |

= 5    = 3    = 1

## 254

Box D

## 255

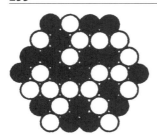

## 256

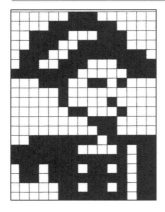

## 257

## 258

2 × (12 + 3) − 9 = 21
2 × 11 − 11 + 10 = 21
5 × 3 + 8 − 2 = 21

## 259

## 260

| 64 | ÷ | 4 | = | 16 | + | 40 | = | 56 |
|---|---|---|---|---|---|---|---|---|
| − | | + | | − | | ÷ | | − |
| 36 | ÷ | 3 | = | 12 | + | 4 | = | 16 |
| = | | = | | = | | = | | = |
| 28 | ÷ | 7 | = | 4 | × | 10 | = | 40 |
| + | | × | | + | | + | | − |
| 13 | − | 4 | = | 9 | + | 4 | = | 13 |
| = | | = | | = | | = | | = |
| 41 | − | 28 | = | 13 | + | 14 | = | 27 |

## 261

| 1 | 2 | 7 | 9 | 3 | 6 | 8 | 5 | 4 |
|---|---|---|---|---|---|---|---|---|
| 9 | 5 | 4 | 7 | 1 | 8 | 6 | 3 | 2 |
| 3 | 8 | 6 | 2 | 5 | 4 | 7 | 9 | 1 |
| 5 | 6 | 9 | 1 | 7 | 3 | 2 | 4 | 8 |
| 4 | 1 | 8 | 5 | 6 | 2 | 9 | 7 | 3 |
| 7 | 3 | 2 | 8 | 4 | 9 | 1 | 6 | 5 |
| 6 | 4 | 1 | 3 | 2 | 7 | 5 | 8 | 9 |
| 8 | 7 | 5 | 4 | 9 | 1 | 3 | 2 | 6 |
| 2 | 9 | 3 | 6 | 8 | 5 | 4 | 1 | 7 |

## 262

1 Senor Pedro's Poodles
2 Fred the Fire-eater
3 Crazy Carvellos
4 Clever Clowns
5 Jim the Juggler
6 Flying Fortresses
7 Agilles Acrobats
8 Madame Poll's Parrots

## 263

Pictures 2 and 5

## 264

| Q | 8 | T | J | J |
|---|---|---|---|---|
| D | D | D | S | D |
| T | 8 | K | J | A |
| C | C | D | H | H |
| J | 9 | K | K | T |
| C | H | S | H | S |
| Q | 9 | Q | 8 | 8 |
| C | D | S | S | H |
| K | 9 | Q | T | 9 |
| C | S | H | H | C |

## 265

## 266

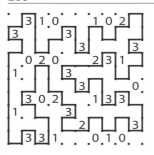

## 267

Billiard room – Lance O'Boyle;
Lounge – Wicklow, the maid;
Card room – Hon. Reginald Ackney;
Morning room – Reverend Rash;
Cloak room – Lady Mole;
Study – Spott, the butler;
Library – Miss Felicity Bytes.

## 268

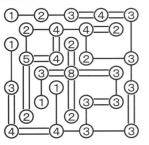

## 269

After numbering the squares 1 to 25 in the conventional manner – arbitrarily assign A to square 10. This means that square 1 is also A since squares 2, 3, 4 or 5 cannot be A as they are in the same shape as square 10 – and square 14 is an A, as squares 9, 15, 20 and 25 are in the same row or column as square 10. Similarly, square 17 has an A, so the remaining A is in square 23.
Assigning arbitrary letter B to square 5 means that square 9 must also contain a B. In turn, this means that square 11 also has a B. Thus neither squares 12, 13, 16 or 21 has a B – and since there is an A in square 17 (above), this means that the requirement cannot be met.

| 1 | 2 | 3 | 4 | 5 |
|----|----|----|----|----|
| 6 | 7 | 8 | 9 | 10 |
| 11 | 12 | 13 | 14 | 15 |
| 16 | 17 | 18 | 19 | 20 |
| 21 | 22 | 23 | 24 | 25 |

## 270

3, 0, 6, 2, 8, 5, 4, 9, 7, 1

## 271

Pictures 4 and 5

## 272

Television 3

## 273

64,512 Multiply the figures that form the numbers
2 x 3 x 4 x 7 = 168.

## 274

A Donner  B Cupid  C Dancer
D Vixen  E Prancer  F Cornet
G Dasher  H Blitzen

## 275

Weights A and B will rise, and weights C and D will fall.

## 276

| C |   | B |   | A | D |
|---|---|---|---|---|---|
| D |   |   | C | B | A |
|   | B | A | D |   | C |
| A | C |   | B | D |   |
|   | A | D |   | C | B |
| B | D | C | A |   |   |

## 277

The matching ducks are: 1+8, 2+3 and 4+6; so the different ducks are 5 and 7.

## 278

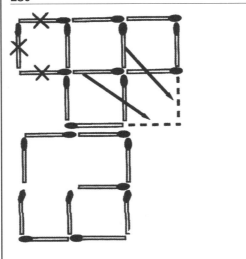

## 279

A  Kate & Naomi
B  Jenny & Lisa
C  Megan & Sally
D  Paula & Rita

## 280

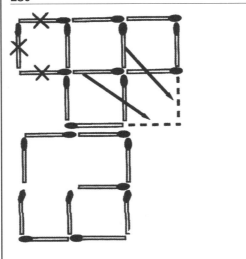

## 281

| | | | | |
|---|---|---|---|---|
| 2nd floor: | Carrol | Farmer | Jenkin | Innish |
| 1st floor: | Grimes | Edgely | Davies | Harris |
| Ground floor: | Levers | Grimes | Edgely | Levers |

## 282

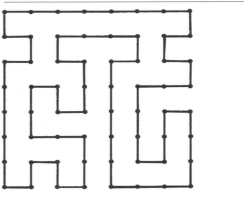

## 283

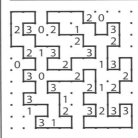

## 284

## 285

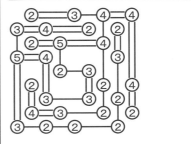

## 286

Eye colour changed, sign on window missing, wheel nut missing, handle different colour, driver's tie missing and tyre tread missing.

### 287

Frown now a smile, shadow on jumper missing, shadow under foot missing, collar now yellow, seed shadow missing, two eyebrows.

### 288

| 6 | 8 | 7 | 2 | 4 | 9 | 1 | 5 | 3 |
|---|---|---|---|---|---|---|---|---|
| 5 | 4 | 2 | 1 | 3 | 6 | 8 | 7 | 9 |
| 3 | 1 | 9 | 7 | 5 | 8 | 4 | 6 | 2 |
| 2 | 9 | 5 | 6 | 8 | 1 | 3 | 4 | 7 |
| 7 | 3 | 1 | 5 | 2 | 4 | 9 | 8 | 6 |
| 8 | 6 | 4 | 3 | 9 | 7 | 2 | 1 | 5 |
| 4 | 5 | 3 | 8 | 6 | 2 | 7 | 9 | 1 |
| 9 | 7 | 6 | 4 | 1 | 3 | 5 | 2 | 8 |
| 1 | 2 | 8 | 9 | 7 | 5 | 6 | 3 | 4 |

### 289

Shape D

### 290

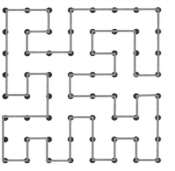

### 291

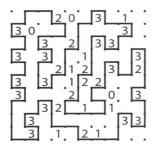

### 292

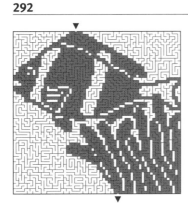

### 293

### 294

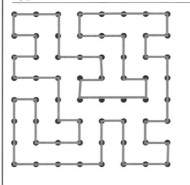

### 295

### 296

| T | 8 | 8 | K | T |
| S | D | H | D | C |
| | | | | |
| J | A | K | 8 | Q |
| S | H | C | C | S |
| | | | | |
| T | 9 | K | 8 | 9 |
| D | C | H | S | S |
| | | | | |
| T | K | Q | Q | 9 |
| H | S | D | C | H |
| | | | | |
| J | J | J | Q | 9 |
| C | H | D | H | D |

### 297

Footballer D

### 298

Pieces 2 and 6

### 299

| 2 | 4 | 1 | | 6 | 9 | 8 | | |
|---|---|---|---|---|---|---|---|---|
| 8 | 7 | 3 | | 8 | 7 | 9 | 6 | |
| | 8 | 5 | 9 | 7 | | 7 | 9 | 8 |
| 7 | 9 | | 6 | 9 | 8 | | 8 | 6 |
| 9 | 6 | 8 | | 5 | 9 | | 7 | 9 |
| | 9 | 3 | | 7 | 1 | | | |
| 1 | 2 | | 1 | 2 | | 2 | 4 | 1 |
| 2 | 3 | | 2 | 4 | 1 | | 1 | 3 |
| 4 | 1 | 2 | | 1 | 3 | 5 | 2 | |
| | 4 | 1 | 2 | 3 | | 1 | 3 | 7 |
| | 3 | 1 | 5 | | 8 | 6 | 9 | |

### 300

| 2 | 0 | 1 | 5 | 4 | 4 | 6 |
|---|---|---|---|---|---|---|
| 5 | 5 | 1 | 6 | 5 | 6 | 6 |

| 3 | 0 | 3 | 1 | 1 | 1 | 0 |
|---|---|---|---|---|---|---|
| 6 | 2 | 5 | 2 | 5 | 3 | 0 |

| 0 | 2 | 2 | 3 | 0 | 0 | 2 |
|---|---|---|---|---|---|---|
| 1 | 4 | 2 | 4 | 3 | 4 | 3 |

| 1 | 5 | 0 | 3 | 2 | 1 | 4 |
|---|---|---|---|---|---|---|
| 6 | 5 | 6 | 3 | 6 | 4 | 4 |

### 301

Betty, surgeon, and Alice, lawyer, are sisters. Frank, surgeon, and Dave, accountant, are brothers. Carol, accountant, and Ed, lawyer are siblings. Marriages are: Betty and Ed; Alice and Dave; and Carol and Frank.

### 302

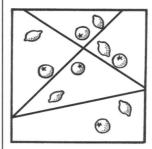

### 303

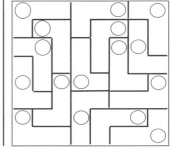

## 304

Nos. 3, 4 and 9

## 305

| | | | | |
|---|---|---|---|---|
| T C | 9 H | K C | J S | 8 H |
| T D | 8 D | Q C | 9 S | Q D |
| 8 C | 8 S | K H | Q S | A H |
| T S | K S | J H | J C | J D |
| Q H | 9 C | T S | 9 D | K D |

## 306

## 307

| B | A | E | C | D |
|---|---|---|---|---|
| E | C | A | D | B |
| D | E | C | B | A |
| C | B | D | A | E |
| A | D | B | E | C |

## 308

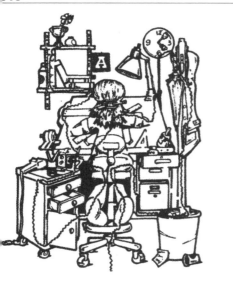

## 309

ZULU = 83 (A=15, B=10, C=4, D=24, E=7, F=16, G=17, H=21, I=6, J=25, K=20, L=8, M=1, N=5, O=13, P=9, Q=14, R=2, S=22, T=3, U=26, V=19, W=12, X=18, Y=11, Z=23)

## 310

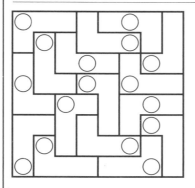

## 311

| C | D | | B | A |
|---|---|---|---|---|
| A | D | B | | C |
| B | C | | A | D |
| D | A | | B | C |
| | C | D | A | B |
| | B | A | C | D |

## 312

| 2 | 5 | 2 | 7 | 2 | 3 | 1 | 5 |
|---|---|---|---|---|---|---|---|
| 6 | 5 | 6 | 4 | 2 | 5 | 6 | 5 |
| 4 | 1 | 1 | 1 | 3 | 4 | 3 | 1 |
| 3 | 5 | 4 | 6 | 2 | 7 | 4 | 1 |
| 2 | 1 | 4 | 2 | 7 | 3 | 3 | 6 |
| 1 | 5 | 3 | 3 | 7 | 4 | 2 | 4 |
| 7 | 5 | 7 | 7 | 6 | 6 | 6 | 7 |

## 313

2 and 5

## 314

Piece no. 4

## 315

5 is the innermost number on strap D (clue 4), so that cannot be the strap referred to in clue 5, nor can strap E (clue 3), or strap C (clue 7), while the outermost numbers on both straps A and F must be single-digit numbers (clue 2), so the strap referred to in clue 5 must be strap B. Clue 8 tells us the 17 is not the innermost number, so, from clue 5, the strap B numbers, reading outwards, must be 12, 1 and 17. So, from clue 8, the innermost number of strap E must be 18, and that on strap 8 therefore 8. We have now placed four innermost numbers, which total 43, so, from clue 1, the other two must total 21. From numbers already placed, we know these cannot be 18 and 3, 17 and 4, 16 and 5, 13 and 8, or 12 and 9, and clue 6 rules out both 15 and 6 and 11 and 10, so they must be 14 and 7. So, from clue 4, the 7 must be on strap C, and the 14 on strap A. We now know the single-digit number in the middle of strap A (clue 2) is not 1, 5, 7 or 8, nor, since the 15 is not an innermost number, can it be 6 (clue 6). It clearly cannot be 2 (clue 2). If it were 3 or 4, then, from clue 2, one of the other two numbers referred to would have to be 1, but we have already placed that number elsewhere, so, by elimination, it must be 9. We know the number outside it is not 7 or 8, nor, since we have placed 7 and 8, can it be 1 or 2 (clue 2). We also know that it is not 5, and, since we have placed the 5, it cannot be 4 (clue 2), so it must be 3 or 6, and so must be the outermost number of strap F (clue 2). But we have placed the only even number on strap F (clue 3), so its outermost number must be 3, and the 6 must be on strap A. We know the 15 is not on strap B, so, from clue 6, it must be the middle number on strap F. Clue 6 now reveals the 10 as an outermost number. The middle number next to it is 16 (clue 6), so they cannot be on strap E, which already has one even number (clue 3), or on C, which has only one two-digit number (clue 7), so they must be on strap D. Since the 2 is not on strap C (clue 7), it must be one of the two even numbers on strap E (clue 3), which leaves the 4 on strap C. Clue 7 also places the 13 on strap C, leaving the 11 on strap E. From clue 3, the 2 must be the outermost number of strap E, and the 13 therefore is the outermost on strap C (clue 7), leaving the 11 and the 4 as the central numbers on their respective straps.

In summary: (Reading outwards)
Strap A: 14, 9, 6.
Strap B: 12, 1, 17.
Strap C: 7, 4, 13.
Strap D: 5, 16, 10.
Strap E: 18, 11, 2.
Strap F: 8, 15, 3.

## 316

| | | 7 | 6 | 5 | 4 | 4 | 5 | 6 | | |
|---|---|---|---|---|---|---|---|---|---|---|
| 6 | 2 | 5 | | 6 | 2 | 3 | | 8 | 9 | 4 |
| 7 | | 7 | 4 | 5 | 0 | 9 | 7 | 5 | | 5 |
| 4 | 3 | 1 | 3 | 6 | 7 | 7 | 7 | 7 | 8 | 6 |
| | 4 | 3 | 2 | 1 | 3 | 4 | 5 | | | |
| 7 | 4 | 2 | | 5 | | 9 | | 8 | 5 | 3 |
| | 4 | 2 | 2 | 4 | 5 | 4 | 5 | | | |
| 5 | 5 | 4 | 4 | 3 | 1 | 3 | 5 | 6 | 6 | 6 |
| 6 | | 5 | 4 | 4 | 3 | 0 | 9 | 9 | | 6 |
| 5 | 2 | 2 | | 5 | 2 | 1 | | 4 | 3 | 2 |
| | 4 | 3 | 1 | 2 | 3 | 4 | 4 | | | |

## 317

Man H is the wanted man.

## 318

13

## 319

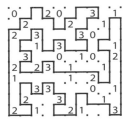

## 320

Numbering the positions 1 (left end) to 5 (right end);
Snuffy is not in positions 1 or 5.
Snuffy is not in position 2 as that would put Basher on the left end and Wilf would have to be next door to either Clogger or Alf, which he cannot be. Snuffy is not in position 4 as that would put Clogger in 5 but he cannot be next to Snuffy. So Snuffy is in position 3. Clogger is in position 5. Wilf cannot be in 2 or 4 and must be in 1. So Alf is in 4 and Basher in 2. Alf was the cloth-headed thief.

## 321

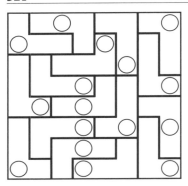

## 322

## 323

| SKIP | LEAD | TWO | THREE |
|------|------|-----|-------|
| REG | PETE | JOAN | DORIS |
| RITA | PAULINE | JIM | DAVE |
| RON | PAMELA | JANET | DENNIS |
| ROSE | PHILIP | JOHN | DEIRDRE |

Reg 24 – Rose 21
Rita 17 – Ron 12

## 324

| B | D |   |   | C | A |
|---|---|---|---|---|---|
| A |   | C |   | B | D |
| C |   | D | A |   | B |
|   | A | B | C | D |   |
|   | B |   | D | A | C |
| D | C | A | B |   |   |

## 325

| 2 | 7 | 3 | 4 | 1 | 9 | 5 | 8 | 6 |
|---|---|---|---|---|---|---|---|---|
| 9 | 5 | 6 | 8 | 7 | 3 | 4 | 2 | 1 |
| 1 | 4 | 8 | 5 | 2 | 6 | 7 | 9 | 3 |
| 7 | 8 | 1 | 9 | 5 | 4 | 6 | 3 | 2 |
| 6 | 2 | 4 | 3 | 8 | 7 | 1 | 5 | 9 |
| 5 | 3 | 9 | 1 | 6 | 2 | 8 | 7 | 4 |
| 4 | 1 | 7 | 2 | 9 | 5 | 3 | 6 | 8 |
| 3 | 9 | 5 | 6 | 4 | 8 | 2 | 1 | 7 |
| 8 | 6 | 2 | 7 | 3 | 1 | 9 | 4 | 5 |

## 326

Each square tile has neighbours – tiles that share an edge. The corners have just two neighbours, those along the edge have three and the ones in the middle have four. For each square, check how many of its neighbours are in the same state (empty, red or blue) as the cell itself. If the score is 0 – the cell becomes empty; if it is 1 or 2 – colour it red and if it is 3 or 4 colour it blue.

## 327

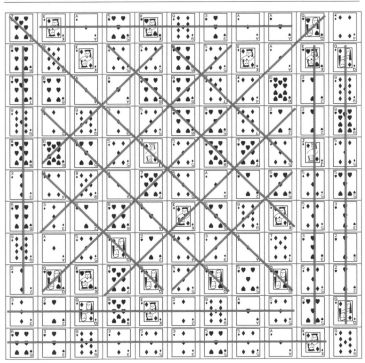

## 328

| GHOST | OF | AT | FEATURE |
|-------|-----|-----|---------|
| A | DYSART | HAM HOUSE | PAPERS |
| B | WINDHAM | FELBRIGG | BOOKS |
| C | BOLEYN | BLICKLING | HEADLESS |
| D | VERNEY | CLAYDON | HAND |
| E | LEGH | LYME PARK | FUNERAL |

## 329

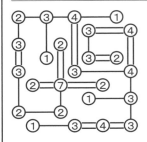

## 330

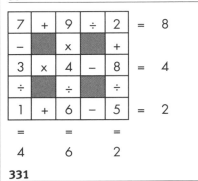

| 7 | + | 9 | ÷ | 2 | = | 8 |
|---|---|---|---|---|---|---|
| − |   | × |   | + |   |   |
| 3 | × | 4 | − | 8 | = | 4 |
| ÷ |   | ÷ |   | ÷ |   |   |
| 1 | + | 6 | − | 5 | = | 2 |
| = |   | = |   | = |   |   |
| 4 |   | 6 |   | 2 |   |   |

## 331

The weights that will go up are 1 and 4 and the weights that will go down are 2, 3 and 5.

**332**

**333**

**334**

| 5 | 5 | 7 | 5 | 6 | 5 | 7 | 5 |
|---|---|---|---|---|---|---|---|
| 3 | 3 | 3 | 1 | 1 | 2 | 1 | 2 |
| 3 | 4 | 6 | 2 | 6 | 7 | 3 | 1 |
| 6 | 1 | 5 | 7 | 1 | 1 | 7 | 7 |
| 2 | 7 | 7 | 4 | 4 | 2 | 6 | 1 |
| 5 | 4 | 4 | 2 | 3 | 2 | 4 | 6 |
| 3 | 6 | 4 | 1 | 2 | 1 | 3 | 6 |

**335**

| B | A |   | C | D |   |
|---|---|---|---|---|---|
| D | A |   |   | B | C |
|   | C | D | A |   | B |
| A | D | B | C |   |   |
| B |   | C | D | A |   |
| C |   |   | B | D | A |

**336**

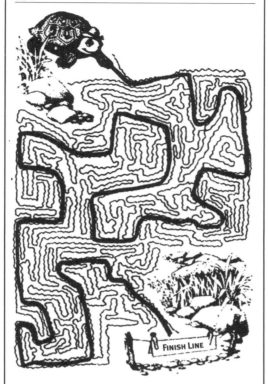

FINISH LINE

**337**

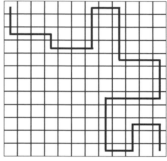

**338**

2

**339**

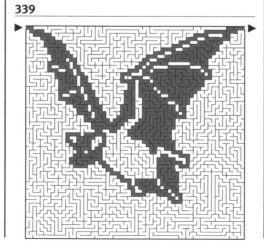

**340**

Piece b

**341**

| FORENAME | SURNAME | FORENAME | SURNAME |
|----------|---------|----------|---------|
| JUAN | FIGN-DIAZ | ISABELLA | DA BOLLA |
| MANUEL | GHIAZ | MARIA | NIDJOTA |
| PANCHO | HEROLE | JUANITA | MEEYA |
| SANCHO | MUCHO | ROSA | SUTAZ |

**342**

| C |   | D |   | B | A |
|---|---|---|---|---|---|
| A | D | B |   | C | A |
| B | C |   | A | D |   |
| D | A |   | B |   | C |
|   |   | C | D | A | B |
|   | B | A | C |   | D |

**343**

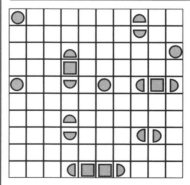

**344**

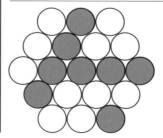

**345**

## 346

Rabbit D

## 347

| 5 | + | 7 | ÷ | 6 | = | 2 |
|---|---|---|---|---|---|---|
| + | | − | | ÷ | | |
| 8 | − | 4 | x | 2 | = | 8 |
| − | | x | | + | | |
| 9 | ÷ | 3 | − | 1 | = | 2 |
| = | | = | | = | | |
| 4 | | 9 | | 4 | | |

## 348

| PANELLIST | GUEST | OCCUPATION | OCCUPATION |
|-----------|-------|------------|------------|
| GERTA | KEN | FLEDGER'S | CRINGE |
| MILES | CONNIE | GRUTTLER'S | HOCKER |
| NOAH | ANN | CRIMPER'S | SLANT |
| WANDA | ENA | TADDLER'S | POSSE |

## 349

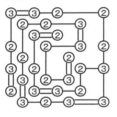

## 350

A = 2
B = 3
C = 1

## 351

## 352

| | | | |
|---|---|---|---|
| TURNIPS | GRAPES | POTATOES | BANANAS |
| DATES | YAMS | FIGS | RADISHES |
| W'CRESS | APPLES | MARROWS | KUMQUATS |
| LYCHEES | PEAS | CHERRIES | ONIONS |

## 353

Flag, fork, candle

## 354

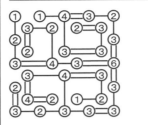

## 355

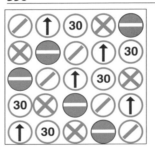

## 356

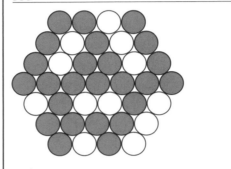

## 357

A1=B5, A2=F1, C1=E5, D5=E2, F2=F5

## 358

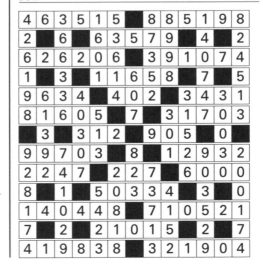

## 359

Letter E

## 360

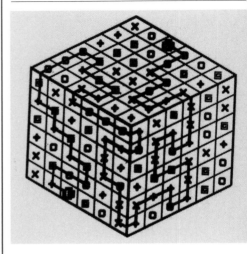

## 361

2 and 4

## 362

| Shop | Customer | Video |
|------|----------|-------|
| Just Flicks | C Nitt | Gosh! |
| More Movies | B Dee-High | Whew! |
| Nite Rates | A Blinkon | Wow! |
| Rent 'n' Rave | D Cryer | Hey! |

## 363

E inner is given as 4, so C inner, which must be an even number (clue 4) cannot be 4 or 8. If it were 2 and D inner 3 from clue 2, B outer and H inner would both be 3 and, from clue 3, the inner 6 could only be in segment G. C outer would therefore also be 6 as would F middle (clue 4). In that case outer would have to be 12, which is impossible. So C inner must be 6 and D inner 3 (clue 4). So, from clue 2, B outer must be 7, H middle 8 and H inner 7, and since those two numbers add up to 15, H outer must be 0. With the inner being in C, the outer 6 must be in G (clue 3) and B inner must therefore be 5 (clue 2). To complete the B quota, B middle must be 3. We know D inner is 3, and, since from clue 4, outer is double D middle, those numbers must be 8 and respectively. F outer must be four times G middle (clue 4) and since the outer circle already has an 8, F outer must be 4, middle 1 and F middle, from the same clue, 2. To complete their quotas, F inner must be 9 and G inner 8. C outer must be 2 (clue 4) and C middle 7. All inner numbers have now been inserted except in A, which is an odd number (clue 2, so it must be 1. To make up A's quota, the remaining odd numbers must be 5 and 9 and from clue 1, the 9 must be outer and 5 A middle. Therefore E outer must also be 5 (clue 4) and E middle 6.

In summary:
Numbers given as outer, middle, inner.
A, 9, 5, 1.
B, 7, 3, 5.
C, 2, 7, 6.
D, 8, 4, 3.
E, 5, 6, 4.
F, 4, 2, 9.
G, 6, 1, 8.
H, 0, 8, 7.

**364**

| C |   | B |   | A | D |
|---|---|---|---|---|---|
| D |   |   | C | B | A |
|   | B | A | D |   | C |
| A | C |   | B | D |   |
|   | A | D |   | C | B |
| B | D | C | A |   |   |

**365**

rint 3

**366**

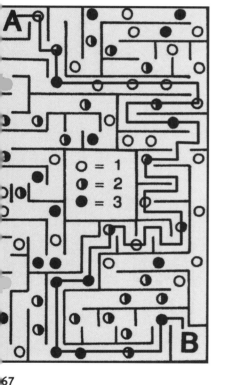

O = 1
◑ = 2
● = 3

**367**

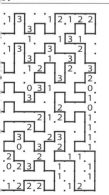

**368**

**369**

|          | Table 1        | Table 2        | Table 3         | Table 4         |
|----------|----------------|----------------|-----------------|-----------------|
| N        | Harry          | Babs           | Tessa (dummy)   | Fred            |
| E        | Susie (dummy)  | Kate           | Connie          | Lola            |
| S        | Jane           | Roger (dummy)  | Dot             | Gordon          |
| W        | Peter          | Alan           | Michael         | Eddie (dummy)   |
| Contract | 2 Diamonds     | 4 Spades       | 1 Heart         | 3 Clubs         |

**370**

|          | Eagle | Birdie | Par | Bogey | Double Bogey | FINAL SCORE |
|----------|-------|--------|-----|-------|--------------|-------------|
| Darma    | 2     | 5      | 1   | 6     | 4            | 77          |
| Jackliss | 4     | 2      | 8   | 3     | 1            | 67          |
| Clayer   | 1     | 4      | 6   | 2     | 5            | 78          |

**371**

| A | E | D | B | C |
|---|---|---|---|---|
| B | D | C | E | A |
| D | C | E | A | B |
| E | A | B | C | D |
| C | B | A | D | E |

**372**

**373**

| 4 | + | 6 | − | 1 | = | 9 |
|---|---|---|---|---|---|---|
| ÷ |   | + |   | × |   |   |
| 2 | × | 8 | − | 9 | = | 7 |
| + |   | ÷ |   | ÷ |   |   |
| 5 | + | 7 | ÷ | 3 | = | 4 |
| = |   | = |   | = |   |   |
| 7 |   | 2 |   | 3 |   |   |

**374**

| 0 | 4 | 1 | 5 | 0 | 0 | 0 |
|---|---|---|---|---|---|---|
| 0 | 5 | 5 | 2 | 5 | 6 | 0 | 1 |

(numbers arranged in domino grid)

| 0 | 4 | 1 | 5 | 0 | 0 | 0 |
| 5 | 5 | 2 | 5 | 6 | 0 | 1 |
| 5 | 2 | 0 | 4 | 3 | 3 | 0 |
| 6 | 4 | 2 | 4 | 3 | 4 | 4 |
| 1 | 4 | 2 | 0 | 1 | 3 | 1 |
| 1 | 6 | 2 | 3 | 6 | 6 | 5 |
| 1 | 1 | 2 | 6 | 3 | 2 | 2 |
| 4 | 3 | 5 | 6 | 5 | 6 | 3 |

**375**

| C | D | E | A | B |
|---|---|---|---|---|
| E | A | B | D | C |
| B | C | A | E | D |
| A | B | D | C | E |
| D | E | C | B | A |

**376**

| NAME     | SANDWICH | CRISPS | FRUIT  |
|----------|----------|--------|--------|
| FELICITY | EGG      | PRAWN  | PEACH  |
| FELIX    | HAM      | SALTED | ORANGE |
| FIONA    | CHICKEN  | CHEESE | BANANA |
| FREDDIE  | CHEESE   | S & V  | APPLE  |

**377**

A – The Old Mill – 1964
B – St Aidan's Church – 1981
C – Crane Bay – 1976
D – Lower Wood – 1992
E – Fiddler's Brook – 1988

**378**

1 and 7
2 and 4
3 and 6
5 and 8

**379**

A – H        D – G
B – F        E – J
C – I

## 380

| Quarter-Finals | Semi-Finals | Final | Winner |
|---|---|---|---|
| Chelsea v Norwich | Chelsea | | |
| | | v | Arsenal |
| Spurs v Arsenal | Arsenal | | |
| | | | EVERTON |
| Everton v Watford | Everton | | |
| | | v | Everton |
| Liverpool v Southampton | Liverpool | | |

## 381

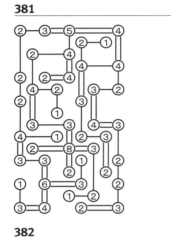

## 382

| J | Q | J | T | 9 |
|---|---|---|---|---|
| C | S | H | S | S |
| Q | 8 | J | T | 9 |
| C | C | D | D | D |
| K | 9 | Q | Q | 9 |
| H | H | D | H | C |
| T | K | 8 | A | K |
| C | S | D | H | C |
| T | 8 | J | 8 | K |
| H | H | S | S | D |

## 383

| 6 0 | 5 | 1 | 1 | 4 | 1 |
|---|---|---|---|---|---|
| 6 2 | 5 | 1 | 3 | 6 | 4 |

| 1 | 2 | 3 | 1 | 3 | 4 |
|---|---|---|---|---|---|
| 5 | 3 | 5 | 2 | 6 | 5 |

| 2 | 2 | 4 | 5 | 0 | 1 |
|---|---|---|---|---|---|
| 2 | 4 | 4 | 6 | 1 | 6 |

| 0 | 0 | 2 | 0 | 2 | 3 |
|---|---|---|---|---|---|
| 3 | 6 | 5 | 4 | 6 | 3 |

## 384

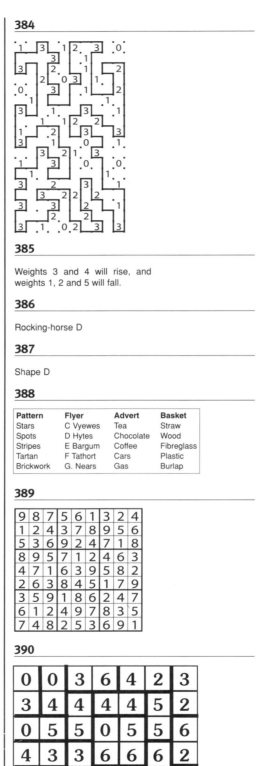

## 385

Weights 3 and 4 will rise, and weights 1, 2 and 5 will fall.

## 386

Rocking-horse D

## 387

Shape D

## 388

| Pattern | Flyer | Advert | Basket |
|---|---|---|---|
| Stars | C Vyewes | Tea | Straw |
| Spots | D Hytes | Chocolate | Wood |
| Stripes | E Bargum | Coffee | Fibreglass |
| Tartan | F Tathort | Cars | Plastic |
| Brickwork | G. Nears | Gas | Burlap |

## 389

| 9 | 8 | 7 | 5 | 6 | 1 | 3 | 2 | 4 |
|---|---|---|---|---|---|---|---|---|
| 1 | 2 | 4 | 3 | 7 | 8 | 9 | 5 | 6 |
| 5 | 3 | 6 | 9 | 2 | 4 | 7 | 1 | 8 |
| 8 | 9 | 5 | 7 | 1 | 2 | 4 | 6 | 3 |
| 4 | 7 | 1 | 6 | 3 | 9 | 5 | 8 | 2 |
| 2 | 6 | 3 | 8 | 4 | 5 | 1 | 7 | 9 |
| 3 | 5 | 9 | 1 | 8 | 6 | 2 | 4 | 7 |
| 6 | 1 | 2 | 4 | 9 | 7 | 8 | 3 | 5 |
| 7 | 4 | 8 | 2 | 5 | 3 | 6 | 9 | 1 |

## 390

| 0 | 0 | 3 | 6 | 4 | 2 | 3 |
|---|---|---|---|---|---|---|
| 3 | 4 | 4 | 4 | 4 | 5 | 2 |
| 0 | 5 | 5 | 0 | 5 | 5 | 6 |
| 4 | 3 | 3 | 6 | 6 | 6 | 2 |
| 4 | 5 | 3 | 0 | 5 | 1 | 3 |
| 6 | 2 | 2 | 0 | 1 | 1 | 1 |
| 1 | 5 | 2 | 0 | 2 | 4 | 1 |
| 1 | 3 | 6 | 6 | 2 | 1 | 0 |

## 391

| 9 | + | 7 | − | 8 | = | 8 |
|---|---|---|---|---|---|---|
| − | | + | | × | | |
| 6 | − | 2 | × | 1 | = | 4 |
| + | | ÷ | | ÷ | | |
| 5 | − | 3 | × | 4 | = | 8 |

| = | | = | | = | | |
| 8 | | 3 | | 2 | | |

## 392

1,7,3,4,2,0,5,8,9,6

## 393

3 and 7

## 394

A – G
B – E
C – D
F – H

## 395

From left to right:
King of Spades – Queen of Spades – King of Clubs – King of Hearts.

## 396

## 397

## 398

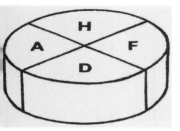

## 399

| SEAT | FORENAME | SURNAME | BUSINESS |
|------|----------|---------|----------|
| 1 | Ella | Vatripp | Tourist |
| 2 | Ron | Waylite | Director |
| 3 | Adelia | Baddand | Croupier |
| 4 | Mahatma | Ghote | Magician |
| 5 | Stewart | Hess | Male Model |
| 6 | Lady | Smayde | Author |

## 400

14 red, 4 yellow, 2 green, 5 blue, 3 pink.

## 401

There are 54 missing bricks.

## 402

| 7 | 3 | 5 | 8 | 6 | 9 | 2 | 1 | 4 |
|---|---|---|---|---|---|---|---|---|
| 9 | 8 | 1 | 7 | 2 | 4 | 6 | 3 | 5 |
| 2 | 6 | 4 | 1 | 3 | 5 | 8 | 9 | 7 |
| 8 | 5 | 7 | 9 | 4 | 1 | 3 | 2 | 6 |
| 3 | 4 | 2 | 6 | 8 | 7 | 9 | 5 | 1 |
| 1 | 9 | 6 | 3 | 5 | 2 | 7 | 4 | 8 |
| 6 | 2 | 3 | 4 | 1 | 8 | 5 | 7 | 9 |
| 4 | 7 | 8 | 5 | 9 | 3 | 1 | 6 | 2 |
| 5 | 1 | 9 | 2 | 7 | 6 | 4 | 8 | 3 |

## 403

## 404

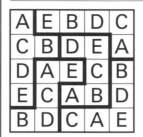

## 405

There are four knots.

## 406

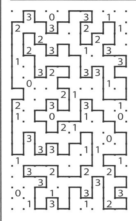

## 407

Weights A and C will rise, and weights E, B and D will fall.

## 408

From the top: blue, red, yellow, lavender, green, orange.

## 409

If you were on the near side of the Moon – the Earth would always be up and never set. If you were on the far side of the Moon – the Earth would never rise and you would not directly know it existed. It just so happens that, as the Moon takes about 29 days to orbit the Earth, so, too it takes the same time to spin once on its axis. So it presents the same side to the Earth all the time.

## 410

From the left: Rachel, blonde, programmer; Teresa, brunette, saleslady; Mavis, redhead, secretary.

## 411

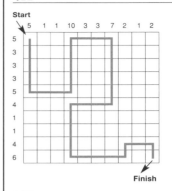

## 412

Card 1

## 413

Pictures 6 and 8.

## 414

| | Eagle | Birdie | Par | Bogey | Double Bogey | FINAL SCORE |
|--------|-------|--------|-----|-------|--------------|-------------|
| Darma | 3 | 5 | 7 | 2 | 1 | 65 |
| Jackliss | 1 | 4 | 8 | 3 | 2 | 73 |
| Clayer | 2 | 7 | 5 | 1 | 3 | 68 |

## 415

| 7 | 9 | | 1 | 3 | 6 | | 8 | 6 |
|---|---|---|---|---|---|---|---|---|
| 9 | 8 | | 2 | 1 | 4 | | 9 | 8 |
| 8 | 6 | 7 | 3 | | 8 | 6 | 7 | 9 |
| | | 9 | 6 | | 7 | 9 | | |
| 9 | 7 | 8 | 4 | | 9 | 8 | 7 | 5 |
| 8 | 2 | | | | | | 3 | 1 |
| 7 | 1 | 2 | 3 | | 2 | 1 | 9 | 3 |
| | | 4 | 8 | | 9 | 7 | | |
| 3 | 5 | 1 | 2 | | 1 | 3 | 2 | 6 |
| 2 | 9 | | 1 | 7 | 3 | | 1 | 8 |
| 1 | 8 | | 4 | 9 | 8 | | 3 | 9 |

## 416

Diagram 1–16 triangles
Diagram 2–10 triangles
Diagram 3–18 triangles
Diagram 4–12 triangles
Ostrich 3 is holding the diagram with the most triangles.

## 417

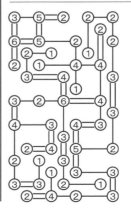

## 418

1 Madame Poll's Parrots
2 Agilles Acrobats
3 Jim the Juggler
4 Flying Fortresses
5 Clever Clowns
6 Fred the Fire-eater
7 Crazy Carvellos
8 Senor Pedro's Poodles

## 419

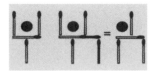

## 420

They match up as follows:
A6, B4, C5, D1, E2, F8, G3, H7.

## 421

Make a circular cut around the inside of the pie, then cut into quarters.

## 422

| 2 | 6 | 1 | 4 | 4 | 3 | 0 | 3 |
|---|---|---|---|---|---|---|---|
| 2 | 3 | 5 | 5 | 6 | 6 | 4 | 2 |
| 0 | 1 | 0 | 2 | 1 | 1 | 1 | 4 |
| 5 | 3 | 0 | 0 | 5 | 3 | 0 | 5 |
| 0 | 6 | 1 | 2 | 1 | 6 | 4 | 1 |
| 4 | 3 | 3 | 4 | 0 | 5 | 5 | 6 |
| 2 | 4 | 6 | 3 | 2 | 2 | 6 | 5 |

## 423

Blocks 1 and 3.

## 424

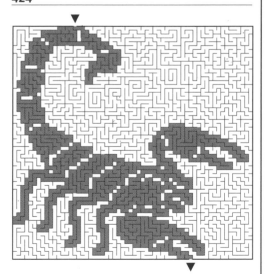

## 425

Arrange to have your body flown eastwards across the International Date Line (where it is still the day before!) and buried immediately.

## 426

Path B

## 427

| 8 | 2 | 5 | 3 | 7 | 1 | 9 | 6 | 4 |
|---|---|---|---|---|---|---|---|---|
| 9 | 4 | 3 | 6 | 2 | 5 | 8 | 7 | 1 |
| 1 | 6 | 7 | 8 | 9 | 4 | 2 | 5 | 3 |
| 3 | 5 | 9 | 2 | 8 | 7 | 1 | 4 | 6 |
| 6 | 1 | 2 | 4 | 5 | 3 | 7 | 8 | 9 |
| 4 | 7 | 8 | 1 | 6 | 9 | 5 | 3 | 2 |
| 5 | 8 | 4 | 9 | 1 | 6 | 3 | 2 | 7 |
| 7 | 9 | 6 | 5 | 3 | 2 | 4 | 1 | 8 |
| 2 | 3 | 1 | 7 | 4 | 8 | 6 | 9 | 5 |

## 428

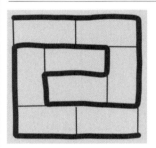

## 429

Amy – orange, Bob – yellow, Chloe – blue, Fiona – violet, Jack – pink, Martin – red, Paul – brown, Sharon – green.

## 430

| 1 | 0 | 7 | 9 | 8 | 9 | ■ | 2 | 1 | 2 | 8 | 0 | 6 |
|---|---|---|---|---|---|---|---|---|---|---|---|---|
| 3 | ■ | 1 | ■ | 3 | 0 | 9 | 4 | 7 | ■ | 1 | ■ | 6 |
| 4 | 5 | 3 | 5 | 2 | 7 | ■ | 5 | 8 | 1 | 9 | 4 | 1 |
| 8 | ■ | 9 | ■ | 6 | 1 | 5 | 1 | 3 | ■ | 2 | ■ | 6 |
| 7 | 6 | 5 | 7 | ■ | 8 | 7 | 4 | ■ | 9 | 0 | 8 | 3 |
| 1 | 0 | 4 | 3 | 9 | ■ | 2 | ■ | 2 | 7 | 1 | 9 | 0 |
| ■ | 1 | ■ | 3 | 0 | 4 | ■ | 4 | 2 | 1 | ■ | 2 | ■ |
| 5 | 7 | 1 | 4 | 7 | ■ | 2 | ■ | 6 | 7 | 3 | 2 | 9 |
| 7 | 5 | 7 | 6 | ■ | 8 | 1 | 5 | ■ | 9 | 4 | 4 | 7 |
| 2 | ■ | 2 | ■ | 1 | 4 | 7 | 5 | 6 | ■ | 1 | ■ | 1 |
| 2 | 1 | 3 | 0 | 7 | 1 | ■ | 3 | 1 | 6 | 2 | 9 | 3 |
| 1 | ■ | 5 | ■ | 4 | 6 | 0 | 2 | 3 | ■ | 6 | ■ | 2 |
| 5 | 5 | 1 | 1 | 0 | 8 | ■ | 6 | 7 | 6 | 8 | 6 | 9 |

## 431

From the top: blue, orange, yellow, lavender, green, red.

## 432

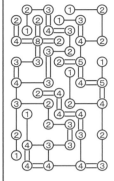

## 433

Kettledrum 7

## 434

| 2 | 0 | 2 | 1 | 1 | 0 | 1 |
|---|---|---|---|---|---|---|
| 6 | 6 | 3 | 3 | 2 | 2 | 0 |
| 4 | 3 | 5 | 4 | 2 | 6 | 6 |
| 0 | 0 | 0 | 4 | 4 | 6 | 3 |
| 1 | 6 | 5 | 4 | 5 | 5 | 1 |
| 6 | 0 | 3 | 5 | 2 | 5 | 4 |
| 0 | 4 | 3 | 5 | 5 | 1 | 2 |
| 3 | 4 | 1 | 3 | 2 | 1 | 6 |

## 435

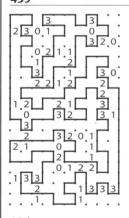

## 436

| 7 | 6 | 8 | 3 | 4 | 1 | 2 | 9 | 5 |
|---|---|---|---|---|---|---|---|---|
| 9 | 3 | 2 | 8 | 6 | 5 | 7 | 4 | 1 |
| 5 | 1 | 4 | 9 | 2 | 7 | 6 | 8 | 3 |
| 2 | 8 | 9 | 1 | 5 | 3 | 4 | 7 | 6 |
| 3 | 5 | 7 | 4 | 9 | 6 | 1 | 2 | 8 |
| 1 | 4 | 6 | 7 | 8 | 2 | 5 | 3 | 9 |
| 6 | 7 | 5 | 2 | 3 | 9 | 8 | 1 | 4 |
| 8 | 2 | 3 | 6 | 1 | 4 | 9 | 5 | 7 |
| 4 | 9 | 1 | 5 | 7 | 8 | 3 | 6 | 2 |

## 437

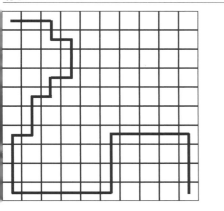

| | B | C | A | D | |
|---|---|---|---|---|---|
| A | D | | | C | B |
| | C | A | B | | D |
| B | | D | | A | C |
| C | | B | D | | A |
| D | A | | C | B | |

## 438

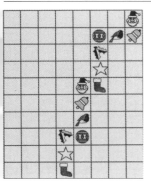

## 439

Alien 4

## 440

The order is:
9, 1, 11, 5, 14, 7, 10, 2, 12, 3, 13, 8, 4, 6.

## 441

## 442

| 2 | 6 | 0 | 6 | 0 | 5 | 3 |
|---|---|---|---|---|---|---|
| 3 | 3 | 3 | 5 | 5 | 6 | 5 |
| 6 | 2 | 0 | 4 | 1 | 6 | 6 |
| 3 | 2 | 1 | 4 | 4 | 3 | 4 |
| 5 | 2 | 4 | 1 | 1 | 1 | 6 |
| 2 | 3 | 0 | 2 | 3 | 2 | 4 |
| 5 | 4 | 1 | 0 | 0 | 1 | 6 |
| 5 | 0 | 1 | 0 | 4 | 5 | 2 |

## 443

| 5 | 0 | 4 | 1 | 1 | 9 | ■ | 8 | 2 | 4 | 3 | 3 | 2 |
|---|---|---|---|---|---|---|---|---|---|---|---|---|
| 1 | ■ | 0 | ■ | 7 | 1 | 0 | 5 | 0 | ■ | 4 | ■ | 1 |
| 1 | 8 | 3 | 5 | 4 | 7 | ■ | 9 | 0 | 1 | 5 | 7 | 0 |
| 4 | ■ | 5 | ■ | 6 | 1 | 1 | 4 | 0 | ■ | 6 | ■ | 9 |
| 3 | 5 | 8 | 4 | ■ | 7 | 5 | 7 | ■ | 4 | 7 | 3 | 8 |
| 3 | 1 | 2 | 5 | 5 | ■ | 5 | ■ | 1 | 2 | 8 | 0 | 7 |
| ■ | 7 | ■ | 6 | 6 | 2 | ■ | 3 | 7 | 7 | ■ | 4 | ■ |
| 8 | 2 | 7 | 1 | 0 | ■ | 4 | ■ | 9 | 1 | 6 | 0 | 6 |
| 5 | 6 | 6 | 6 | ■ | 2 | 8 | 1 | ■ | 6 | 6 | 5 | 6 |
| 6 | ■ | 6 | ■ | 7 | 4 | 8 | 2 | 8 | ■ | 5 | ■ | 7 |
| 4 | 5 | 6 | 4 | 8 | 9 | ■ | 3 | 1 | 7 | 5 | 0 | 6 |
| 7 | ■ | 6 | ■ | 6 | 3 | 4 | 2 | 2 | ■ | 4 | ■ | 8 |
| 2 | 1 | 5 | 0 | 3 | 2 | ■ | 1 | 2 | 3 | 4 | 5 | 6 |

## 444

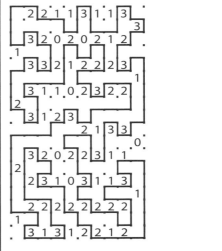

## 445

| | B | | D | C | A |
|---|---|---|---|---|---|
| C | A | B | | D | |
| A | | D | B | | C |
| B | | C | A | | D |
| | D | A | C | B | |
| D | C | | | A | B |

## 446

| 9 | 8 | 5 | 3 | 1 | 4 | 2 | 6 | 7 |
|---|---|---|---|---|---|---|---|---|
| 6 | 3 | 1 | 7 | 2 | 5 | 9 | 4 | 8 |
| 7 | 4 | 2 | 8 | 9 | 6 | 1 | 5 | 3 |
| 8 | 7 | 3 | 9 | 5 | 2 | 6 | 1 | 4 |
| 4 | 2 | 9 | 1 | 6 | 3 | 8 | 7 | 5 |
| 5 | 1 | 6 | 4 | 8 | 7 | 3 | 9 | 2 |
| 2 | 5 | 4 | 6 | 3 | 9 | 7 | 8 | 1 |
| 1 | 9 | 7 | 2 | 4 | 8 | 5 | 3 | 6 |
| 3 | 6 | 8 | 5 | 7 | 1 | 4 | 2 | 9 |

## 447

| 1 | 3 | ■ | 1 | 2 | ■ | ■ | 9 | 7 |
|---|---|---|---|---|---|---|---|---|
| 4 | 2 | 5 | 3 | 1 | ■ | 9 | 8 | 6 |
| 2 | 1 | 3 | ■ | 4 | 9 | 8 | 6 | ■ |
| ■ | ■ | 1 | 2 | ■ | 7 | 6 | ■ | ■ |
| 1 | 3 | 2 | 4 | 6 | ■ | ■ | 7 | 8 |
| 3 | 2 | ■ | 1 | 8 | 2 | ■ | 9 | 1 |
| ■ | 1 | 2 | ■ | 9 | 6 | 8 | 7 | 5 |
| ■ | 3 | 7 | ■ | 1 | 9 | ■ | ■ | ■ |
| 8 | 6 | 9 | 7 | ■ | 7 | 2 | 1 | ■ |
| 2 | 7 | 1 | ■ | 2 | 4 | 6 | 1 | 3 |
| 7 | 9 | ■ | 1 | 9 | ■ | 4 | 2 | ■ |

## 448

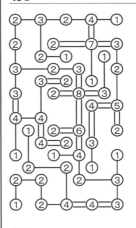

## 449

From the top: A, C, E, B, D, F

## 450

| ■ | ■ | ■ | ■ | ■ | ■ | ■ | 4 |
|---|---|---|---|---|---|---|---|
| ■ | 3 | ■ | 2 | ■ | 2 | ■ | 3 |
| 2 | ■ | ■ | ■ | 4 | ■ | ■ | ■ |
| ■ | ■ | ■ | ■ | ■ | ■ | ■ | ■ |
| ■ | 4 | ■ | 2 | ■ | ■ | ■ | 3 |
| ■ | ■ | ■ | ■ | ■ | 3 | ■ | ■ |
| ■ | ■ | ■ | ■ | ■ | 2 | ■ | 3 |
| 3 | ■ | 3 | ■ | ■ | ■ | ■ | ■ |

## 451

(grid of connected numbered circles)

## 452

Number 3

## 453

| 6 | 4 | 3 | 9 | 5 | 7 | 2 | 8 | 1 |
|---|---|---|---|---|---|---|---|---|
| 8 | 5 | 2 | 4 | 3 | 1 | 6 | 9 | 7 |
| 9 | 1 | 7 | 8 | 6 | 2 | 5 | 3 | 4 |
| 2 | 8 | 9 | 1 | 7 | 3 | 4 | 5 | 6 |
| 5 | 3 | 1 | 2 | 4 | 6 | 9 | 7 | 8 |
| 4 | 7 | 6 | 5 | 9 | 8 | 3 | 1 | 2 |
| 7 | 9 | 5 | 6 | 8 | 4 | 1 | 2 | 3 |
| 3 | 2 | 4 | 7 | 1 | 9 | 8 | 6 | 5 |
| 1 | 6 | 8 | 3 | 2 | 5 | 7 | 4 | 9 |

## 454

Architect: Mark Jones; Barber: Neil Franklin; Critic: Luke Harkness; Dentist: Otto Ives; Economist: Karl Gainor.

## 455

## 456

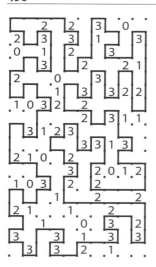

## 457

| N | F | Y | K | C |
|---|---|---|---|---|
| Q | J | W | H | T |
| G | U | R | B | M |
| A | L | D | V | O |
| X | P | I | S | E |

## 458

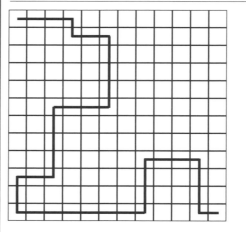

## 459

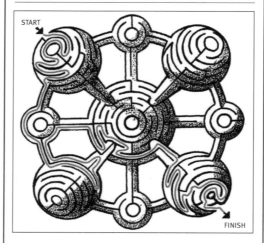

## 460

A Hebe    B Cary
C Alan    D Fred
E Bess    F Enid
G Dave    H Gina

## 461

## 462

| 7 | 0 | 3 | 8 | 9 | 1 | ■ | 8 | 8 | 4 | 2 | 7 | 1 |
|---|---|---|---|---|---|---|---|---|---|---|---|---|
| 7 | ■ | 4 | ■ | 2 | 9 | 0 | 1 | 7 | ■ | 1 | ■ | 0 |
| 6 | 2 | 4 | 8 | 9 | 6 | ■ | 5 | 4 | 3 | 2 | 1 | 0 |
| 9 | ■ | 0 | ■ | 3 | 5 | 7 | 0 | 9 | ■ | 2 | ■ | 2 |
| 7 | 4 | 7 | 5 | ■ | 8 | 3 | 7 | ■ | 7 | 2 | 8 | 0 |
| 6 | 9 | 1 | 7 | 7 | ■ | 6 | ■ | 9 | 1 | 3 | 7 | 0 |
| ■ | 8 | ■ | 6 | 2 | 3 | ■ | 5 | 4 | 7 | ■ | 1 | ■ |
| 4 | 3 | 5 | 8 | 1 | ■ | 4 | ■ | 1 | 0 | 6 | 7 | 9 |
| 6 | 2 | 1 | 9 | ■ | 2 | 1 | 3 | ■ | 5 | 3 | 4 | 2 |
| 3 | ■ | 5 | ■ | 4 | 0 | 2 | 3 | 3 | ■ | 5 | ■ | 1 |
| 3 | 1 | 2 | 1 | 1 | ■ | 4 | 5 | 3 | 3 | 2 | 4 | ■ |
| 2 | ■ | 5 | ■ | 7 | 8 | 9 | 0 | 5 | ■ | 4 | ■ | 0 |
| 2 | 4 | 3 | 4 | 4 | 4 | ■ | 1 | 2 | 1 | 3 | 1 | 4 |

## 463

| 3 | 6 | 8 | 4 | 4 | 0 | 4 |
|---|---|---|---|---|---|---|
| 6 | 2 | 5 | 9 | 0 | 3 | 3 |
| 8 | 5 | 6 | 2 | 7 | 5 | 1 |
| 4 | 9 | 2 | 4 | 8 | 4 | 3 |
| 4 | 0 | 7 | 8 | 0 | 2 | 1 |
| 0 | 3 | 5 | 4 | 2 | 4 | 3 |
| 4 | 3 | 1 | 3 | 1 | 3 | 2 |

## 464

| PLOT | FAMILY | FROM | SIZE |
|---|---|---|---|
| WEST | LARKITTS | FRUMLEY | 4 |
| NORTH | SPENCERS | CHEAPHILL | 3 |
| EAST | GROVES | WELMSIDE | 6 |
| SOUTH | HUGGINS | TYNEHAM | 5 |

## 465

## 466

| | | | | |
|---|---|---|---|---|
| Q | T | T | Q | 9 |
| C | H | S | S | H |
| K | 9 | T | J | J |
| C | C | C | S | C |
| K | 8 | J | 9 | J |
| D | S | H | D | D |
| 9 | Q | 8 | K | Q |
| S | H | H | S | D |
| K | A | 8 | T | 8 |
| H | H | C | D | D |

## 467

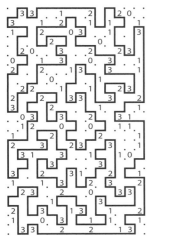

## 468

| FORENAME | SURNAME | SUBJECT | UNIVERSITY |
|---|---|---|---|
| ANNA | JONES | MATHS | YALE |
| BARBARA | BROWN | PHYSICS | HARVARD |
| CLARE | TAYLOR | CHEMISTRY | MIT |
| DIANA | MOORE | BIOLOGY | PRINCETON |

## 469

| | | | | | | | | |
|---|---|---|---|---|---|---|---|---|
| 6 | 4 | 9 | 2 | 5 | 1 | 7 | 8 | 3 |
| 5 | 1 | 8 | 4 | 7 | 3 | 9 | 6 | 2 |
| 3 | 7 | 2 | 9 | 8 | 6 | 1 | 4 | 5 |
| 8 | 2 | 4 | 6 | 1 | 7 | 3 | 5 | 9 |
| 7 | 6 | 3 | 5 | 4 | 9 | 2 | 1 | 8 |
| 1 | 9 | 5 | 3 | 2 | 8 | 6 | 7 | 4 |
| 2 | 5 | 6 | 1 | 3 | 4 | 8 | 9 | 7 |
| 9 | 3 | 7 | 8 | 6 | 5 | 4 | 2 | 1 |
| 4 | 8 | 1 | 7 | 9 | 2 | 5 | 3 | 6 |

## 470

1 Crazy Carvellos
2 Agilles Acrobats
3 Clever Clowns
4 Fred the Fire-eater
5 Jim the Juggler
6 Senor Pedro's Poodles
7 Flying Fortresses
8 Madame Poll's Parrots

## 471

| | | | | | | | | |
|---|---|---|---|---|---|---|---|---|
| 3 | 1 | 9 | 6 | 7 | 5 | 8 | 4 | 2 |
| 5 | 8 | 2 | 3 | 9 | 4 | 6 | 7 | 1 |
| 6 | 7 | 4 | 2 | 1 | 8 | 9 | 3 | 5 |
| 4 | 6 | 7 | 5 | 2 | 9 | 1 | 8 | 3 |
| 1 | 2 | 3 | 7 | 8 | 6 | 4 | 5 | 9 |
| 8 | 9 | 5 | 4 | 3 | 1 | 2 | 6 | 7 |
| 9 | 3 | 1 | 8 | 4 | 7 | 5 | 2 | 6 |
| 2 | 4 | 6 | 1 | 5 | 3 | 7 | 9 | 8 |
| 7 | 5 | 8 | 9 | 6 | 2 | 3 | 1 | 4 |

## 472

| 3 | 6 | 10 | 1 | 8 | 4 | 9 | 2 | 7 | 5 |
|---|---|---|---|---|---|---|---|---|---|
| I | C | G | E | B | J | A | D | H | F |

## 473

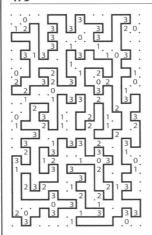

## 474

 Each square tile has neighbours – tiles that share an edge. The corners have just two neighbours, those along the edge have three and the ones in the middle have four. For each square, check how many of it and its neighbours are not white. If the score is 0 or 1 – colour it red; if it is 2 or 3 – colour it black and if it is 4 or 5 leave it empty.

## 475

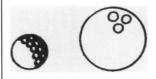

## 476

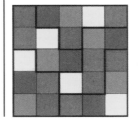

## 477

9018

## 478

From the top: B, E, D, C, F, A

## 479

Piece 8

## 480

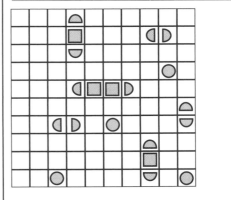

## 481

| | | | | | | | | |
|---|---|---|---|---|---|---|---|---|
| 7 | 3 | 5 | 9 | 2 | 1 | 4 | 8 | 6 |
| 6 | 1 | 4 | 5 | 7 | 8 | 2 | 9 | 3 |
| 9 | 8 | 2 | 6 | 4 | 3 | 5 | 7 | 1 |
| 4 | 9 | 6 | 1 | 5 | 2 | 8 | 3 | 7 |
| 3 | 5 | 1 | 7 | 8 | 6 | 9 | 4 | 2 |
| 8 | 2 | 7 | 3 | 9 | 4 | 6 | 1 | 5 |
| 2 | 6 | 9 | 8 | 1 | 7 | 3 | 5 | 4 |
| 5 | 7 | 3 | 4 | 6 | 9 | 1 | 2 | 8 |
| 1 | 4 | 8 | 2 | 3 | 5 | 7 | 6 | 9 |

## 482

| | | | | | | | | | | | | | |
|---|---|---|---|---|---|---|---|---|---|---|---|---|---|
| 7 | 5 | 9 | 6 | 5 | 7 | ■ | 1 | 6 | 2 | 5 | 6 | 4 |
| 1 | ■ | 5 | ■ | 2 | 9 | 1 | 1 | 0 | ■ | 8 | ■ | 7 |
| 5 | 3 | 8 | 4 | 5 | 8 | ■ | 8 | 4 | 3 | 3 | 5 | 8 |
| 2 | ■ | 5 | ■ | 4 | 2 | 4 | 0 | 7 | ■ | 2 | ■ | 4 |
| 2 | 6 | 5 | 6 | ■ | 8 | 3 | 2 | ■ | 1 | 1 | 3 | 3 |
| 7 | 0 | 5 | 9 | 6 | ■ | 0 | ■ | 3 | 0 | 8 | 7 | 9 |
| ■ | 4 | ■ | 2 | 5 | 6 | ■ | 7 | 7 | 7 | ■ | 2 | ■ |
| 4 | 1 | 2 | 9 | 6 | ■ | 1 | ■ | 8 | 0 | 9 | 0 | 3 |
| 1 | 7 | 6 | 2 | ■ | 5 | 6 | 2 | ■ | 3 | 6 | 7 | 5 |
| 2 | ■ | 3 | ■ | 8 | 9 | 1 | 3 | 4 | ■ | 5 | ■ | 7 |
| 2 | 1 | 6 | 4 | 3 | 2 | ■ | 3 | 8 | 4 | 8 | 5 | 8 |
| 4 | ■ | 4 | ■ | 9 | 7 | 1 | 2 | 6 | ■ | 6 | ■ | 7 |
| 1 | 1 | 6 | 2 | 8 | 5 | ■ | 6 | 4 | 5 | 4 | 4 | 4 |

## 483

She's blown 79 bubbles.

**484**

START

FINISH

**485**

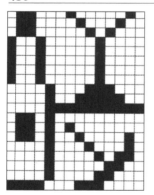

**486**

**487**

| | C | | D | A | B |
|---|---|---|---|---|---|
| B | D | C | | | A |
| A | | B | | D | C |
| D | | A | C | B | |
| C | B | | A | | D |
| | A | D | B | C | |

**488**

72694

**489**

| 6 | 5 | 7 | 1 | 2 | 3 | 4 | 9 | 8 |
|---|---|---|---|---|---|---|---|---|
| 1 | 9 | 4 | 5 | 6 | 8 | 3 | 7 | 2 |
| 2 | 3 | 8 | 7 | 9 | 4 | 5 | 1 | 6 |
| 5 | 8 | 1 | 6 | 3 | 2 | 7 | 4 | 9 |
| 9 | 4 | 2 | 8 | 7 | 5 | 1 | 6 | 3 |
| 3 | 7 | 6 | 4 | 1 | 9 | 8 | 2 | 5 |
| 4 | 2 | 9 | 3 | 8 | 7 | 6 | 5 | 1 |
| 8 | 1 | 5 | 9 | 4 | 6 | 2 | 3 | 7 |
| 7 | 6 | 3 | 2 | 5 | 1 | 9 | 8 | 4 |

**490**

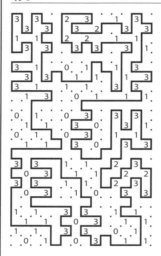

**491**

From the top: green, yellow, red, blue, orange, lavender.

**492**

**493**

1 – 9, 2 – 4, 3 – 10, 5 – 8, 6 – 7

**494**

Path 3

**495**

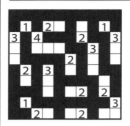

**496**

| SHE | SURNAME | HE | SURNAME |
|---|---|---|---|
| ANN | BRAKES | GARY | STAMPS |
| BELLA | NOBLE | HORACE | LYNES |
| CHER | DARALL | ED | COPES |
| DAWN | CHOVIES | FRANK | BALDY |

**497**

Horse/Robin
Unicorn/Simon
Peacock/Biddie
Zebra/Sheila
Dragon/Tom
Emu/Rose
Camel/Tess
Elephant/Brian

**498**

**499**

| 3D | 8C | 7D |
|---|---|---|
| 10S | 6H | 2S |
| 5D | 4C | 9D |

**500**

Simply move the 1 in the right-hand column to the left of any number in the left-hand column. e.g. turn the 0 into 10! Then both columns will total 27.

**501**

| 2 | 3 | 5 | 6 | 9 | 7 | 4 | 8 | 1 |
|---|---|---|---|---|---|---|---|---|
| 8 | 9 | 4 | 1 | 3 | 2 | 7 | 5 | 6 |
| 1 | 6 | 7 | 5 | 8 | 4 | 9 | 3 | 2 |
| 6 | 5 | 8 | 4 | 2 | 3 | 1 | 9 | 7 |
| 7 | 2 | 3 | 9 | 1 | 6 | 5 | 4 | 8 |
| 9 | 4 | 1 | 7 | 5 | 8 | 6 | 2 | 3 |
| 5 | 8 | 9 | 3 | 7 | 1 | 2 | 6 | 4 |
| 4 | 7 | 2 | 8 | 6 | 9 | 3 | 1 | 5 |
| 3 | 1 | 6 | 2 | 4 | 5 | 8 | 7 | 9 |

**502**

| 2 | 3 | 5 | 7 | 9 | 4 | 1 | 6 | 8 |
|---|---|---|---|---|---|---|---|---|
| 6 | 9 | 1 | 8 | 2 | 5 | 4 | 3 | 7 |
| 7 | 8 | 4 | 3 | 6 | 1 | 5 | 2 | 9 |
| 9 | 6 | 7 | 5 | 4 | 8 | 2 | 1 | 3 |
| 5 | 1 | 2 | 6 | 3 | 7 | 9 | 8 | 4 |
| 8 | 4 | 3 | 2 | 1 | 9 | 6 | 7 | 5 |
| 4 | 2 | 6 | 9 | 8 | 3 | 7 | 5 | 1 |
| 3 | 5 | 9 | 1 | 7 | 6 | 8 | 4 | 2 |
| 1 | 7 | 8 | 4 | 5 | 2 | 3 | 9 | 6 |

**503**

| 5 | 8 | 9 | 1 | 3 | 7 | 6 | 4 | 2 |
|---|---|---|---|---|---|---|---|---|
| 6 | 1 | 7 | 9 | 2 | 4 | 3 | 8 | 5 |
| 3 | 2 | 4 | 8 | 5 | 6 | 7 | 1 | 9 |
| 2 | 7 | 8 | 4 | 6 | 1 | 5 | 9 | 3 |
| 9 | 4 | 6 | 5 | 7 | 3 | 8 | 2 | 1 |
| 1 | 5 | 3 | 2 | 9 | 8 | 4 | 7 | 6 |
| 4 | 6 | 5 | 7 | 1 | 2 | 9 | 3 | 8 |
| 7 | 9 | 2 | 3 | 8 | 5 | 1 | 6 | 4 |
| 8 | 3 | 1 | 6 | 4 | 9 | 2 | 5 | 7 |

**504**

| 3 | 8 | 2 | 1 | 4 | 7 | 6 | 5 | 9 |
|---|---|---|---|---|---|---|---|---|
| 4 | 7 | 5 | 8 | 9 | 6 | 1 | 2 | 3 |
| 9 | 6 | 1 | 3 | 2 | 5 | 4 | 7 | 8 |
| 2 | 4 | 3 | 9 | 7 | 1 | 5 | 8 | 6 |
| 8 | 5 | 9 | 6 | 3 | 4 | 2 | 1 | 7 |
| 7 | 1 | 6 | 2 | 5 | 8 | 3 | 9 | 4 |
| 5 | 2 | 4 | 7 | 8 | 3 | 9 | 6 | 1 |
| 6 | 3 | 7 | 5 | 1 | 9 | 8 | 4 | 2 |
| 1 | 9 | 8 | 4 | 6 | 2 | 7 | 3 | 5 |

**505**

| 7 | 4 | 3 | 9 | 1 | 8 | 2 | 5 | 6 |
|---|---|---|---|---|---|---|---|---|
| 8 | 5 | 1 | 2 | 6 | 7 | 9 | 4 | 3 |
| 9 | 6 | 2 | 5 | 3 | 4 | 7 | 1 | 8 |
| 1 | 9 | 6 | 7 | 8 | 3 | 5 | 2 | 4 |
| 3 | 2 | 8 | 4 | 5 | 1 | 6 | 9 | 7 |
| 5 | 7 | 4 | 6 | 2 | 9 | 8 | 3 | 1 |
| 6 | 1 | 9 | 3 | 7 | 5 | 4 | 8 | 2 |
| 2 | 3 | 5 | 8 | 4 | 6 | 1 | 7 | 9 |
| 4 | 8 | 7 | 1 | 9 | 2 | 3 | 6 | 5 |

**506**

| 8 | 4 | 7 | 9 | 2 | 3 | 5 | 1 | 6 |
|---|---|---|---|---|---|---|---|---|
| 9 | 3 | 1 | 6 | 5 | 7 | 8 | 2 | 4 |
| 6 | 2 | 5 | 1 | 4 | 8 | 3 | 7 | 9 |
| 2 | 5 | 3 | 4 | 1 | 9 | 6 | 8 | 7 |
| 4 | 7 | 8 | 2 | 3 | 6 | 9 | 5 | 1 |
| 1 | 6 | 9 | 8 | 7 | 5 | 4 | 3 | 2 |
| 3 | 8 | 4 | 7 | 6 | 2 | 1 | 9 | 5 |
| 5 | 1 | 2 | 3 | 9 | 4 | 7 | 6 | 8 |
| 7 | 9 | 6 | 5 | 8 | 1 | 2 | 4 | 3 |

**507**

| 6 | 1 | 7 | 5 | 4 | 3 | 2 | 8 | 9 |
|---|---|---|---|---|---|---|---|---|
| 2 | 5 | 9 | 7 | 8 | 1 | 6 | 4 | 3 |
| 3 | 8 | 4 | 6 | 2 | 9 | 5 | 7 | 1 |
| 8 | 6 | 3 | 4 | 1 | 2 | 7 | 9 | 5 |
| 7 | 9 | 2 | 3 | 5 | 6 | 4 | 1 | 8 |
| 1 | 4 | 5 | 9 | 7 | 8 | 3 | 6 | 2 |
| 9 | 3 | 8 | 2 | 6 | 4 | 1 | 5 | 7 |
| 5 | 2 | 6 | 1 | 9 | 7 | 8 | 3 | 4 |
| 4 | 7 | 1 | 8 | 3 | 5 | 9 | 2 | 6 |

**508**

| 1 | 7 | 9 | 2 | 5 | 8 | 3 | 4 | 6 |
|---|---|---|---|---|---|---|---|---|
| 4 | 3 | 8 | 1 | 9 | 6 | 2 | 5 | 7 |
| 2 | 5 | 6 | 4 | 7 | 3 | 1 | 9 | 8 |
| 5 | 9 | 2 | 7 | 1 | 4 | 6 | 8 | 3 |
| 8 | 1 | 3 | 6 | 2 | 9 | 5 | 7 | 4 |
| 6 | 4 | 7 | 8 | 3 | 5 | 9 | 1 | 2 |
| 3 | 8 | 4 | 5 | 6 | 1 | 7 | 2 | 9 |
| 9 | 2 | 1 | 3 | 4 | 7 | 8 | 6 | 5 |
| 7 | 6 | 5 | 9 | 8 | 2 | 4 | 3 | 1 |

**509**

| 2 | 8 | 1 | 6 | 9 | 5 | 4 | 3 | 7 |
|---|---|---|---|---|---|---|---|---|
| 5 | 3 | 4 | 2 | 7 | 1 | 9 | 8 | 6 |
| 6 | 7 | 9 | 8 | 3 | 4 | 5 | 1 | 2 |
| 3 | 2 | 6 | 1 | 4 | 7 | 8 | 5 | 9 |
| 9 | 1 | 7 | 5 | 8 | 6 | 2 | 4 | 3 |
| 8 | 4 | 5 | 9 | 2 | 3 | 6 | 7 | 1 |
| 1 | 5 | 3 | 4 | 6 | 2 | 7 | 9 | 8 |
| 7 | 9 | 2 | 3 | 5 | 8 | 1 | 6 | 4 |
| 4 | 6 | 8 | 7 | 1 | 9 | 3 | 2 | 5 |

**510**

| 1 | 9 | 4 | 2 | 6 | 5 | 3 | 8 | 7 |
|---|---|---|---|---|---|---|---|---|
| 3 | 8 | 2 | 9 | 7 | 1 | 4 | 6 | 5 |
| 7 | 5 | 6 | 3 | 8 | 4 | 2 | 9 | 1 |
| 2 | 4 | 5 | 7 | 3 | 9 | 8 | 1 | 6 |
| 6 | 1 | 8 | 4 | 5 | 2 | 9 | 7 | 3 |
| 9 | 3 | 7 | 8 | 1 | 6 | 5 | 4 | 2 |
| 4 | 7 | 1 | 5 | 9 | 3 | 6 | 2 | 8 |
| 8 | 2 | 3 | 6 | 4 | 7 | 1 | 5 | 9 |
| 5 | 6 | 9 | 1 | 2 | 8 | 7 | 3 | 4 |

**511**

| 8 | 9 | 6 | 3 | 1 | 4 | 5 | 7 | 2 |
|---|---|---|---|---|---|---|---|---|
| 4 | 5 | 1 | 9 | 7 | 2 | 3 | 6 | 8 |
| 2 | 7 | 3 | 5 | 8 | 6 | 1 | 4 | 9 |
| 6 | 2 | 8 | 4 | 9 | 5 | 7 | 1 | 3 |
| 3 | 4 | 7 | 1 | 2 | 8 | 6 | 9 | 5 |
| 9 | 1 | 5 | 6 | 3 | 7 | 2 | 8 | 4 |
| 7 | 3 | 2 | 8 | 6 | 9 | 4 | 5 | 1 |
| 1 | 8 | 4 | 7 | 5 | 3 | 9 | 2 | 6 |
| 5 | 6 | 9 | 2 | 4 | 1 | 8 | 3 | 7 |

**512**

| 8 | 9 | 6 | 5 | 3 | 7 | 2 | 1 | 4 |
|---|---|---|---|---|---|---|---|---|
| 5 | 2 | 7 | 6 | 1 | 4 | 3 | 8 | 9 |
| 1 | 3 | 4 | 2 | 8 | 9 | 6 | 7 | 5 |
| 6 | 8 | 5 | 7 | 9 | 1 | 4 | 2 | 3 |
| 9 | 1 | 2 | 4 | 5 | 3 | 7 | 6 | 8 |
| 4 | 7 | 3 | 8 | 2 | 6 | 5 | 9 | 1 |
| 3 | 6 | 8 | 9 | 4 | 2 | 1 | 5 | 7 |
| 7 | 4 | 9 | 1 | 6 | 5 | 8 | 3 | 2 |
| 2 | 5 | 1 | 3 | 7 | 8 | 9 | 4 | 6 |

**513**

| 9 | 7 | 4 | 5 | 3 | 8 | 6 | 2 | 1 |
|---|---|---|---|---|---|---|---|---|
| 1 | 3 | 5 | 6 | 4 | 2 | 7 | 8 | 9 |
| 8 | 2 | 6 | 9 | 1 | 7 | 5 | 3 | 4 |
| 2 | 9 | 1 | 3 | 7 | 5 | 8 | 4 | 6 |
| 5 | 4 | 7 | 1 | 8 | 6 | 3 | 9 | 2 |
| 3 | 6 | 8 | 4 | 2 | 9 | 1 | 5 | 7 |
| 4 | 5 | 9 | 8 | 6 | 1 | 2 | 7 | 3 |
| 6 | 8 | 2 | 7 | 9 | 3 | 4 | 1 | 5 |
| 7 | 1 | 3 | 2 | 5 | 4 | 9 | 6 | 8 |

**514**

| 5 | 3 | 8 | 2 | 4 | 7 | 9 | 1 | 6 |
|---|---|---|---|---|---|---|---|---|
| 2 | 1 | 7 | 5 | 9 | 6 | 4 | 8 | 3 |
| 9 | 4 | 6 | 8 | 1 | 3 | 2 | 7 | 5 |
| 7 | 2 | 9 | 3 | 6 | 4 | 8 | 5 | 1 |
| 6 | 5 | 4 | 1 | 7 | 8 | 3 | 9 | 2 |
| 1 | 8 | 3 | 9 | 2 | 5 | 7 | 6 | 4 |
| 3 | 7 | 2 | 6 | 5 | 9 | 1 | 4 | 8 |
| 8 | 9 | 5 | 4 | 3 | 1 | 6 | 2 | 7 |
| 4 | 6 | 1 | 7 | 8 | 2 | 5 | 3 | 9 |

**515**

| 7 | 2 | 3 | 6 | 5 | 9 | 8 | 1 | 4 |
|---|---|---|---|---|---|---|---|---|
| 6 | 4 | 9 | 8 | 3 | 1 | 7 | 5 | 2 |
| 8 | 5 | 1 | 2 | 7 | 4 | 9 | 6 | 3 |
| 3 | 6 | 4 | 9 | 2 | 7 | 5 | 8 | 1 |
| 1 | 9 | 2 | 3 | 8 | 5 | 6 | 4 | 7 |
| 5 | 7 | 8 | 1 | 4 | 6 | 3 | 2 | 9 |
| 2 | 1 | 6 | 5 | 9 | 3 | 4 | 7 | 8 |
| 4 | 3 | 5 | 7 | 1 | 8 | 2 | 9 | 6 |
| 9 | 8 | 7 | 4 | 6 | 2 | 1 | 3 | 5 |

**516**

| 5 | 4 | 9 | 7 | 3 | 8 | 1 | 6 | 2 |
|---|---|---|---|---|---|---|---|---|
| 7 | 2 | 3 | 1 | 6 | 4 | 8 | 9 | 5 |
| 1 | 6 | 8 | 2 | 9 | 5 | 4 | 7 | 3 |
| 9 | 1 | 2 | 3 | 8 | 6 | 5 | 4 | 7 |
| 6 | 7 | 4 | 5 | 1 | 9 | 3 | 2 | 8 |
| 3 | 8 | 5 | 4 | 2 | 7 | 9 | 1 | 6 |
| 8 | 5 | 1 | 6 | 4 | 2 | 7 | 3 | 9 |
| 2 | 3 | 7 | 9 | 5 | 1 | 6 | 8 | 4 |
| 4 | 9 | 6 | 8 | 7 | 3 | 2 | 5 | 1 |

**517**

| 7 | 3 | 5 | 4 | 8 | 9 | 6 | 2 | 1 |
|---|---|---|---|---|---|---|---|---|
| 4 | 8 | 2 | 6 | 3 | 1 | 7 | 5 | 9 |
| 9 | 6 | 1 | 5 | 7 | 2 | 8 | 4 | 3 |
| 1 | 9 | 7 | 2 | 4 | 6 | 3 | 8 | 5 |
| 8 | 2 | 6 | 3 | 1 | 5 | 9 | 7 | 4 |
| 5 | 4 | 3 | 8 | 9 | 7 | 1 | 6 | 2 |
| 2 | 7 | 9 | 1 | 6 | 4 | 5 | 3 | 8 |
| 6 | 5 | 8 | 9 | 2 | 3 | 4 | 1 | 7 |
| 3 | 1 | 4 | 7 | 5 | 8 | 2 | 9 | 6 |

**518**

| 7 | 3 | 4 | 1 | 8 | 9 | 6 | 5 | 2 |
|---|---|---|---|---|---|---|---|---|
| 8 | 6 | 9 | 2 | 3 | 5 | 4 | 7 | 1 |
| 1 | 5 | 2 | 7 | 6 | 4 | 8 | 3 | 9 |
| 5 | 9 | 6 | 4 | 1 | 3 | 7 | 2 | 8 |
| 4 | 8 | 3 | 5 | 7 | 2 | 9 | 1 | 6 |
| 2 | 7 | 1 | 6 | 9 | 8 | 5 | 4 | 3 |
| 6 | 1 | 8 | 3 | 5 | 7 | 2 | 9 | 4 |
| 3 | 2 | 7 | 9 | 4 | 6 | 1 | 8 | 5 |
| 9 | 4 | 5 | 8 | 2 | 1 | 3 | 6 | 7 |

**519**

| 9 | 2 | 6 | 8 | 4 | 5 | 1 | 7 | 3 |
|---|---|---|---|---|---|---|---|---|
| 1 | 4 | 5 | 7 | 3 | 9 | 2 | 8 | 6 |
| 7 | 8 | 3 | 6 | 2 | 1 | 4 | 5 | 9 |
| 3 | 1 | 4 | 5 | 7 | 2 | 9 | 6 | 8 |
| 8 | 6 | 2 | 9 | 1 | 3 | 7 | 4 | 5 |
| 5 | 7 | 9 | 4 | 8 | 6 | 3 | 1 | 2 |
| 6 | 3 | 7 | 2 | 5 | 4 | 8 | 9 | 1 |
| 4 | 5 | 1 | 3 | 9 | 8 | 6 | 2 | 7 |
| 2 | 9 | 8 | 1 | 6 | 7 | 5 | 3 | 4 |

**520**

| 8 | 3 | 7 | 6 | 5 | 2 | 1 | 9 | 4 |
|---|---|---|---|---|---|---|---|---|
| 2 | 6 | 1 | 4 | 7 | 9 | 3 | 5 | 8 |
| 9 | 4 | 5 | 1 | 3 | 8 | 6 | 7 | 2 |
| 3 | 7 | 6 | 9 | 8 | 1 | 2 | 4 | 5 |
| 1 | 5 | 9 | 3 | 2 | 4 | 8 | 6 | 7 |
| 4 | 2 | 8 | 7 | 6 | 5 | 9 | 1 | 3 |
| 7 | 9 | 3 | 8 | 4 | 6 | 5 | 2 | 1 |
| 5 | 1 | 4 | 2 | 9 | 3 | 7 | 8 | 6 |
| 6 | 8 | 2 | 5 | 1 | 7 | 4 | 3 | 9 |

**521**

| 7 | 4 | 3 | 5 | 1 | 9 | 2 | 6 | 8 |
|---|---|---|---|---|---|---|---|---|
| 6 | 9 | 8 | 3 | 2 | 4 | 7 | 5 | 1 |
| 2 | 1 | 5 | 8 | 6 | 7 | 9 | 3 | 4 |
| 4 | 3 | 7 | 1 | 9 | 8 | 5 | 2 | 6 |
| 9 | 8 | 6 | 2 | 3 | 5 | 1 | 4 | 7 |
| 1 | 5 | 2 | 4 | 7 | 6 | 3 | 8 | 9 |
| 8 | 7 | 4 | 9 | 5 | 3 | 6 | 1 | 2 |
| 5 | 6 | 1 | 7 | 8 | 2 | 4 | 9 | 3 |
| 3 | 2 | 9 | 6 | 4 | 1 | 8 | 7 | 5 |

**522**

| 9 | 5 | 1 | 4 | 3 | 8 | 6 | 7 | 2 |
|---|---|---|---|---|---|---|---|---|
| 2 | 4 | 6 | 5 | 7 | 1 | 8 | 9 | 3 |
| 3 | 7 | 8 | 9 | 6 | 2 | 1 | 4 | 5 |
| 8 | 2 | 7 | 6 | 1 | 9 | 5 | 3 | 4 |
| 5 | 3 | 4 | 8 | 2 | 7 | 9 | 6 | 1 |
| 1 | 6 | 9 | 3 | 4 | 5 | 2 | 8 | 7 |
| 6 | 1 | 2 | 7 | 8 | 4 | 3 | 5 | 9 |
| 4 | 8 | 5 | 1 | 9 | 3 | 7 | 2 | 6 |
| 7 | 9 | 3 | 2 | 5 | 6 | 4 | 1 | 8 |

**523**

| 4 | 8 | 3 | 6 | 1 | 5 | 9 | 7 | 2 |
|---|---|---|---|---|---|---|---|---|
| 1 | 5 | 9 | 7 | 2 | 4 | 3 | 6 | 8 |
| 7 | 2 | 6 | 8 | 9 | 3 | 1 | 4 | 5 |
| 9 | 6 | 7 | 2 | 3 | 8 | 5 | 1 | 4 |
| 8 | 3 | 5 | 9 | 4 | 1 | 7 | 2 | 6 |
| 2 | 4 | 1 | 5 | 7 | 6 | 8 | 9 | 3 |
| 6 | 9 | 4 | 3 | 5 | 7 | 2 | 8 | 1 |
| 3 | 7 | 8 | 1 | 6 | 2 | 4 | 5 | 9 |
| 5 | 1 | 2 | 4 | 8 | 9 | 6 | 3 | 7 |

**524**

| 3 | 6 | 5 | 2 | 4 | 8 | 9 | 1 | 7 |
|---|---|---|---|---|---|---|---|---|
| 2 | 4 | 7 | 9 | 1 | 5 | 8 | 3 | 6 |
| 1 | 8 | 9 | 6 | 7 | 3 | 5 | 4 | 2 |
| 8 | 5 | 3 | 7 | 6 | 4 | 1 | 2 | 9 |
| 4 | 2 | 1 | 8 | 5 | 9 | 6 | 7 | 3 |
| 9 | 7 | 6 | 1 | 3 | 2 | 4 | 5 | 8 |
| 7 | 3 | 8 | 4 | 9 | 1 | 2 | 6 | 5 |
| 6 | 9 | 4 | 5 | 2 | 7 | 3 | 8 | 1 |
| 5 | 1 | 2 | 3 | 8 | 6 | 7 | 9 | 4 |

**525**

| 9 | 3 | 7 | 8 | 5 | 6 | 1 | 2 | 4 |
|---|---|---|---|---|---|---|---|---|
| 5 | 8 | 4 | 2 | 9 | 1 | 6 | 3 | 7 |
| 1 | 6 | 2 | 4 | 7 | 3 | 8 | 9 | 5 |
| 8 | 9 | 5 | 3 | 6 | 4 | 2 | 7 | 1 |
| 3 | 4 | 6 | 7 | 1 | 2 | 5 | 8 | 9 |
| 7 | 2 | 1 | 5 | 8 | 9 | 3 | 4 | 6 |
| 4 | 5 | 8 | 1 | 2 | 7 | 9 | 6 | 3 |
| 2 | 7 | 9 | 6 | 3 | 5 | 4 | 1 | 8 |
| 6 | 1 | 3 | 9 | 4 | 8 | 7 | 5 | 2 |

**529**

| 9 | 2 | 1 | 4 | 8 | 6 | 7 | 3 | 5 |
|---|---|---|---|---|---|---|---|---|
| 6 | 7 | 4 | 3 | 5 | 9 | 1 | 2 | 8 |
| 3 | 5 | 8 | 2 | 1 | 7 | 4 | 6 | 9 |
| 7 | 8 | 3 | 1 | 9 | 2 | 5 | 4 | 6 |
| 2 | 1 | 6 | 5 | 4 | 3 | 8 | 9 | 7 |
| 4 | 9 | 5 | 6 | 7 | 8 | 3 | 1 | 2 |
| 5 | 6 | 9 | 8 | 3 | 4 | 2 | 7 | 1 |
| 1 | 4 | 7 | 9 | 2 | 5 | 6 | 8 | 3 |
| 8 | 3 | 2 | 7 | 6 | 1 | 9 | 5 | 4 |

**526**

| 2 | 3 | 6 | 1 | 8 | 9 | 7 | 4 | 5 |
|---|---|---|---|---|---|---|---|---|
| 4 | 7 | 5 | 2 | 3 | 6 | 1 | 8 | 9 |
| 8 | 9 | 1 | 7 | 5 | 4 | 6 | 3 | 2 |
| 5 | 6 | 9 | 4 | 2 | 7 | 8 | 1 | 3 |
| 1 | 4 | 7 | 3 | 9 | 8 | 5 | 2 | 6 |
| 3 | 2 | 8 | 6 | 1 | 5 | 9 | 7 | 4 |
| 9 | 5 | 3 | 8 | 4 | 1 | 2 | 6 | 7 |
| 7 | 1 | 2 | 9 | 6 | 3 | 4 | 5 | 8 |
| 6 | 8 | 4 | 5 | 7 | 2 | 3 | 9 | 1 |

**530**

| 7 | 6 | 8 | 2 | 5 | 9 | 1 | 4 | 3 |
|---|---|---|---|---|---|---|---|---|
| 1 | 9 | 2 | 3 | 4 | 7 | 8 | 5 | 6 |
| 5 | 3 | 4 | 8 | 6 | 1 | 2 | 9 | 7 |
| 2 | 5 | 3 | 9 | 1 | 8 | 7 | 6 | 4 |
| 4 | 8 | 7 | 6 | 3 | 5 | 9 | 1 | 2 |
| 9 | 1 | 6 | 4 | 7 | 2 | 5 | 3 | 8 |
| 8 | 4 | 1 | 7 | 9 | 3 | 6 | 2 | 5 |
| 3 | 7 | 9 | 5 | 2 | 6 | 4 | 8 | 1 |
| 6 | 2 | 5 | 1 | 8 | 4 | 3 | 7 | 9 |

**527**

| 5 | 6 | 3 | 2 | 1 | 7 | 8 | 4 | 9 |
|---|---|---|---|---|---|---|---|---|
| 2 | 7 | 4 | 6 | 9 | 8 | 1 | 3 | 5 |
| 8 | 9 | 1 | 5 | 3 | 4 | 7 | 2 | 6 |
| 7 | 8 | 6 | 3 | 4 | 5 | 9 | 1 | 2 |
| 3 | 5 | 9 | 8 | 2 | 1 | 6 | 7 | 4 |
| 1 | 4 | 2 | 9 | 7 | 6 | 5 | 8 | 3 |
| 4 | 2 | 8 | 7 | 5 | 9 | 3 | 6 | 1 |
| 9 | 1 | 7 | 4 | 6 | 3 | 2 | 5 | 8 |
| 6 | 3 | 5 | 1 | 8 | 2 | 4 | 9 | 7 |

**531**

| 7 | 6 | 3 | 1 | 4 | 8 | 5 | 2 | 9 |
|---|---|---|---|---|---|---|---|---|
| 5 | 1 | 4 | 2 | 6 | 9 | 3 | 8 | 7 |
| 8 | 9 | 2 | 3 | 7 | 5 | 6 | 4 | 1 |
| 4 | 8 | 6 | 7 | 9 | 1 | 2 | 5 | 3 |
| 9 | 3 | 7 | 8 | 5 | 2 | 4 | 1 | 6 |
| 2 | 5 | 1 | 6 | 3 | 4 | 9 | 7 | 8 |
| 3 | 4 | 9 | 5 | 8 | 7 | 1 | 6 | 2 |
| 1 | 7 | 5 | 9 | 2 | 6 | 8 | 3 | 4 |
| 6 | 2 | 8 | 4 | 1 | 3 | 7 | 9 | 5 |

**528**

| 4 | 3 | 6 | 5 | 2 | 8 | 1 | 9 | 7 |
|---|---|---|---|---|---|---|---|---|
| 8 | 9 | 5 | 7 | 1 | 3 | 2 | 4 | 6 |
| 7 | 1 | 2 | 4 | 9 | 6 | 3 | 8 | 5 |
| 6 | 7 | 9 | 3 | 8 | 5 | 4 | 2 | 1 |
| 5 | 2 | 8 | 9 | 4 | 1 | 7 | 6 | 3 |
| 1 | 4 | 3 | 2 | 6 | 7 | 9 | 5 | 8 |
| 9 | 5 | 1 | 6 | 3 | 4 | 8 | 7 | 2 |
| 2 | 8 | 7 | 1 | 5 | 9 | 6 | 3 | 4 |
| 3 | 6 | 4 | 8 | 7 | 2 | 5 | 1 | 9 |

**532**

| 2 | 1 | 5 | 8 | 3 | 6 | 9 | 4 | 7 |
|---|---|---|---|---|---|---|---|---|
| 9 | 3 | 4 | 2 | 5 | 7 | 8 | 6 | 1 |
| 8 | 6 | 7 | 4 | 9 | 1 | 2 | 5 | 3 |
| 7 | 8 | 3 | 9 | 4 | 2 | 5 | 1 | 6 |
| 1 | 4 | 9 | 5 | 6 | 8 | 3 | 7 | 2 |
| 6 | 5 | 2 | 1 | 7 | 3 | 4 | 9 | 8 |
| 4 | 7 | 8 | 3 | 1 | 5 | 6 | 2 | 9 |
| 5 | 2 | 6 | 7 | 8 | 9 | 1 | 3 | 4 |
| 3 | 9 | 1 | 6 | 2 | 4 | 7 | 8 | 5 |